60926R

M c GRAW-HILL **T**ECHNICAL **E**DUCATION **S**ERIES

McGRAW-HILL TECHNICAL EDUCATION SERIES

Norman C. Harris, Series Editor

Introductory Applied Physics, 2d ed. • Harris and Hemmerling

Experiments in Applied Physics • Harris

Introduction to Microwave Theory and Measurements • Lance

Specifications Writing for Architects and Engineers • Watson

(Other volumes in preparation.)

McGraw-Hill Book Company

New York

Toronto

London

Donald A. Watson, CSI, AIA

Associate Professor of

Architecture,

Pasadena City College

Vice President,

Los Angeles Chapter,

Construction Specifications Institute

Specifications Writing for Architects and Engineers

SPECIFICATIONS WRITING FOR ARCHITECTS AND ENGINEERS

Copyright © 1964 by McGraw-Hill, Inc.

All Rights Reserved.

Printed in the United States of America.

This book, or parts thereof, may not be reproduced in any form

without permission of the publishers.

Library of Congress Catalog Card Number 63-22555

68473

To my wife, Evelyn

Preface

This book is intended as both a guide and a reference work for architectural and engineering students. Many architects and engineers have completed prescribed college courses in architecture or engineering with no more than a perfunctory glance at the problems involved in the extremely exacting skill of specifications writing. Fortunately, many universities and colleges are now adding courses in specifications writing to their curricula or are including this training as a portion of courses labeled Professional Practice, Construction Management, or a similar designation. The writing of good specifications is closely related to modern design and construction practices. Consequently, the material presented here covers the entire field. A knowledge of office organization, professional practice and ethics, and construction management is essential for the specifications writer. The material has been arranged in such a manner that the book can be used as a text for related subjects, with proper emphasis placed on the importance of good specifications, as well as for one expressly called Specifications.

Questions have been included at the end of most chapters and in the Appendix. These can be used as a teaching aid to regularly established courses or as a review for those preparing for state board examinations.

The writing of good specifications is, in many ways, as important in the design and construction of a successful building as the careful preparation of the other construction documents. Many architects and engineers who have designed buildings for years copy old specifications job after job and never look at the form or content. As a consequence, specifications have grown more wordy and involved with each repetition or addition. Stilted legal terms, indefinite instructions, and escape clauses have been included in specifications in place of a thorough analysis of the problems involved. It is hoped that this book, along with others in the field, will help to raise the level of specifications produced by architectural and engineering offices throughout the country.

The basic principles involved in the use of words, the description of materials and processes, and the methods of analyzing problems and conducting the research necessary to produce good specifications remain the same. It is this basic information that is covered here. Where there is a difference of opinion among members of the construction industry or specifications writers, an attempt has been made to show both sides. The individual specifications writer must evaluate the information given and follow that which best suits his purpose.

It would be impossible to list all sources of information that appear in this book. Many of the ideas and principles presented here have been the result of extensive reading in the excellent books and articles by such authorities as Harold Sleeper, Ben John Small, Goldwin Goldsmith, D. W. Gale, H. Griffith Edwards, Harold Rosen, and the many contributors to Specifications Digest, the national magazine of the Construction Specifications Institute.

Many discussions, programs, committee meetings, and conferences of the CSI have influenced my thinking on specifications methods. My experience as a construction superintendent, draftsman, specifications writer, specifications consultant, architect, and teacher has pointed up the need for good specifications.

I would like to thank those who reviewed portions of the manuscript or granted permission for the use of published material. Special thanks are due R. Redmond Coghlan, Jr. (AIA, FCSI), Raymond Whalley (AIA, CSI), Dr. Oscar E. Marsh (CSI) and the staff of the Ralph M. Parsons Company, F. C. Frost, Fred F. Van Atta, Charles Joseph Shoenberg, and my many friends and associates in the Construction Specifications Institute for their help and encouragement in the preparation of this book. My daughter-in-law, Donna, gave freely of her time in the skillful typing and retyping of the manuscript.

This book could not have been completed without the encouragement, understanding, and patience of my wife. Her helpful suggestions during the writing, typing of rough drafts, and proofreading have made this work possible.

Donald A. Watson

Contents

Chapter 4
Construction Management and Supervision

CHAPTER 1 Introduction to Specifications

During the next ten years approximately one million private and public buildings will be constructed. Nearly thirty thousand school buildings will be constructed during this period. An equal number of attempts will be made at defining, by use of the written word, the thousand and one parts that make up one phase of the construction of these buildings. These definitions, planned to supplement and be supplemented by drawings and illustrations, are called "specifications."

DEFINITION

Before proceeding further, let us attempt to define the word "specifications." A specification has been described as a statement containing a minute description or enumeration of particulars, as of the terms of a contract or the details of construction not shown in an architect's drawings. A specification is definite, determinate, distinctly and plainly set forth, and stated in full and explicit terms. The reader will note from this definition that specifications are expected to be all-encompassing and exact. We may say simply that specifications should be clear, concise, complete, and correct.

HISTORY

Historically, specifications were the only instructions for a building project. Let us consider a specification for what might be called the first mass housing project.

And God said unto Noah. . . "Make thee an ark of gopher wood; rooms shalt thou make in the ark, and shalt pitch it within and without with pitch. And this is the fashion which thou shalt make it of: The length of the ark shall be three hundred cubits, the breadth of it fifty cubits, and the height of it thirty cubits. A window shalt thou make to the ark. . .and the door of the ark shalt thou set in the side thereof; with lower, second, and third stories shalt thou make it."

Role of Specifications. The earliest specifications were simply written instructions complemented by sketches or pictures that conveyed the idea of the master builder or architect. Today, we have reached the point where complex, detailed working drawings are considered by some persons in the construction industry to be of primary importance: The specifications, or written instructions, are relegated to a minor role. In too many instances, the writing of specifications is "pushed off" on a draftsman who has little or no training or interest in the very important, extremely complex, and exacting task of writing specifications.

Catalog Specifications. Thirty to forty years ago, it was necessary to draw full-sized details of nearly every part of a building. The small local manufacturers or job shops were able and willing to fabricate almost anything the engineer or architect wished to include in a building, as long as there was a full-sized drawing to act as a pattern. Common practice now is simply to pick an article from the catalog of a national manufacturer, examine samples and models submitted by producers, and make a choice. This new trend will undoubtedly continue and even increase. This puts the responsibility of careful detailing and of establishing the validity of distributors' claims made in sales literature on the producer.

Mass-produced Products. The architect, engineer, or specifications writer, although he may feel that a better product could be designed, chooses a prefabricated product and puts down only a catalog number in the specifications. For reasons of economy or because of the time element involved in a custom-made product, the specifications writer may be forced to include in his specifications mass-produced items that are not quite what he visualized in preliminary studies.

IMPORTANCE OF SPECIFICATIONS WRITING

To many, the writing of specifications is a boring task to be put off or disposed of in an offhand manner. However, others find as much pleasure in the writing of detailed instructions necessary to construct a pleasant, workable, and economically sound building as the designer finds in the creation of a fine facade. The general public may see only the pleasing outside or attractive work spaces; but the owner who is satisfied because the building was produced within his budget and because it is easy to maintain and economical to operate will sing the praises of the architect or engineer who produced it. This is the kind of advertising that can make or break a reputation. While the writing of specifications may not be romantic or lend itself to flights of fancy, it is creative and interesting work, requiring an analytical mind and the ability to visualize a project from its inception to its completion.

CONSULTANTS

The problem of preparing specifications is becoming more complex every day. The development of modern techniques and the diversity of new materials available for construction call for research, investigation, and ingenuity from the specifications writer. The specifications writer cannot hope to solve all the mechanical, electrical, and technical problems involved in a modern building. He must depend on engineers, consultants, manufacturers, associations, and distributors to assist him in the solution of these problems. He cannot afford to disregard new techniques and materials and continue to specify only those that have been proved to be successful through long use, nor can he throw out all that is old and try only the latest fads and fancies. He must reevaluate that which is proved and, through research and testing, use that which best fits a particular process or project.

SPECIFICATIONS: A Team Effort

A team is a group of highly specialized people who contribute their individual skills to the total effort and therefore assume great responsibility. In specifications writing, the general contractor and his group of subcontractors, specialty contractors, and materials dealers are very much a part of the

Fig. 1-1. The specifications department of a large firm of architects-engineers.

team. The scope of the team is thought, by some, to go even further than this. They believe that the real estate operator, the lender, the insurer, the business analyst, and the production men should also be considered a part of the team.

BACKGROUND OF SPECIFICATIONS WRITER

Each team member must live with specifications even though he may never write them. The draftsman who makes notes on the margin of his drawings for the specifications writer must know what kinds of information will be helpful. The draftsman checking shop drawings against specifications must know where to look, and for what. The materials supplier must be able to tell, from the manner in which the specification is written, when he can and when he cannot bid his products. The experienced field supervisor or field inspector, who must struggle for good performance and who desires clear-cut instructions to follow, knows the good from the bad in specifications. All these men may eventually write good specifications because of their intimate relationship with both adequate and inadequate specifications. However, their viewpoint will always be colored by their particular limited experiences.

Practical Experience. The person who is best qualified to write specifications should be able to see a project from every team member's point of view. One who has had practical experience in all fields could do this, but the person with this type of background is rare indeed. The only substitute for experience is to work through organizations such as the Construction Specifications Institute (CSI), which includes members from all parts of the construction industry who are interested in good specifications. A member of the CSI will sit down and talk with materials suppliers and will work on technical committees composed of all segments of the industry. By working in this way with people in related fields, the specifications writer will be able to visualize the entire process of construction and write specifications that will better service the industry as a whole.

An Analytical Mind Needed. Some people, highly qualified in other phases of work, could never write specifications successfully. Specifications writing requires an analytical mind. The specifications writer must be able to distinguish between important and unimportant details. The many problems involved in modern building construction must be seen in detail and fitted into a well-integrated whole. The specifications writer must be able to see through walls, in his mind's eye, and describe the construction from the inside out. A partition must be more to him than a conveniently placed divider; he must think of a partition as a structure which may consist of a series of metal studs erected by the lathing contractor, attached to a slab floor with prepositioned bolts set in concrete by the cement contractor, supported at the top with clips attached to steel erected by structural-steel men, covered by metal lath, attached with other types of clips to the studs by a lather, and given a scratch coat, a brown coat, and a finish coat of plaster by the plasterers, and painted by the painters. Only if a specifications writer can see all these separate parts and processes can he write a comprehensive specification.

Word Usage. Knowledge of the technical or trade terms commonly used is very important. The specifications writer must know for whom these instructions are written and must make certain that what he is describing is identified in terms that will be understood by all concerned. He must sort out and discard those terms whose meanings are in doubt or which are applicable and understood only in a particular trade or locale.

Business Law. Business law, in general, may be said to consist of rules for guidance of man in his relationships with other men and in his relation to organized society. A knowledge of business law is a prime requisite for the specifications writer. The rules laid down in the specifications deal as much with human relationships, duties, delegation of authority, and acceptance of responsibility as with the quality and kinds of materials. The good specifications writer can foresee those human relationships that will affect a project and the frictions that could develop if he does not consider all the implications of what he is writing. He must be concerned not only with written or statutory law but with unwritten law, common law, and legal precedent in controversies over past differences of opinion.

TIME ELEMENT

The time element is important to the person who is writing specifications. The specifications cannot be completed until all decisions have been made and the drawings are well under way, or in some cases, even completed. The specifications writer must be able to visualize the overall job and quickly separate it into its component parts. The pressure of time is always on his work. Every minute counts, and the greater part of his time should be spent in solving unusual or difficult problems. Matters of format or of organization of a section should be established in advance by the office. Adequate descriptions of standard practices and necessary reference material should be readily available to him. The final compilation and assembling of all the data can then proceed in a simple and orderly manner that can be performed under the stress of time.

SPECIALISTS

The design and construction of a modern building require the knowledge, research, and talent of many specialists, who produce the instructions necessary for this complex operation. Architects and engineers must study the relation of the building to its site, analyze the owner's needs, determine building use, organize the flow of traffic through the building, create the aesthetic qualities desired, and select the construction methods or systems that will best meet these requirements and still keep within what is usually a tight budget. Preliminary studies in the form of renderings, models, schematics, and cost estimates are prepared and presented for discussion and approval by the owner. Detailed instructions, consisting of graphic and written instructions that will assure faithful reproduction of those specifications agreed upon, must be prepared.

CONTRACT DOCUMENTS

These instructions, called the "contract documents," include:
1. Working drawings—graphic representations of work to be done
2. Agreements—written documents setting forth, or contracts pertaining to, the execution of the work
3. General conditions—written instructions governing and defining the responsibilities of all parties concerned (usually the same for all projects from one office)
4. Special conditions—modifications or extensions of the general conditions
5. Addenda—changes in, or additions to, the contract documents before the submission of bids
6. Specifications—detailed written instructions covering each phase of the construction project

The preparation of these detailed written instructions requires a thorough knowledge of all the contract documents and their interrelationships; the organization of, and the part played by, each segment of the construction industry; and the laws, codes, and other outside factors controlling the various phases of building construction. Knowledge of this background material is important to the specifications writer if he is to describe in detail each item that will make up the whole.

GUIDE SPECIFICATIONS

The preparation of clear, concise, and complete specifications for the construction industry is part of the team effort that assures satisfactory completion of any building project. The complexity of the modern building, the rapid change in construction methods, and the multitude of new materials developed and placed on the market each year demand continual revision of standards and constant research into the use of new materials and methods. A number of books have been published that could be considered "guide" specifications. Those listed below are meant to be copied directly or in part, with only specific items entered in appropriate places:

"The American Specification Manual," The Architectural and Building Press, Inc., 1927.

Dyer, B. H.: "Specification Work Sheet," American Institute of Architects, Washington, D. C., 1951.

Sleeper, H. R.: "Architectural Specifications," John Wiley & Sons, Inc., New York, 1940.

Small, B. J.: "Streamlined Specifications Standards," vols. I and II, Reinhold Publishing Corporation, New York, 1956.

Stevens, F. B.: "Stevens Master Specifications," Stevens Master Specifications, Inc., Chicago, 1932.

Limitations of Guide Specifications. Because of the rapid development of the construction industry, guide specifications must be used with extreme care. Another reason for the limited usefulness of universal guide specifications is that the regional practices and local trade jurisdictional regulations in recent years have not followed an identical pattern throughout the country. Each guide specification must be carefully checked to make sure that it conforms to local or regional customs.

EXPERIENCED SPECIFICATIONS WRITERS

Before the specifications writer can hope to write complete specifications, he must have a good knowledge of working drawings and their preparation. In addition to experience as a draftsman in an architect's or engineer's office, he should have as much experience as possible on the job itself. He should see how the specifications actually are used under job conditions. One who knows from firsthand job experience the problems caused by inadequate, inaccurate, or misleading specifications will avoid many of the mistakes made in the construction documents by those who have not had such experience. If those who prepared the specifications were forced to supervise, interpret, and enforce the specifications on the job, we would see a progressive improvement in the relationship between the various segments of the industry.

TECHNICAL INFORMATION

It would be an endless task to attempt to give all the technical information necessary for specifications writing. This would involve the preparation of many volumes, and, because of the rapid technological advances within the industry, the information would quickly be outmoded. Source materials and references will be identified, their value and reliability analyzed, and their use explained. The student of specifications must carry on from there.

BOOK NOT A GUIDE

This book is not a guide to be copied and so produce a set of specifications. It is a discussion of the reasons for the contract documents, of how they will be used, and of the interpretations that have been made in the field.

QUESTIONS

1. Define the word "specifications."
2. State briefly the background needed by a specifications writer.
3. How are specifications writers selected in some offices?
4. Where can guide specifications be obtained?
5. Discuss the education desirable to develop competent specifications writers.
6. Discuss the training in specifications writing that has been received by most graduates of architectural and engineering schools.

CHAPTER 2 Preliminary Studies and Specifications

The person who writes specifications must have a knowledge of the entire planning process that precedes a modern construction project. He must be able to visualize the role of each of the many persons involved. It has been said that modern construction is the result of team action. Certainly, then, the person who is writing the instructions to be used in this cooperative endeavor must understand the place of each team member. He must be able to visualize, if he is not a principal, what has already been done before he is able to start writing. He must know what sorts of decisions have been made, and by whom, and who can give him the information needed in the preparation of specifications. The authority and responsibilities of each party in the undertaking must be considered.

PRELIMINARY STUDIES

The preliminary stages of design set the overall pattern of the project. The architect surveys the locations, property values, zoning requirements, and sites that will be involved. Agreement between the owner and the architect must be reached at this point on many items that will affect the preparation of drawings and specifications. Building use and locations, in regard to fire zones, may preclude certain types of construction or materials. Local ordinances must be checked and their effect on the project considered. Soil conditions and special site requirements must be studied, and the adaptability of various types of construction and the relationship of each type of construction to the site must be carefully analyzed. The studies made by the architect and associated engineers will result in a recommendation to the owner of a particular type of construction best suited to the project. In some instances, this recommendation includes alternative methods of construction, use of materials, and mechanical equipment.

Availability of Preliminary Studies. These studies and recommendations must be available to the specifications writer and will be referred to many times throughout the entire planning stage. He must understand the reasons behind the choice of construction methods to be used in order to write meaningful instructions. As the drawings and specifications are prepared, many decisions must be made, and many of these decisions must be based on the preliminary studies.

Preliminary Sketches. During the preliminary stage of the planning process, a series of preliminary sketches is made in an attempt to study fully the possibilities of the problem and to find a solution that is acceptable to both the architect and the owner. These sketches and studies, even though the ideas expressed are often discarded for others, may prove to be of great value after further study. The preservation of these preliminary sketches will constitute a record of the process by which a final decision is reached. As such, they will be of value for further reference.

Models and Renderings. In order for the owner to visualize what is intended, he must be presented with drawings or pictures he can understand. The owner is frequently unable to interpret drawings and view the meaning and wisdom of the scheme proposed. The architect or engineer must present these drawings and explain them in such a manner as to preclude future misunderstandings. He may have to prepare models that will enable him fully to visualize the mass, proportion, scale, and relation of all parts and that will enable the owner better to understand the design of the building.

RECORDS OF CONVERSATION

It is absolutely essential that a record be kept of all conversations between the architect and the owner during the preliminary stages of design. The decisions reached at this point will govern many of the planning stages of a building. Stated preferences and tastes of the owner must be noted and considered. Commitments made and opinions

Fig. 2-1. Specifications writer with preliminary studies.

expressed at this point can lead to misunderstanding at a future date if not recorded for reference. The record may consist, in the case of a small project, of quick notes preserved on scratch paper or, for a larger project, of a detailed stenographic record of all conferences and meetings between the architect and client. Some large offices, where many persons will be employed in the planning and supervision of the work, summarize this information and duplicate the summary for the use of all involved in the project. One large office, doing a series of schools for several school districts, compiled these summaries into what was called a "school district idiosyncrasy sheet." The title was subsequently changed, although the system was maintained, when employees began calling it an "idiot sheet." Care must be taken that information such as this that might come to the attention of the owner be discreet and correct.

PRELIMINARY SPECIFICATIONS

Preliminary or outline specifications of projects must be prepared during an early stage in the design process. This is necessary in the preparation of a preliminary estimate of probable costs. The architect and owner must have a mutually understood program of requirements and a schedule of materials and special items that will go into the finished project. The specifications will include a brief description of materials and finishes and the results expected from each. The detailed "how" necessary in the final specifications is not included unless this would

materially affect costs. These outline specifications are prepared for the benefit of the owner, architect, designer, draftsman, and specifications writer. Some architects and writers use a checklist of all materials that may be used for any job. This checklist could run as high as 10,000 individual items that might be included. The Federal Housing Administration (FHA) list includes 1,500 items. Each office should develop a checklist of a usable length in which each item can be covered in a broader category of work. These headings or categories could be used at a later time as section headings when writing the construction specifications trade sections. See Appendix A for an example of a preliminary checklist.

PRELIMINARY COST ESTIMATES

The broad outline specifications are then broken down into units that can be used to estimate costs. The preliminary estimate to be presented to the owner can now be prepared. The actual preparation of accurate preliminary cost estimates requires a great deal of experience. The specifications writer may be called in to estimate quantities needed and the extent of the project. The architect, engineer, or estimator will then be able to make his preliminary estimate. This estimate will be based on past experience with similar projects and investigation of current price trends. Any estimate made before the working drawings are completed will probable be inaccurate. If the preliminary estimate is within 20 percent of the actual cost, it can be considered close. The temptation to give a low estimate in order to please a client is very great, but this can lead to unpleasantness and an unhappy client. A high estimate, if it is within a budget, can convince a client that he has obtained a bargain when a low bid comes in. The architect or engineer does not guarantee an estimate, but the client will remember the first figure given him throughout the entire planning and construction process. After the sketches and preliminary specifications are presented to the owner for his approval, a careful record should be kept of any decisions that would amplify or modify these preliminary specifications. Each of these records should be dated to avoid any chronological misunderstanding. These should then be incorporated with the notes taken from earlier conferences and used as references by all who will be involved in the preparation of the construction documents.

CONSULTANTS

The working drawings are a part of the construction documents. It is the architect's duty to make these as complete and clear as possible. Although the architect may be able to visualize the project as it will appear when completed and will be responsible for it, he must, in many instances, call in experts to assist him in accomplishing his objective. These experts may include civil, soil mechanics, structural, mechanical, and electrical engineers who will assist him in the planning of the project. Each will concern himself with only a portion of the planning activity. These engineers must be in on the initial planning of this very complex endeavor or be called in for conferences at an early stage in the architect's preparation of the working drawings and specifications. Their assistance

Fig. 2-2. A soil engineer making a test boring. (By permission of Converse Foundation Engineers.)

to the architect may consist only of advice given in conversation, or they may provide sketches and calculations to be used by the architect in the preparation of working drawings or actually prepare a portion of the drawings to be used on the job. The extent of their participation will vary with the size and type of the project and the personnel and office organization of the architect. These consultants must be brought into the planning early if they are to offer efficient service. They must be given access to all information compiled during the preliminary stage of design in order to coordinate their efforts with others on this design team. In addition to the preparation of working drawings, several sections of the specifications may be prepared by the engineers.

ENGINEERING PRELIMINARIES

Engineers' drawings are limited to specific parts of the total project. The soil mechanics engineer will be concerned with subsurface conditions and will recommend methods to be used in order to utilize or overcome certain soil characteristics. The civil engineer may determine grades, contours, boundaries, property lines, drainage, roads, and other site problems. The structural engineer will calculate the forces that may be exerted on the building and will design the component parts to resist the forces involved. The mechanical engineer will concern himself with the electrical, plumbing, heating, and air-conditioning phases of the project.

COORDINATION OF PRELIMINARY INFORMATION

The information given, the drawings made, and the specifications prepared by the engineers must be coordinated and integrated into the overall design of the project by the architect or his staff of draftsmen and specifications writers. The structural requirements must be analyzed. Space for equipment and power requirements needed by the mechanical engineers must be provided. This initial cooperation during the preliminary stage of design of the many persons involved in this rapidly changing, advancing, and expanding industry is necessary if the specifications writer is to take advantage of and utilize new and better techniques.

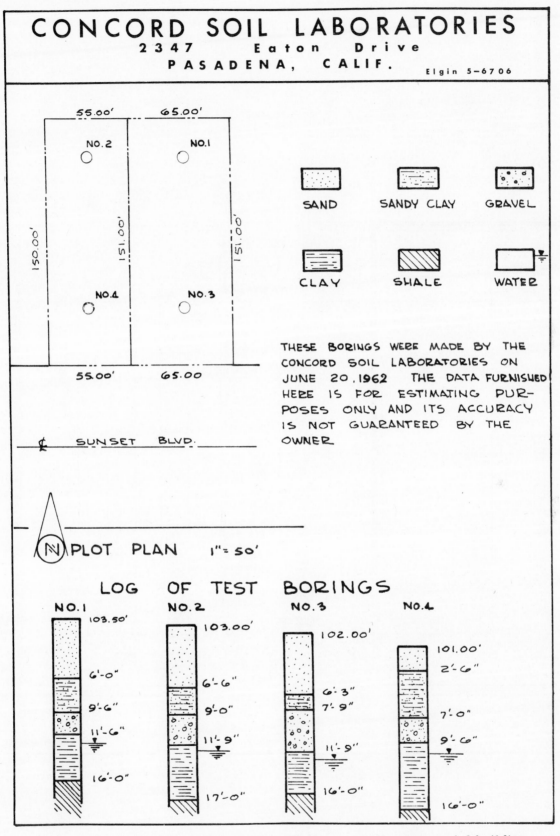

Fig. 2-3. A copy of a soil survey made for a small commercial building.

GENERAL NOTES:
1. USE 3000# CONCRETE AND INTERMEDIATE REINFORCING STEEL.
2. PROVIDE 2" MINIMUM CONCRETE FIREPROOFING FOR STRUCTURAL STEEL
3. RIVETED, BOLTED, OR WELDED CONNECTIONS OPTIONAL

FOUNDATION PLAN 1/8"= 1'-0"

TYPICAL FLOOR FRAMING 1/8"= 1'-0"

NORTH

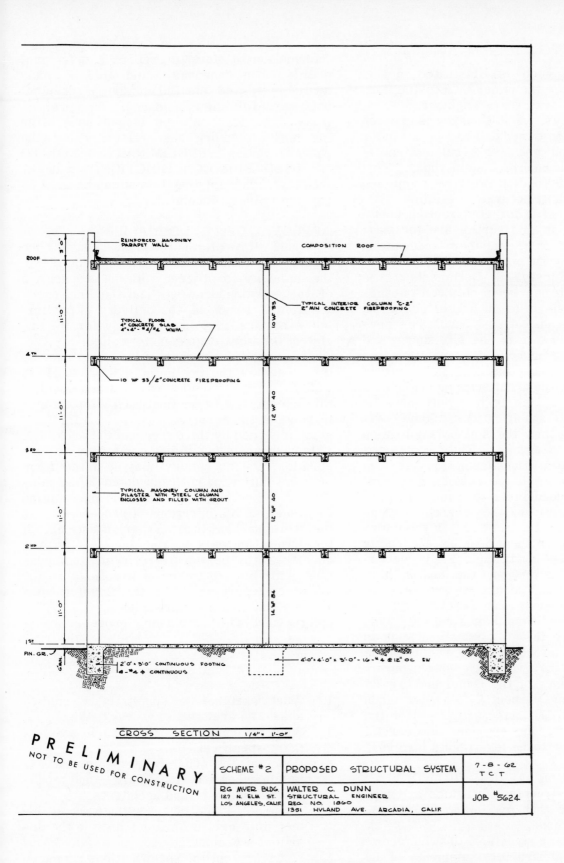

Fig. 2-4. Example of a preliminary structural drawing.

SOIL SURVEYS

Soil surveys such as illustrated in Fig. 2-3 are made for the owner by a testing laboratory or a soil mechanics engineer.

Use of Surveys. A soil survey is ordered and paid for by the owner and will be the basis of the structural engineer's calculations of footing size and underpinning methods. This preliminary investigation must be completed before a reasonably accurate preliminary estimate can be made for construction costs. The data given in this survey are for estimating purposes only, and their accuracy is not guaranteed by the owner.

Location of Surveys in Documents. The information that has been obtained on subsurface conditions is to be presented for the contractor's use and can be handled in several ways. Reference to the site survey and soil tests can be made in the specifications with a notation stating that copies of the tests are available at the architect's or engineer's office. A copy of the test report may be bound in with the specifications. Some engineers prefer to show the soil-boring logs on the structural drawings. The contractor cannot then claim that information has been withheld from him. If the results of the soil survey are included in the drawings or bound with the specifications, they thereby become part of the contract documents. If the information furnished in them does not accurately show the subsurface conditions actually encountered during construction, the courts have held that the contract documents are defective and that the contractor can recover for any additional expense over his original bid. This would be so even though a statement such as the following is inserted: "The results of the test borings by the owner are shown purely for the convenience of the owner and are not guaranteed in any respect." The use made of soil surveys can cause problems for the owner, architect, or engineer if careful thought is not given to the legal points involved.

PRELIMINARY STRUCTURAL DRAWINGS

Preliminary structural drawings are necessary in order that preliminary cost estimates may be made.

The preliminary structural drawing shows only the principal structural elements of the building and sometimes the quantities of materials needed. The purpose of this type of drawing is to furnish the architect with enough information to start to prepare architectural details. The drawings would also be made available to the electrical and mechanical engineers for their guidance. This preliminary drawing should be issued soon after the initial planning has started. Note the rubber stamp: "PRELIMINARY - NOT TO BE USED FOR CONSTRUCTION." It is extremely important that this stamp be used on any preliminary document.

APPROVAL OF PRELIMINARIES

When all preliminary studies have been made, the architect or engineer must obtain the authority to proceed with the preparation of the working drawings and the final specifications. Proof of the delivery of preliminary studies may be necessary for the architect or the engineer to collect his fee. There must be evidence of the acceptance by the owner of the preliminary studies. It is well to secure from the owner a statement of this acceptance in writing. This acceptance may be in the form of a copy of preliminary studies signed by the owner and the architect. If the owner is a building committee or corporation, the acceptance may be in the form of a resolution passed and noted in the minutes of a meeting. The architect may inform the owner of his intentions of proceeding with the working drawings and specifications. If the owner knows that the architect is proceeding with the working drawings and confers with him or gives instructions to the architect regarding them, the architect may assume that the preliminaries are accepted and continue with the planning process.

QUESTIONS

1. What sketches or preliminary studies should an architect preserve? Why?
2. What information is included in preliminary specifications?
3. Describe the usual relationship that exists between structural, civil, and mechanical engineers and architects.
4. Name six kinds of consultants an architect may call in for assistance in the design of a project.
5. When are outline specifications prepared and used?
6. Describe the procedure used in making a soil survey.

CHAPTER 3   Office Organization and the Preparation of Construction Documents

Let us review briefly the documents necessary for a construction project. These may be divided into three distinct types according to their functions: (1) bidding documents, (2) contract forms, and (3) specifications and drawings.

BIDDING DOCUMENTS

Those parts of the construction documents that are written for, and of interest to, all who may bid on a project are considered "bidding documents." The information given here need not be repeated in any other part. The bidding documents are divided into several sections: the invitation to bid, instructions to bidders, the proposal, and bid bonds.

CONTRACT FORMS

These are documents to be used only by the successful bidders. They consist of various legal and contractual documents that make up a portion of the contract documents, such as the agreement forms, subcontractor agreement forms, surety bonds, wage rates, and similar legal documents.

SPECIFICATIONS AND DRAWINGS

These are the detailed instructions, both written and in picture form, that will be used on the construction project by all involved.

Each of the documents mentioned above will be taken up in detail in later chapters, but it is necessary first to understand the organization of, and the relationships between, the architects and engineers and their employees who prepare or assist in the preparation of these documents.

OFFICE TYPES

The responsibility for the preparation of the various contract documents will vary with the size, scope, and personnel of the architect's office. The architect's office may consist of a small skilled work force that performs all parts of the design function. It may include many persons, each skilled or specializing in a particular phase of planning.

This type of office may complete extremely complicated projects with a limited force by calling in, or associating with, specialists or consultants for certain phases of the work. The complexity of modern construction demands a diversity of talent to cover adequately all phases of design. The graduate from an architectural school who hopes to set up his own practice, the draftsman who may move from office to office as work loads vary, and the specifications consultant who may do work for many offices must understand the various types of office organization they will encounter and know what will be expected of them under each type of organization.

One Principal. The office which consists of an architect or an engineer and one or more senior draftsmen is very common in the United States. In this type of office, the architect or engineer usually assumes the responsibility of making the preliminary studies and laying out the work for his draftsmen. In this case, each draftsman must be thoroughly competent and familiar with all phases of the design process. He must be able to take preliminary studies and from them prepare an entire set of working drawings. The architect or engineer will then be able to concentrate on client contracts, preliminary presentations, and construction supervision. The architect or engineer will, in most instances, write the specifications and assist the owner in the preparation of other contract documents. While this type of organization is extremely simple, the responsibilities of the architect or engineer are great. The architect or engineer must be an artist, a businessman, a personnel manager, and a lawyer.

Abilities and Interests. Architectural schools may attempt to turn out future architects who are proficient in all phases of design and who have a basic knowledge of construction techniques. Architectural schools are, however, unable to change natural abilities, nor can they create a uniform interest in all phases of the work that is the architect's responsibility. The fact that a man has finished his classroom work, college work, and architectural or engineering training and has become an architect or an engineer does not necessarily mean that his talent is in design. His talent may be in the handling of clients, in construction management, or in business management. In the course of his education in school and on the job, the student discovers abilities and develops interests that help him become more skilled at one phase of the business of architecture or engineering than another. To one, design and presentation will be of prime interest; to another, the preparation of working drawings that reproduce exactly the basic design in detail will seem the most important phase of architecture. Structural analysis and the new and exciting use of modern framing systems are extremely fascinating to some. The business of meeting people and exchanging ideas; of working with materials dealers, contractors, and tradesmen; and of observing and participating in the actual construction is handled best by a certain type of individual. The legal and technical aspects of contracts, documents, and specifications, which spell success or failure of a project, may be challenging to some. It is important to the construction industry that there be people who possess varying degrees of interest and ability. Many extremely successful architectural practices have been so because of an association of two or more architects or of several architects and engineers having different interests and talents. In any business, including architecture and engineering, the greatest result comes when the greatest talent and interest of each individual are used to the fullest.

Partnerships. In business, individuals usually group together in order to obtain enough capital to operate successfully. An architectural or structural engineering practice does not necessarily need a large amount of capital (although this helps) for its successful prosecution. What it does need is a grouping together of persons with the various capabilities and talents that are required in a profession where such dissimilar traits as artistic, engineering, public relations, and business ability must all be present. The grouping together of two or more of these individuals often makes for a successful practice. The partnership of two or more architects can, in most states, be simply an oral agreement. If each party engages in some phase of the business, and if they divide any profits and assume all losses between themselves, this is considered a partnership. It is more usual for the partnership to be formalized by a written contract which sets forth the conditions of the partnership. Each partner will then assume certain primary responsibilities, although they may each be called upon to grab a pencil and help out on the board, attend meetings, write specifications, or supervise construction when needed.

Architects-Engineers. There has been a trend for architects and engineers to join together in partnerships in order for each to broaden his field of endeavor. This association has proved, in some instances, advantageous for both the architect and the engineer. The architect so associated does not have to call in as many outside consultants to assist him in the complete planning of a project. He is assisted in the design of a complicated structure by the ready and close association with a specialist. The engineer is in on the planning from the start and thus can steer the architect away from designs impossible or uneconomical to execute. The engineer is able to take advantage of the possibly broader background in planning, functions, aesthetics, or artistic perception of the architect. This association can be very advantageous when a project is controlled by a governmental agency which may by law require the services of both an architect and a structural, mechanical, or electrical engineer.

Associated Architects. The architect operating a small office with a limited number of draftsmen, in what is possibly a limited office space, sometimes has the opportunity to secure a commission more extensive than he can handle with his own staff. He may then associate with another architect in what may be considered a limited partnership. This partnership may last only through a single project. With this arrangement, two or more architects or engineers may be associated on one project but at the same time be carrying on separate individual commissions. This type of association is very handy for the young architect who has not established a well-rounded practice or located a sufficient number of clients to provide a steady income. The limited association of two architects may be advantageous when an owner desires the design services of an architect remote from the site of the project. Two architects can associate and divide the work in such a manner that the architect near the site could take over the business arrangements and supervision of the project, while the other would handle the design. The fee would be split, usually on a percentage basis between the two architects, in proportion to the amount of time spent on the project by each office. Several architects may occupy a small building, pool their resources, and jointly hire one receptionist or secretary to act for all. They may have a central conference room available for the use of each. Draftsmen within such an office can easily be shifted from the work of one architect to another as the work load varies. This type of organization can, in many instances, keep several draftsmen and a specifications writer busy. It is then a matter of allocating the hours spent on each project by the draftsmen and specifications writer. Each architect can, by this method, have the services of a specialist closely associated with him but avoid the problem of finding work for several draftsmen and a specifications writer or of finding it necessary to lay them off when not needed.

SUPERVISING ARCHITECTS

Large corporations planning building programs that may extend over a period of years or be separated in widely spaced geographical locations many times wish their programs to be coordinated by one architect or engineer. They may commission several architects for individual projects which will be designed under the overall direction of a "supervising architect." This helps to assure a continuity of design in a building program that may be widely separated by time or distance. States, counties, cities, school districts, large universities, and other public bodies may employ architects on a fee basis or as full-time employees to supervise their entire construction programs.

INCORPORATION

Architectural practice does not seem to lend itself to incorporation except in the extremely large offices. In fact, according to provisions written into licensing or registration laws in some states, architects—like doctors, lawyers, and other professional people—are not permitted to conduct their business in corporate form. In other states, they may do so but are under stringent regulations. There are seeming advantages to incorporation of even the small office. The limiting of liabilities and risk, the permanence of the practice, and the flexibility of operation are advantages. However, the practice of architecture is a very personal undertaking, and nothing can be more impersonal than a corporaation. When a client engages an architectural firm, it is with the understanding that he can be assured that all major decisions on both the design and the technical aspects of the building program will receive the personal attention of the architect. The hiring of an impersonal corporation does not fit into most clients' idea of this personalized service. Also, the additional taxes, state control, complicated records, and bookkeeping systems required soon make the apparent advantages of questionable value to the individual architect.

OFFICE ORGANIZATION

The internal organization of an architectural office, whether it is under one principal, a partnership, or an association must set up a procedure for communication and operations. The chain of command and the designation of responsibilities must be understood by all. Each new employee should be informed of office practices, his responsibilities, and the benefits he may expect. Offices may be classed as having a vertical or a horizontal type of management.

Vertical Management. If one individual has charge of a project from the start to the completion, the management is classified as having a vertical organization. It makes no difference whether this individual is a principal or an associate. He might be an architect employed by an architectural firm and called a "project architect." He acts as designer, project manager, assigner, job management head, supervisor, crew supervisor, specifications writer, and chief draftsman. The advantages of this type of organization are the continuity of effort and the ease and simplicity of communication. The responsibilities are clear-cut, and all phases of design, planning, and construction are coordinated. While this type of organization may work well in small offices, it tends to

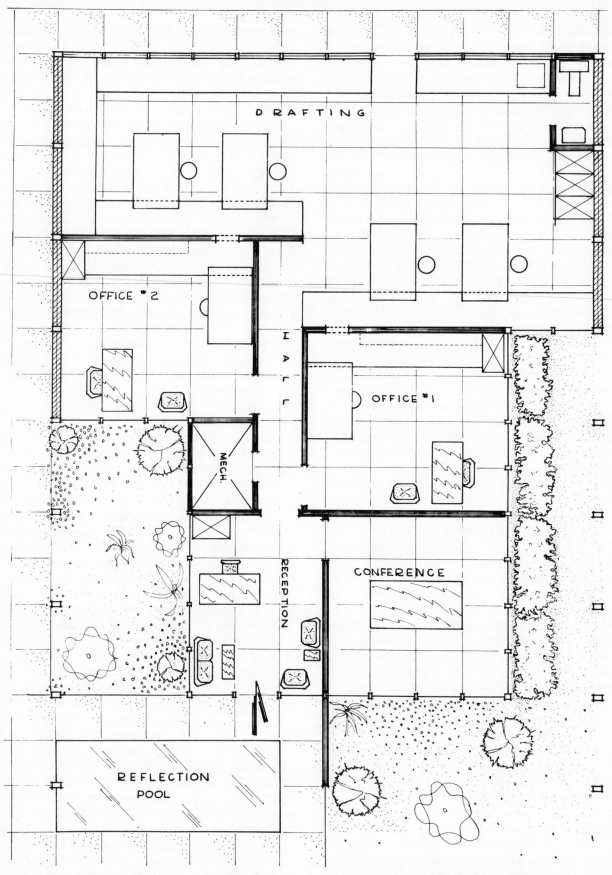

Fig. 3-1. Floor plan for a small architectural office of associated architects.

become inefficient when the work force is increased beyond twenty or thirty employees. Since all phases of the design and construction process do not proceed at the same pace, each employee must be able to perform several tasks well or be idle a portion of the time.

Horizontal Management. If an office is large enough, departments can be formed. Each department or section then has charge of only one phase of the work under the overall direction of a production manager. This type of organization tends to be more efficient in some ways. If the volume of work is sufficient, full use can be made of the abilities and experience of each employee. Each project has a project architect or a project coordinator who, while he does not have direct control over all members of the staff, expedites and coordinates the work of each department. The organization chart shown in Fig. 3-2 illustrates the line of command and departmentalization of one large office.

PERSONAL CONTACTS WITH INDUSTRY

Few people realize the personal contacts that are behind the preparation of a set of contract documents. People who contact the architect or engineer daily seldom do the actual drawing or writing, but their assistance is invaluable in the design of a complex building. Industry, through its literature, societies, institutes, and associations, influences governmental agencies. Industry sets standards, provides facilities, and supports testing programs that would not be possible for the architect to carry out. There are few specifications that do not require some personal contact with an industry representative. Often, industry-employed scientists are needed in the search for the right materials or methods to accomplish a particular result. These people come into the architect's or engineer's office and work with him on special problems. In most instances, they can be trusted to give reliable information. However, there are always some who attempt to take advantage of this opportunity to sell their product, regardless of its adaptability. It takes experience to weed out this type of individual. The honest representative of industry will so advise an architect or engineer if his product will not work and will suggest another, even though it may be the product of a competitor. He thereby earns the architect's confidence and can be assured that his product will be considered for other jobs in the future. The architect must be able to trust a consultant in order to do his job.

CONSULTANTS

Even the largest offices, though they may employ many persons, find the services of consultants valuable in planning a complex project. The services of these consultants may be made available to the architect or engineer by one specific manufacturer or an association of manufacturers, or a consultant with a private practice may be employed. Experts in a particular phase of the construction industry will assist the architect or engineer in the preparation of the contract documents.

Manufacturers' Representatives. As an example of the first type of consultant, the representative of a manufacturer of air-conditioning equipment may come into the architect's or engineer's office, calculate the requirements for heating and cooling, and make recommendations of equipment to be used to meet the needs. To be sure, he will recommend that the equipment to be used be manufactured by his company. However, this equipment may be installed by any number of contractors who distribute or install this product, thereby not eliminating competition entirely. Most firms have architectural representatives whose entire responsibility is to keep architects and engineers informed on the latest products manufactured by their firms and to recommend methods of installation. They furnish literature, information, and guide specifications on their products. The architect or engineer may call in several competitors, at different times, to advise him. It is then his responsibility to evaluate this information and make a choice of one or to specify several and leave the final choice to the contractor.

Hardware Consultants. Most large building-hardware firms employ members of the American Society of Hardware Consultants to assist architects in selecting the correct hardware for a building. Members of this organization can usually be depended upon for unbiased advice on hardware problems. They have gone through a prescribed period of training and passed a rather rigid examination. They must agree to a strict code of ethics before they can become members of

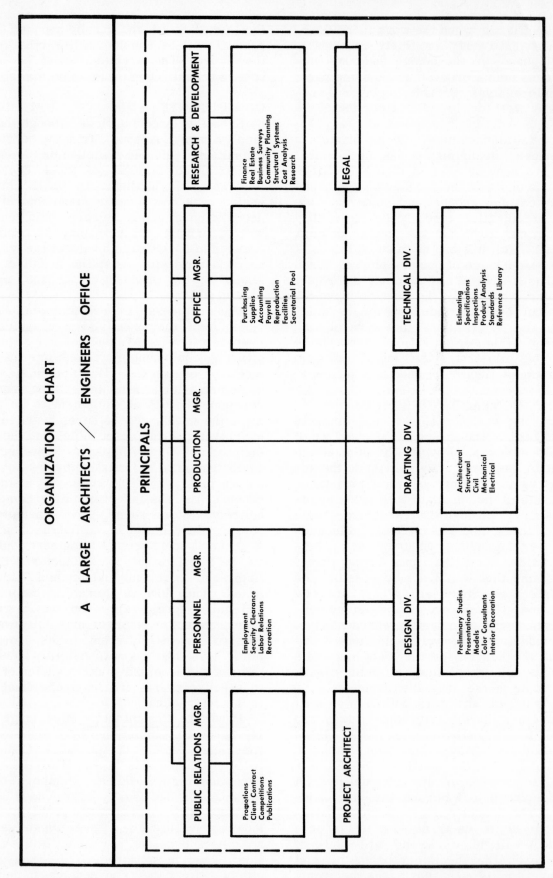

Fig. 3-2. An organization chart for a large office of architects-engineers.

18

the society. They come into the architect's or engineer's office and, at no charge, advise him on installation problems and take off a list of the items that will be necessary and suitable for the job. They give the name, make, and catalog number of each item. In addition to designating items distributed by the company which employs them, they usually list items they believe to be comparable in quality and cost that are manufactured by their competitors. The architect soon learns whether the items they have specified are not competitive by the reaction of contractors bidding on a job. The architect must learn from experience whether the advice of a consultant, called in to assist him, is dependable.

Association Representatives. A group of manufacturers, distributors, or applicators of a basic product may join together for industry-wide promotion. This association then hires experts, possibly architects or engineers, to assist other architects and engineers in solving the problems peculiar to their product. Among these are the Ceramic Tile Institute, American Institute of Steel Construction, Portland Cement Association, and many others. Most of these associations offer their services to investors, architects, consulting engineers, contractors, and governmental agencies to assist in choosing and utilizing the most suitable type of construction. If they are asked the name of a contractor, they generally name several who, because of plant, work force, and location, would be satisfactory. Under the classification "association representatives" could be included engineers who are employed by local gas or electric companies to assist the architect.

Consulting Engineers. Mention has been made of the role of soil mechanics engineers, structural engineers, civil engineers, mechanical engineers, and electrical engineers in the preparation of preliminary studies. These engineers also assist in the preparation of the working drawings and specifications. In addition to these engineers, the architect may need, on certain projects, the services of sanitation engineers, hydraulic engineers, electronic engineers, accoustical engineers, and other specialists.

Consulting Architects. Certain architects have made a specialty of, or had extensive experience in, a particular phase of construc-

tion, building type, or building use. There are architects who have had wide and intimate experience in the design of banks. Others have become expert in the operations of hospitals. Recently a promoter advertised for an architect who would be willing to study the operation of bowling alleys and to travel throughout the country assisting local architects in the design and planning necessary for the successful operation of bowling alleys. Such architects assist a local architect either on a fee basis or as an associate for a particular project. Landscape architects can be of great assistance on many projects requiring extensive site work combined with planting.

ARTISTS

The role of the artist in architecture is coming to be recognized more and more. Actually, this is not a new development. The artists of the Renaissance were the architects of their day. After many years, we are beginning to rediscover the importance of integrating art forms, prepared by artists, with our buildings. The painter, mosaicist, color consultant, and sculptor are being consulted, associated with, or retained by the architect to assist in the planning and integration of the various art forms to be used on an entire project. Many architects do not have the time or, possibly, the skill necessary to prepare large presentations in watercolor, tempera, or ink that are needed to show the appearance of a project to a client. This work may be turned over to artists for preparation. The number of artists, or architectural delineators, as they are sometimes called, that have set up studios or offices of their own, in order to assist architects, has greatly increased in recent years. They usually work on a fee basis or an hourly basis in producing these presentations for several architects. Many talented young designers find this a profitable business or sideline while they are preparing themselves and studying the more technical aspects of building construction which they must master to become architects.

ARCHITECTURAL PHOTOGRAPHERS

Photographs of project sites, work under construction, and completed projects are constantly assuming more importance. The taking of pictures of architectural and engineering projects has become a specialty of a large number of photographers. Architectural photography requires certain unique skills and techniques in order to be entirely effective. The architect usually calls in a professional photographer if he does not feel he can do the photography himself. Many clients insist that a photographic record be made of the project, and the time, type, and number of photographs will be described by the specifications writer. This item can be costly, and the responsibility for payment of this expense must be clearly stated in the specifications.

SPECIFICATIONS CONSULTANTS

Many small offices, and some large offices, find it is more efficient to entrust the writing of the specifications to a specifications consultant, sometimes called a "free-lance" specifications writer. This is done in preference to employing a man to do the writing for all projects or using a draftsman or an associate to do this work. By calling in a specialist in specifications writing only when he is needed, an office can avoid carrying on its staff a well-paid employee whose full capabilities cannot always be used because of variations in work load. The specifications consultant usually sets up an office and employs stenographers and helpers necessary to turn out and reproduce complete sets of specifications for several architectural or engineering firms. He may even employ writers to assist him as he develops contacts and expands his consulting practice. The free-lance specifications writer may be an engineer, an architect, or a person who has the inclination, ability, and knowledge to write good specifications. Many talented people, desiring to operate their own businesses, have entered the field of free-lance specifications writing.

Status of a Specifications Consultant. The practice of architecture and engineering is regulated by each state, and the question has arisen of whether the specifications consultant, who prepares the specifications for an architect or engineer on an hourly basis, on a lump-sum basis agreed upon in a contract, or on the basis of a percentage of project cost, is practicing architecture or engineering. The specifications writer, in this instance, operates in an office separate from that of the architect or engineer. A survey

was made several years ago to determine the attitude of each state on this question.[1] All but one state replied to the effect that, inasmuch as the specifications consultant works under the direction of the architect or engineer, who checks the work while in progress and who checks and signs the specifications before they are issued, is not practicing architecture or engineering without a license. The state of Indiana, the one exception, stated that such a practice would be considered, by definition, the practice of architecture and would require a license.

ORDER OF PREPARATION

The contract documents usually cannot all be prepared by the architect's or engineer's office at the same time. The invitation to bid, unit prices, alternate proposals, wage rates, and others must be based on the nearly completed working drawings and specifications. Although the basic outline specifications may be prepared during the preliminary stages of design, the specifications writer cannot proceed with the final instructions until he is sure that most of the details and construction problems have been solved. The exact time that will be required to prepare each of the contract documents is very difficult to determine. The architect or engineer must estimate the time that will be needed to complete each document and then organize his work force in such a manner that all documents will reach completion in plenty of time for checking before they are issued to contractors. In a small office, handling only one or two projects at a time, this can be quite simple; but in a large office, involved in many and diversified projects, the scheduling can become very complicated. The scheduling or budgeting of time and money to be spent on each phase of design tends to run to extremes. In one office, the philosophy may be that the time spent in preparing a set of documents is not of primary importance. All that matters is that they be entirely complete in every respect, no matter how long this takes. The other extreme is illustrated by the office that sets up an unrealistic budget and, when that budget—in either time or money—is used up, says, "Roll up the drawings and send them

[1]As reported in Progressive Architecture, January, 1956, in an article by Joseph A. McGinnis, former national president of the CSI.

out, complete or not. We have to make a profit on this job. If any problems come up on the job, we'll take care of them there. Maybe the contractor is smart enough to figure it out for himself." A realistic, flexible budget can be set up only after a careful analysis has been made of the project.

PREPARATION OF THE WORKING DRAWINGS

When the client or owner has given a written approval of the preliminary plans, the architect and engineers may begin the preparation of the working drawings. The method of preparing working drawings has undergone considerable change in recent years. In the past, many beginning draftsmen were employed in tracing drawings, in ink on linen cloth, from pencil drawings made by senior draftsmen. While some clients may still demand this, and although a few architects still prefer to follow this procedure, the majority of drawings today are made in pencil on a good grade of transparent rag paper. The advantages of drawing in ink on linen are the long-lasting quality of linen and the nonfading property of india ink. However, nonfading long-lasting "autopositive" photographic reproductions of original drawings can now be made on linen that are acceptable to most clients who at one time insisted upon ink on linen.

APPEARANCE OF WORKING DRAWINGS

The appearance of a set of drawings prepared by an architect's or engineer's office usually reflects the philosophy of the principal. At its extremes, this philosophy may vary greatly. One architect may feel that these drawings are merely instructions to the workman on the job, and he therefore insists that all notes be written in bold letters and that details of every item on the project be drawn at as large a scale as possible. If every item could be drawn at full scale, he would be happy. If the notes are on the drawings—even though they are written in longhand—this is satisfactory, as long as they are big. Dimensions and sizes, according to some, should appear on each plan, section, and detail, even though they are repeated elsewhere, with the possibility of error being multiplied at each repetition. No matter where a workman looks, he will find a dimension. Details and notes are scattered over drawings near the larger sections, elevations, or plans, wherever there is a vacant space.

A second architect may believe that the appearance of a set of drawings issued by his office is of extreme importance. He says, "The drawings issued by my office are the only means of advertising that is available to me. I want all who look at these drawings to realize how careful and professional I am. I do not want a client to think that I continually forget items and must crowd in details wherever I can find room. When a client shows, with pride, a good-looking set of my drawings to friends and associates, I have potential new clients. Every note, drawing, or detail must be aligned and organized in such a manner as to present a neat appearance. Dimensions will appear only once, and then only in a specific location.

RESPONSIBILITIES OF THE DRAFTSMAN

In most offices, the number of draftsmen employed at any one time will vary. This means that many architectural or engineering draftsmen will move from one office to another. The draftsman who works in only one office throughout his career, is rare, and in order to be successful, a draftsman must be able to adapt to the changing conditions found as he moves from one job to another. While most offices do not conform entirely to either of the philosophies mentioned earlier, the new employee must discover and analyze existing office practices and strive to conform. Originality in design may be a desirable quality, but working drawings most present a uniform appearance regardless of which draftsman prepares them. A unique alphabet developed by a draftsman may be interesting to a designer, but the new draftsman must look for the particular style of lettering used most commonly by that particular office and be able to match that style. He must be able to produce drawings that will present a uniform appearance in content, line quality, and lettering and that will fit in with all others produced in that office. There is no definite point in time or experience when a junior draftsman becomes a senior draftsman or job captain. This depends upon the gradual accumulation of additional knowledge of construction processes and the ability to adapt to changing drafting techniques. A draftsman may be considered a senior man in an office specializing in residences but be unsatisfactory in an office with a broad practice.

JOB CAPTAIN

In a small office, the preliminary studies may be turned over to one senior or experienced draftsman, and in some instances he will prepare all the working drawings. In a larger office, a particular senior draftsman will be assigned as a job captain. This job captain will have the responsibility of carrying out the preparation of all working drawings for that job. He will analyze the preliminary studies and prepare a list of the drawings that will be needed to present a clear picture of exactly what will be involved in the project. The job captain must organize and give titles to each sheet that will be needed. The titles must be comprehensive but brief. These titles will be copied on the index to the drawings and must indicate exactly what will be included on each.

INFORMATION TO SPECIFICATIONS CONSULTANTS

Specifications consultants who are not working in the architect's office and who will prepare the specifications must have access to all information on a project as soon as possible. Most consultants have checklists which they furnish to the architect. They also have forms that can be filled out by the draftsman as he prepares the detailed drawings necessary for the project. The consultant must receive constant reports on the progress being made in the preparation of the drawings so that he can schedule his time in such a way as to complete the specifications when they are needed. It is a mistake to expect an outside consultant to take a completed set of drawings and, with no advance information, turn out a complete, accurate, and comprehensive set of specifications in an impossibly short period of time and under the pressure of all concerned who are constantly insisting on speed.

CHECKING OF DOCUMENTS

No matter how experienced or how careful a draftsman, specifications writer, or consultant has been, there is always the possibility of errors or omissions in the drawings or specifications. If sufficient time has been allowed, a final and complete check should be made of all contract documents, one against the other. Unfortunately, because of improper scheduling this is not always possible, and many times this lack of checking can lead to serious discrepancies. The checking should be performed by a third party to be completely successful. The person who has been intimately involved in the preparation of the specifications or the drawings may overlook items or inconsistencies in his work because of his very familiarity with it. His language or wording may convey clear and definite meanings to him but may be interpreted quite differently by another. One large office insists that all drawings and specifications be checked thoroughly by the inspector who will supervise the actual construction. It is felt that by following this procedure, the number of embarrassing and possibly costly questions that may come up after contracts are signed can be reduced. In some offices, the job captain checks the completed specifications against his drawings, and the specifications writer checks the completed drawings against the specifications he has prepared. This double checking is very important in assuring the conformity and completeness of all construction documents.

THE BIDDING PERIOD

The period between the completion of the contract documents and the awarding of a contract to the successful bidder is known as the "bidding period." Many problems that arise during this period can be avoided if careful attention is given to the wording of the instructions to the bidder. If the bidders are made aware of the procedures required during this period, there will be less chance of a bidder being disqualified at the bid opening because of a technicality. The exact information to be included in the instructions to bidders will be covered later; these instructions must not be taken lightly or considered to be of minor importance.

ADDENDA

After the contract documents have been prepared, they are picked up at the architect's office by contractors who will prepare bids for the project. It is usually necessary to give additional instructions or clarifications to the bidders during the bidding period. These instructions, if they cover only one item, constitute an "addendum." If the instructions are concerned with several different items or issues, they become the "addenda." Addenda are issued before the contractor submits his bid. They are added to, and become part of, the original contract and are noted as such when a contract is signed by the owner and the contractor. Any instructions issued by the architect after the contract is signed constitute a "change order" and alter the terms of the contract. Addenda may be necessary to clear up points or discrepancies in the contract documents. The form to follow and precautions to be observed when writing addenda will be covered later; however, a brief description of the reasons for addenda is given here.

Verbal Instructions. Errors, discrepancies, and omissions are often called to the attention of the architect or engineer during the bidding period. It is not fair to the other bidders if clarifications are given over the telephone or in person to only one bidder because the bidder who receives the verbal instructions then has an advantage over the others. Only written instructions should be given, and then each bidder must receive a copy. A bidder may be informed that an addendum will be issued, but he should read and interpret this for himself when he receives it. Only written instructions can be made a part of the contract documents when an agreement is signed.

Purpose of Addenda. Addenda are necessary to correct any discrepancies between the drawings and the specifications, to increase or decrease the scope of the project, to change the quality of the work, to extend the bidding period, or to make other similar changes. Addenda are written and issued to each bidder during the bidding period to clear up any discrepancies that may be found at this time. These addenda may include drawings or sketches prepared by a draftsman to eliminate any possible misunderstanding. It is difficult, and in many instances dangerous, to make changes on the original drawings, make new prints, call in the drawings that the various bidders are using to prepare bids, substitute the altered drawings, and return them to the bidders, all in the usually short time the bidder has in which to prepare a bid. Instead of this type of change, addenda are sent to all bidders explaining in detail the proposed change. Any revision of the original drawings should be deferred until after the contract has been awarded. These addenda must be prepared and issued in time for the contractors who are bidding to make adjustments in their bids. Some offices set this date as five days prior to the bid opening. A statement must appear in the proposal that the addenda have been received and their numbers listed.

PLAN CHECK BY GOVERNMENTAL AGENCIES

During the bidding period or, in some instances, before the final completion of all documents, the engineering calculations, drawings, and specifications must be submitted to various governmental agencies, zoning commissions, or building departments by the architect for a "plan check." This checking of all the contract documents may be very extensive and may be done by several agencies. It may consist of simply a routine submission of the drawings with a request for a building permit to be issued by a local building department. The plan check may require as little as a week's time, or it may consume many months as the documents are sent from one office to another of the state and local fire marshall, division of architecture, state department of education, state division of schoolhouse planning, national hospital board, county engineers, city planning commissions, and any other agency that may be involved in a particular project. Unfortunately, many of these agencies have different or even conflicting requirements that must be met, and an agreement must be reached to resolve any conflicts caused by these divergent requirements. Drawings and specifications must be altered if the plans are to be approved before the project is let out to bid. If the checking is not completed until sometime during the bidding period, addenda must be written that will alter the contract documents so that they will comply with all agency requirements or requests. It would seem logical to obtain answers or rulings from each agency before the planning is completed. However, these are usually difficult or, in some cases, impossible to obtain until the documents are complete.

PROPOSAL

At the completion of the bidding period, each contractor must submit a proposal. This is a document prepared by the architect or engineer for use by each contractor who submits a bid on the project. In order for the architect to analyze the proposals, the same form must be used by all bidders. The proposal should be so written that all bidders will be bidding on the same basis. To avoid any possible controversies, only bids submitted on the prepared form should be considered. The opening statements of this form are usually in the form of a letter, addressed to the owner and signed by the contractor, stating that the contractor agrees to furnish all work listed in the bid schedule in accordance with drawings and specifications if he is awarded a contract within the stated time, usually thirty days.

BID SCHEDULE

The bid schedule is part of the proposal and itemizes exactly what type of bid will be accepted. Usually the bidder is asked to state a certain amount of money, or a lump sum, for which he agrees to complete the entire project. On certain projects where it is difficult to determine exact quantities of work to be done, the bidders may be asked to submit unit prices for portions of the work.

UNIT PRICES

Unit prices are usually asked for on items of work which are variable, such as unexpected rock encountered during excavation, additional fill material needed, and extra paving requested by the owner. Unit prices should be asked only for items that are indefinite or impossible to estimate. Usually a limit is placed on the amount of work to be required above or below the estimated quantities, say, plus or minus 25 percent. The units should be of a small enough size and of such a nature that they are easy to estimate and evaluate.

ALTERNATE BIDS

If the owner desires to know how certain items will affect costs and wishes to take advantage of these price differences, the architect will include a description of alternate bids in the proposal. The proposal must state whether all bidders must submit alternate bids or not and on what basis the contract will be awarded. A bidder who has submitted a low lump-sum on a project may lose out because a higher bidder on a lump-sum basis has submitted lower bids on alternates. The bidder must know exactly on what basis the contract will be awarded.

TIME OF COMPLETION

The proposal must state the time of completion. In some instances this time is to be filled in by the contractor. If the time element is a major factor in the project and will affect the awarding of the contract, the bidder should

be notified of the fact. It is fairer to all concerned if the architect establishes this time of completion and notes it in the information to bidders. The only variable is then price.

BID BONDS

Along with submission of the proposal, certain documents are required. The contractor may be required to submit a bond made out by a surety company to assure the owner that the contractor will sign a contract if it is awarded to him. If the contractor does not sign the contract, the bid bond is forfeited and the owner can then choose another bidder. The bid bond is usually for an amount between 5 and 10 percent of the bid. The contractor is sometimes allowed to post a certified check or to use the form of a surety company, or he may be limited to a form prepared or furnished by the architect or engineer. The bid bond is canceled or the check returned after the contract is signed. See Fig. 3-3 for an example of a bid bond.

LIST OF SUBCONTRACTORS

A list of subcontractors whom the general or prime contractor proposes to use is sometimes required. This list is sometimes used by the architect in analyzing the bids that are close and is required by some governmental agencies. The use of such a list is believed by some architects to eliminate the practice of some contractors of attempting to cut their costs by playing one subcontractor against another. This is sometimes called "bid shopping" and is usually unfair to subcontractors. The subcontractor may lower his bid and then attempt to cut corners to make a profit. A list of subcontractors is sometimes required only of the successful bidder.

MATERIALS LISTS

In some instances, the specifications list several materials that will be acceptable, and the choice of which material actually will be installed is left to the contractor. He may be required to furnish a list of the exact materials he will use. If he wishes to furnish a substitute for a material specified, he is sometimes allowed to state the materials or processes he proposes to use and the cost savings that will be made possible for the owner by this substitution. The use of this procedure is questionable in that all bidders are not bidding on the same basis. If the owner wishes to accept

AIA DOCUMENT
SEPT. 1963 ED.

A310

BID BOND

KNOW ALL MEN BY THESE PRESENTS, that we

as Principal, hereinafter called the Principal, and

a corporation duly organized under the laws of the State of
as Surety, hereinafter called the Surety, are held and firmly bound unto

as Obligee, hereinafter called the Obligee, in the sum of

Dollars ($),

for the payment of which sum well and truly to be made, the said Principal and the said Surety, bind ourselves, our heirs, executors, administrators, successors and assigns, jointly and severally, firmly by these presents.

WHEREAS, the Principal has submitted a bid for

NOW, THEREFORE, if the Obligee shall accept the bid of the Principal and the Principal shall enter into a contract with the Obligee in accordance with the terms of such bid, and give such bond or bonds as may be specified in the bidding or contract documents with good and sufficient surety for the faithful performance of such contract and for the prompt payment of labor and material furnished in the prosecution thereof, or in the event of the failure of the Principal to enter such contract and give such bond or bonds, if the Principal shall pay to the Obligee the difference not to exceed the penalty hereof between the amount specified in said bid and such larger amount for which the Obligee may in good faith contract with another party to perform the work covered by said bid, then this obligation shall be null and void, otherwise to remain in full force and effect.

Signed and sealed this   day of   A.D. 19   ,

_____ {
———————————————————— (Seal)
Principal

———————————————————————
Title

_____ {
———————————————————— (Seal)
Surety

———————————————————————
Title

BID BOND
AIA DOC. A310   SEPT. 1963 ED.   ONE PAGE

© 1963 The American Institute of Architects   PAGE 1
1735 New York Ave NW., Washington, D. C.

Fig. 3-3. AIA Document No. A-310, Bid Bond, 1958 edition. (By permission of the American Institute of Architects.)

a substitute, he can do so after the contract is signed by issuing a change order.

SUBMISSION OF BIDS

The moment when bids are submitted and opened is a dramatic and tense one for all concerned. The owner has waited anxiously for months to see whether the project is within his budget. The architect is concerned with the accuracy of his preliminary estimate. Will the actual bid be above or below the figure he has designed toward? Each contractor is thinking of the possible thousands of dollars he has spent in estimating this project. Will it be wasted or paid for out of the profits he will receive from a successful building project? From this point on, the architect and engineers will be dealing with only the successful contractor. The architect and his employees are not through but are now starting on the construction management and supervision phase of the building project.

QUESTIONS

1. List eight duties of the architect after entering a contract with the owner.
2. Describe four types of architectural offices and give the advantages of each.
3. Discuss the advantages of an architect-engineer association.
4. What are the qualifications of a senior architectural draftsman?
5. Should an architectural draftsman develop a distinctive style of lettering? Why?
6. What is a limited association of architects?

AWARD OF CONTRACT

If only qualified contractors have been invited or allowed to bid on a project, the contract should generally be awarded to the lowest bidder. In most work for a public agency, the contract must, by law, be awarded to the lowest qualified bidder. If the lowest bid received is for an amount of money above that allocated for the project, all bids may be rejected and the architect may be asked to revise the drawings and specifications and prepare a new invitation for bid. If there are minor changes required in the drawings and specifications, changes in the bid can be negotiated with the successful bidder only before the agreement is signed.

ERRORS IN BID

If the bidder has not used the correct form for the submission of his bid, he may be disqualified and the next lowest bid accepted. If the error is not serious, the low bidder is usually allowed to correct his mistake and submit his bid on the proper form. If, after the bids have been opened, the lowest bidder claims that an appreciable error has been made, such as an error in addition, a transposition of numbers by a typist, or other such mistake, he is sometimes allowed to withdraw his bid and his bid bond is returned. He must prove, however, that there was no attempt to defraud. In some instances the contractor has been forced to proceed with the project even though he claims that there has been an appreciable error. It is not always in the best interests of the architect, engineer, or owner to insist on the signing and carrying out of an unprofitable contract. In many instances, the only way a contractor in this situation can stay in business is by cutting corners or substituting inferior materials. The architect can expect a satisfactory finished project only when the contractor expects to receive a fair profit from his work.

RETURN OF DRAWINGS AND SPECIFICATIONS

Each contractor who has submitted a bid on the project has been issued a set of drawings and specifications. It is the usual practice for the architect to require each bidder to post a deposit for these contract documents. This deposit is returned to each of the bidders when the drawings and specifications are returned. It is essential that all documents be accounted for at this time. A subcontractor may have removed a sheet of the drawings and several pages of specifications and retained them for future use. The official project drawings may subsequently be changed as the project progresses, and the subcontractor may bring the uncorrected sheets he has retained or sections of the specifications to the job with no knowledge of the subsequent changes. It is best to collect all documents, even from the successful bidder, and to reissue the documents to be used on the project. In this way, an accurate record of documents issued and their dates can be maintained in the architect's office. If any change is made during the progress of the project, notification of this change can be sent to everyone who has been issued a set of the contract documents.

ACCEPTANCE PERIOD

After the bids have been opened, the owner usually has thirty days or some other specific length of time (the acceptance period) in which to analyze the bids and to make an award of a contract. This time limit is designated in the bidding documents. If the owner wishes more time than is set forth in the bidding documents, he must expect a possible rise in the costs of labor and materials during this longer period of time. The contractor must assure himself that his materials dealers or subcontractors will guarantee their prices during this interval.

LETTER OF INTENT

There are times when it is to the owner's advantage that the contractor start construction before the formality of signing a contract is accomplished. When this is the case, the owner often issues a "letter of intent" to the contractor. This letter is signed by both parties and obligates both the owner and the contractor to enter into a contract at a later date. In the letter, there must be a statement that provides for suitable compensation to be made to the contractor should the owner not wish to sign a formal contract.

SIGNING OF AGREEMENT

The agreement is the formal contract signed by the owner and the contractor. It is usually not necessary to have witnesses present. The only purpose of witnesses would be to establish the validity of the signatures, and, except where forgery is involved, this is easily done. This document unites all the contract documents by reference. It identifies all the documents, including addenda, to be used on the project and acts as a condensation of the contract elements. The agreement contains clauses that designate the work to be done, the price to be paid, the time of starting, the time of completion, particulars concerning payments to the contractor, and other items necessary to regulate the work. Each party of the construction contract must sign the agreement. If it is an unincorporated company, the usual practice is to enter the company name followed by a signature and the title of the person signing. If either or both parties are corporations, it may be necessary to attach a corporate seal to the document or to include the minutes of the corporate board meeting with a resolution of the board of directors. If the contract is to be with a public agency, the contractor must be sure that the officer of the public agency has the authority to sign. Municipal ordinances sometimes provide that no department of the municipality can legally make a contract unless an appropriation has been previously made. In all large or complicated projects, it is always wise for both parties to obtain the services of an attorney to investigate all aspects of the agreement to be signed.

NOTICE TO PROCEED

The start of formal construction operations is usually preceded by a written "notice to proceed." This paper is prepared by the owner or the architect and informs the contractor of the time he can enter the property and start operations. The contractor has whatever amount of time is stated in the contract—usually ten days—in which to start construction.

PLAN CHECKING FEES

Before the contractor can start actual construction, a building permit must have been issued, in most instances by the local building department. Before this building permit is issued, the local building authority must have checked the plans and specifications to see that they follow the codes that will apply to the project. In many localities, the checking of the plans requires a plan-checking fee. The architect submits the plans and specifications to the building department for checking before the invitations to bid are issued. In this manner, any changes in the drawings or specifications that may be required can be made before the project is submitted to bid. If changes are required by the building department during the bidding period, it will be necessary for the architect to issue addenda in order to comply with new requirements. If the corrected drawings and specifications are received after the bid has been opened and a contract signed, a change order must be written which may affect the contract price. This fee is usually paid by the architect or the owner.

BUILDING PERMITS

The question of who will pay for the actual building permit is somewhat controversial. If the local building agency has set up separate fees for plan checking and building permits, and if the architect has had the documents approved, the contractor can ascertain exactly what the cost of the building permit will be and include the cost in his bid. The contractor knows the plans have been approved and can feel sure the contract documents will be followed. In this manner, the owner pays for the building permit eventually, but many feel that it is the owner's responsibility to apply and pay for the building permit directly. If the contractor is left the responsibility of putting the documents through the building department, how can he know what changes will be required? It will be the architect's responsibility to make any changes in the contract documents, so why should he not have the responsibility of presenting the drawings and applying for the

Speediset ® Moore Business Forms, Inc. e

INSTRUCTION: USE BALL POINT PEN, TYPEWRITER, OR HARD PENCIL. PRESS FIRMLY. BE SURE ALL COPIES ARE LEGIBLE. NO ERASURES PERMITTED. **A DOUBLE FEE WILL BE CHARGED IF WORK IS STARTED BEFORE PERMIT IS ISSUED.**

JOB ADDRESS

NUMBER	STREET

APPLICATION FOR A
BUILDING PERMIT
DEPARTMENT OF BUILDING, PASADENA, CALIF.

CONTRACTOR	STATE LIC. NO.
MAILING ADDRESS	TEL. NO.
☐ ARCH. ☐ ENGR.	STATE LIC. NO.
MAILING ADDRESS	TEL. NO.
OWNER	TEL. NO.
MAILING ADDRESS	

NEW ☐ ADD'N ☐ ALTER. ☐ REPAIR ☐ DEMOLISH ☐

FLOOR AREA (SQ. FT.)	NO. OF STORIES	NO. OF DWELLING UNITS
PRESENT BLDG. USE	PROPOSED BLDG. USE	

DESCRIBE WORK TO BE DONE

EXTERIOR WALL MATERIAL	ROOF FRAMING MATERIAL
PARTITIONING MATERIAL	ROOF COVERING MATERIAL

LOT WIDTH	LOT DEPTH	NO. OF EXISTING BLDGS. ON LOT

VALUATION NOTE: INCLUDE LABOR, MAT. WIRING, PLUMB., HEAT., ETC. $_____

INFORMATION PROVIDED BY ENGR. - ST. DEPT.

LEGAL DESCRIPTION_____

INFORMATION PROVIDED BY BLDG. SECTION

USE ZONE	FIRE ZONE	OCCU-PANCY	TYPE
REQ'D SET BACKS	FRONT	RIGHT SIDE	LEFT SIDE	REAR

APPEAL NO.	USE PERMIT OR VARIANCE NO.	PARK. SPACES REQ'D.

PLAN CHECK FEE	PERM. PLAN ☐	APPROVED BY
PERMIT FEE	APPROVED W/O PLAN ☐	

I have carefully read and examined the above application and find the same to be true and correct. All provisions of the Laws and Ordinances governing building construction will be complied with whether specified herein or not. No person shall be employed in violation of the Labor Code of the State of California. I agree not to occupy or allow occupancy of any building authorized by this permit until final building inspection has been received.

SIGNATURE OF OWNER OR AUTHORIZED AGENT ℗ e

PERMANENT

CK. CASH M.O. PLAN CHECK VALIDATION

CK. CASH M. O. NOTE: WHEN PROPERLY VALIDATED IN THIS SPACE, THIS FORM CONSTITUTES A BUILDING PERMIT TO DO THE WORK PRESCRIBED HEREIN.

INSPECTION RECORD

ITEM	REMARKS	DATE	INSPECTOR
SET BACKS			
EXCAVATIONS FORMS FTG, WIDTH & DEPTH, FTG. REINE ETC.			
SUB-FRAME			
MASONRY-CONCRETE REINE WALLS COLUMNS SLABS CHIMNEYS FENCES RETAIN. WALLS			
FRAME GLU. LAM. BMS.			
LATH INTERIOR EXTERIOR			
PLASTER SCRATCH BROWN			
PARKING			
SPECIAL CONDITIONS			
FINAL			

CORRECTIONS

Fig. 4-1. Application for plan check. (By permission of the Department of Building and Safety, city of Pasadena.)

permit? A common practice is for the owner to secure the building permit for the project as a whole and for the contractor to secure permits for work of a temporary nature, such as those for installing temporary power, doing work on public property, breaking curbs, repairing sidewalks, and building temporary barricades.

CONSTRUCTION PERSONNEL

The direct supervision of the project, including assignment of jobs to tradesmen, is handled by a contractor's superintendent or foreman. This superintendent may handle several small projects at one time or, if the project is large enough, be assigned to the one project from start to finish. Most architects will insist that a contractor's superintendent or foreman be on the job site at all times. This man has, in many instances, risen from the ranks and many times has a strong union background, which may make him inefficient as a member of management. The trend is toward using men who are graduate engineers.

Foremen. Under the direction of the construction superintendent may be foremen or leadmen of several crews, each performing a special type of work. These foremen and their crews may, in a large contractor's organization, be retained on a more or less permanent basis. However, unless the contractor has a large volume of work, the crew will be maintained only for the duration of its particular work on the project. A new crew would be formed for the next project. A man may form a crew of masons or painters, for instance, and work for several contractors during any given year.

Tradesmen. Most construction workers today are union members. Thus their wages, conditions of employment, hours, and permissible work are covered by agreements dictated by collective bargaining. Some areas of the country are more intensely organized than others. The architect who prepares the contract documents, especially the specifications, must understand the labor practices prevailing in the area in which the project is located. While labor unions have without a doubt bettered the position of the laboring man, they have not as yet settled all differences and disputes between themselves, nor have they been able to establish uniform acceptable trade practices throughout the country. The architect, engi-

neer, specifications writer, contractor, and estimator must all thoroughly understand the local practices and the limits imposed on each tradesman.

ARCHITECT'S SUPERVISION

Much litigation has come about because of differences of opinion regarding the responsibility and authority of the architect or engineer during the construction process. The architect acts as an agent of the owner and endeavors to protect him from any deviations from the drawings and specifications. He also attempts to guard against any defects in the project. His authority and duty are confined to seeing that the work is done according to the drawings and specifications. This he must do through periodic visits to the site. How often the architect or engineer visits the site will depend on the type, complexity, and size of the project. The frequency of his visits will be determined by what he feels, in his professional judgment, is sufficient to keep the owner informed on the progress of the work. This may be once a day, twice a week, weekly, or monthly, depending on the stage of the work. It is the architect's responsibility to issue certificates to the contractor when certain phases of the work have been completed or at the end of a particular period. These certificates are then presented to the owner by the contractor for payment of an agreed sum.

ARCHITECT'S SUPERINTENDENT

The owner who wishes to maintain a closer contact with the work than is provided by this periodic visitation must employ someone to be present on the job throughout working hours. Most architects and engineers recommend the hiring of such a person on all but the smallest jobs. This will be someone who is acceptable to the owner, the architect, and the engineer. He will be employed by the architect at a salary satisfactory to the owner and at the owner's expense. As such, he will be an agent of the architect who will be responsible for his actions or failures to act. The person stationed at the work may be called a "clerk of the works," "inspector," "project inspector," "superintendent," "project representative," "engineer's superintendent," or "architect's superintendent." Any of these titles may be used; however, the duties and responsibilities involved are similar. Here we shall call him the "architect's superintendent," as distin-

Department of Building — City of Pasadena
COMMERCIAL CONSTRUCTION REQUIREMENTS

LOCATION_____OWNER_____

To owner, architect, engineer and contractor: you are required to comply with the Pasadena Building, Electrical and Plumbing Codes and all other applicable ordinances within the City of Pasadena. The following minimum requirements are particularly pertinent to commercial construction and are listed only for your information and convenience.

PARKING

1. Complete plans showing parking layout, grading and drainage shall be submitted to Engineering-Street Department for approval.
2. Parking areas shall be enclosed with a concrete or masonry wall having a height of not less than two (2) feet and not more than six (6) feet. Where a parking area abuts the side or rear of a lot in a residential zone, a solid masonry or concrete wall five (5) feet in height shall be erected between the parking and residential areas.
3. A permit shall be obtained from the City Engineer before:
   a. Driving over or removing curb or sidewalk.
   b. Changing the slope of the area between curb and property line by more than one-quarter inch per foot.
   c. Constructing any paving in, or placing materials, fences, barricades or other obstruction upon or over any public street, alley, sidewalk or parkway.
4. The placing of temporary (Construction) toilets on or in any public street, sidewalk or parking is prohibited and any such installation may be removed by the City at the property owner's expense.
5. For all commercial and multiple dwellings which require automobile parking areas to be approved by the Engineering-Street Department, a plot plan and detailed parking layout are to be submitted to the Engineering-Street Department for checking at the time plans are submitted to the Building Department. (The Engineering-Street Department should be contacted regarding minimum parking lot requirements before final plans are submitted for checking).

VENTILATION

1. For office buildings, retail stores, garages, factories, workshops and similar uses:
   a. Ventilation by windows or skylights with an area of not less than one-eighth of total floor area.
   b. Ventilation by mechanical means requires two changes of air per hour.
2. Storage garages require mechanical ventilation sufficient to supply one complete change of air every 15 minutes.
3. For assembly buildings:
   a. Ventilation by windows or skylights with an area of not less than one-eighth of the total floor area.
   b. Ventilation by mechanical means requires a minimum of five (5) cubic feet per minute of outside air with a total circulated of not less than fifteen (15) cubic feet per minute per occupant.

HEAT AND VENTILATION DUCTS

1. Return air must be in incombustible ducts or one hour shafts. Corridors can not be used as return air plenums in forced air systems.
2. Duct openings in a required fire resistive ceiling shall be protected by fire dampers.
3. Air ducts passing through a floor shall be enclosed in fire resistive shafts. Dampers are required where ducts pierce shaft enclosure walls.
4. Openings for air ducts in a one hour corridor wall or occupancy separation shall be protected with fire dampers.
5. The passing of ducts through area separation walls shall be avoided wherever possible. When ducts pass through area separation walls they shall be provided with approved automatic fire doors on both sides of the wall. For openings less than eighteen (18) inches in diameter, a three-eighths inch steel plate may be used in lieu of fire doors.

TOILET ROOMS

1. Separate toilet facilities are required for each sex and the minimum number of facilities shall be as specified in Appendix C of the Pasadena Plumbing Code.
2. Floors and walls of toilet rooms in all commercial buildings and industrial buildings shall be finished with a smooth, hard surface of cement, tile or an approved equal. Walls shall be so finished to a height of four (4) feet above the floor.

ATTIC SEPARATION AND DROPPED CEILINGS

1. In wood frame roof construction, attic separations shall be divided into areas of not more than 2,500 square feet. Attic scuttles are required from the corridors into the attic.
2. In wood frame floor construction, where suspended ceilings occur, a separation between the ceiling and the floor above shall be divided into areas not exceeding one thousand square feet. An eighteen (18) inch by twenty-four (24) inch access crawl hole shall be provided into underfloor space.
3. Where drop ceilings occur below a required fire resistive ceiling:
   a. If an incombustible support system is used, either Class I finish material shall be used or three-eighths inch sheetrock backing installed under finish material other than Class I.
   b. If a combustible support system is used, a plastered ceiling or a five-eighths inch sheetrock ceiling is required.
4. Fire resistive ceilings may have openings for incombustible electrical outlets provided the total area of such openings do not exceed one hundred (100) square inches in one hundred (100) square feet. Openings in excess of this amount in a required one hour fire resistive ceiling must be covered with lath and plaster or five-eighths inch sheetrock.

DOORS AND EXITS

1. All exits are required to be openable from the inside without the use of a key or any special knowledge or effort. F or G occupancy buildings need not comply with this requirement if an approved metal permanent sign is located adjacent to the door stating in letters not less than one (1) inch high "THIS DOOR TO REMAIN UNLOCKED DURING BUSINESS HOURS".
2. Every door serving an occupant load of more than ten (10) shall open into a corridor, enclosed stairway, exterior stairway, exterior court or public way.
3. No openings are permitted into exit enclosures except doorways and openings in exterior walls.
4. In every building more than two stories in height, one stairway shall extend to the roof unless the roof has a slope greater than four in twelve.

MISCELLANEOUS

1. Masonry walls must be adequately braced at each floor during construction. Additional bracing at the midpoint of all walls shall be provided where the distance between lateral supports exceeds twenty (20) feet in height.
2. The building permit shall expire if work is not commenced within 60 days from the date of such permit or if work is suspended or abandoned at any time after work is commenced for a period of 120 days.

I understand that the above notes are now a permanent part of these plans and I agree to comply with all of the existing applicable ordinances of the City of Pasadena and understand that any less restrictive notations or details shown on my plans are superseded by these ordinances.

Signature_____   Date_____

Fig. 4-2. Building department correction sheet.

PUT IN A CONSPICUOUS PLACE ON THE JOB
INSPECTION RECORD CARD
DEPARTMENT OF BUILDING
City of Pasadena
Telephone SYcamore 2-6161

Location..

Permit No...................... Date..........................

Owner..

Contractor...

Excavation & Setback Inspections

To be Made Before Concrete is Poured	Setback...................
	Excavation................
	Ground Lines.............
	Sewer Grade..............

Masonry, Concrete & Reinforcing Inspections

To be Made Before Grouting or Placing of Concrete	Wall Forms...............
	Reinforcing
	Footings..............
	Walls.................
	Cells....................
	Bond Beam.............

Sub-Floor Inspections

To be Made Before Sub-Floor is laid	Foundations..............
	Joists & Sills............
	Plumbing.................
	Gas Lines................

Rough Inspections

To be Made Before Lath is Applied	Rough Plumbing..........
	Gas Lines................
	Wiring...................
	Heating..................
	Chimney.................
	Roofing..................
	Framing.................

Plaster and Stucco Inspections

To be Made After Lath and Wire are Applied	Scratch	
	Lath...........	
		Brown
	Wire...........	

Sewer Approved....................................

Finish Inspections

Do not Occupy Building Until These are Signed	Electrical...............
	Plumbing...............
	Building................

Note: Signature of Inspector after item designates approval. When properly signed this card is a Certificate of Occupancy.

1m 2-28-63 P4

Fig. 4-3. Sample building permit.

guished from the "contractor's superintendent."

Responsibilities of the Architect's Superintendent. The architect's superintendent is not on the job to direct the workmen, but to interpret the drawings and specifications. He should have the training of an architect and a fair knowledge of engineering principles if he is to make a true interpretation of the drawings and specifications. His job is not simply to see that the work proceeds according to the best practices of the trade; he must also be able to visualize a final effect that will be other than was intended in time to notify the architect before it is too late. While an intimate knowledge of the drawings and specifications and an understanding of his duties in enforcing the provisions found in them are important, the architect's superintendent must have the qualities of diplomacy and tact. In order for the job to run smoothly, he must make the workmen on the job feel that he is there to help them, not to spy on them. A spirit of cooperation should exist where each is doing his part to complete a successful project. In attempting to gain the confidence and cooperation of the contractor and tradesmen, however, the architect's superintendent must realize that he does not have the authority to relax, change, or nullify the requirements of the contract documents.

Clerical Duties of the Architect's Superintendent. The records kept by the architect's superintendent are extremely important. He must report regularly to the architect on the progress of the work. He must keep the contractor or any interested persons informed of all rulings, bulletins, or change orders issued by the architect or engineer. An accurate chart of the progress of each portion of the work must be kept up to date. Quantities of materials delivered to the job, erected, or installed must be noted carefully. A schedule of values must be set up at the beginning of the job. By dividing the total value set for a unit of work by the percentage of completion, a close check can be made of the time and money spent. From these schedules and charts, the architect can calculate the amount of money due the contractor and issue certificates for payment.

INSURANCE

The liability of all persons on the job must be considered. The architect may wish to take out errors and omissions insurance to protect himself in case of discrepancies in the contract documents which were not found during the bidding period. The contractor must carry insurance required by law, such as social security, federal old-age and survivors insurance, and workmen's compensation. He should carry public liability, property damage, and some form of contractor's protective insurance to protect himself. The owner, through his architect, must be certain that he receives certificates or notification from the contractor's insurance company that all required insurance is in effect before work is started. While the contractor must carry insurance to protect his workmen and should carry insurance to protect himself, this is not enough from the owner's point of view. The owner must carry insurance to protect himself from any claims. In case of an accident, the claimant will, in all probability, sue the contractor, the architect, and the owner. The owner must also carry insurance protecting the property in case of fire, theft, or damage. It is to the contractor's advantage to make sure the owner carries this insurance. The contractor should require that all his subcontractors carry compensation insurance and should decide which subcontractors should carry public liability insurance. The builder should require a certificate of insurance showing the coverage carried by his subcontractors on both types of insurance.

OWNER'S RESPONSIBILITY

Although the owner has appointed an architect or an engineer to act as an agent for him on the job, he still has certain responsibilities in relation to the work. Some of these were pointed out in the discussion of preliminary studies, such as the site and soil surveys he must furnish the contractor. It is the owner's responsibility to be sure that no acts of his delay the work. Instructions to the contractor must be in writing, submitted through the architect or his representative, in order to avoid confusion. If the owner intends to use a portion of the property during the progress of the work, this fact must be included in the contract documents. The fact that the owner intends to use a portion of the property before completion of the project may materially affect costs. The owner must pay promptly all bills presented in an approved manner through the architect.

OWNER'S RIGHTS

The owner has the right to stop the work and do work on the project if he follows the procedure set up in the contract documents. If the contractor should neglect the work, the owner, three days after he has given notice to the contractor of his intentions, may himself make good any deficiencies of the contractor. This notice of his intentions must be signed by the architect. The owner may then deduct the cost involved from the money due the contractor. This is a very delicate situation, and the owner or architect must proceed with extreme care if he wishes to avoid legal action. If the contractor can satisfy the owner that he has remedied the defects, the owner may refuse to take action or may take action at any reasonable time after the three days. The owner may terminate the contract upon the certificate of the architect that sufficient cause exists to justify such action. This may be done seven days after the contractor has been notified of the action. This procedure is undertaken only after all other attempts have failed and is usually a prelude to court action.

OWNER'S INSPECTORS

In addition to the architect's superintendent, in certain instances the owner may have other personnel on the site to check the progress of the work. This is especially true with large corporations or where the owner is a governmental agency. School boards in the larger municipalities usually have inspection departments composed of specialists who assist the architect's superintendent in certain phases of the control. Their job is usually more specific than that of the architect's superintendent, who must oversee the entire job. The owner's inspector comes on the job during certain phases of construction and, while there, conducts a detailed inspection of a particular installation or method. His report is then made to the architect's superintendent for follow-up.

LOCAL BUILDING DEPARTMENT INSPECTORS

It is the duty of local departments of building and safety to ensure that every building constructed in the area conforms to the local code. The field inspection provided by a building department is an important function in assuring that buildings are constructed properly and that the provisions of the codes are lived up to. Building permits are granted by building departments after a careful check of the plans and specifications. This checking, no matter how painstaking, is not absolute assurance that there is nothing contained in the documents that violates some section of the code. The building inspector, therefore, must know the code thoroughly in addition to being familiar with the drawings and specifications. Work that violates the code, even though detailed on the drawings which were passed during the plan check, must be stopped and brought to the attention of the contractor. There is sometimes a tendency on the part of the building inspector to enforce personal ideas about how things should be done. In doing this, the inspector removes himself from the protection of the code and becomes personally responsible for any damage done by his requiring something which is illegal. The contractor and the architect's superintendent cannot rely on the building inspector to supervise the work. If the superintendence by the architect's superintendent is lacking, it is not safe to assume that the local building department will fulfill the need. In some instances, notably projects by school boards and state and national agencies, the local building departments have no authority to act. If the local building department does not have authority to act on a particular project, there are usually agencies that take over this responsibility. It may be the state division of architecture, the state division of school house planning, the state hospital board, or any one of several governmental agencies. It is well for both the architect's representative and the contractor to find out exactly who has authority over a particular project.

REPORTS TO GOVERNMENTAL AGENCIES

On certain types of projects, for example, construction of a school, the contractor must agree to make a report from time to time, upon prescribed forms, that the work has been performed in accordance with approved drawings and specifications. Several states have this regulation.

FIRE MARSHAL INSPECTORS AND OTHER AGENCIES

Most states, municipalities, and communities have established offices of fire marshals for the purpose of promoting fire-safety campaigns and eliminating fire hazards. This function is usually assigned to the local fire department. Many communities have a housing division which is interested in what is going into a project. There may be a department of public safety that will inspect a project for compliance with its rulings. Departments of public welfare and public streets, the Industrial Accident Commission, the Federal Housing Administration, and the state housing authority all may have inspectors on the project from

time to time. To satisfy all these agencies, which unfortunately sometimes have conflicting regulations, requires an unlimited amount of understanding, patience, diplomacy, and tact on the part of the owner, the architect, the engineer, and the contractor.

MANUFACTURERS' INSPECTORS

Certain manufacturers and associations employ inspectors who check on the quality of materials delivered and installation procedures followed where their products are involved. The manufacturers provide this service for two reasons. First, it is a means of checking on those applicators who have been approved and recommended or have been given agencies to apply the manufacturer's product. The manufacturer knows that unless his product is installed properly, it will fail. Secondly, this type of service to the architect is good public relations. The manufacturer's representative comes on the job, inspects the surfaces or structures to which his product will be attached, watches during application, and checks the finished work. Manufacturers of roofing materials, in most instances, provide this service. It is sometimes necessary to require this inspection in the specifications and, in the case of a bonded roof, pay for it. Associations of manufacturers will check materials and installations and stamp approved material or work.

CONTRACTOR CLASSIFICATION

In the past, it was not unusual for a contractor to carry, as employees, tradesmen who were proficient in many crafts. With a work force which was large and versatile and which he paid by the hour or the week, he was able to complete a complicated project himself. He was the boss, and any problems with workmen on the job could be handled by him. However, the advent of unions, the age of specialization, and the growing complexity of modern construction have made it impossible for one contractor to control all workmen on the job directly. The general or prime contractor, as he is now called, contracts with members of his crew to handle a portion of the work on a lump-sum basis. In this manner, the contractor delegates small parts of his authority and concentrates on larger portions of the construction process. This specialization in only small portions of the work has progressed to the point where one state now licenses over thirty-three separate categories of contractors. Following is a partial list of the contractors licensed by this state:

General (engineering)
General (building)
Insulation
Boilers, hot-water heating, steam fitting
Cabinet and millwork
Cement and concrete
Electrical (general)
Elevator installation
Excavating, grading, trenching, paving, surfacing
Flooring (wood)
Fire-protection engineering
Glazing
Warm-air heating, ventilating, air conditioning
House and building moving
Structural pest control
Ornamental metals
Lathing
Landscaping
Masonry
Painting, decorating, paperhanging
Plastering
Plumbing
Refrigeration
Roofing
Sewer, sewage disposal, drain, cement, pipe laying
Sheet metal
Electrical signs
Steel (reinforcing)
Steel (structural)
Swimming pools
Tile (ceramic or mosaic)
Well drilling
Welding
Classified specialists

SUBCONTRACTORS

The practice of general contractors of dividing up the work necessary to complete a project and entering into a contract with others to perform a portion of the work has become established in the construction industry. In fact, in many areas, the general contractor has become simply a broker, not a builder at all. He assumes as little responsibility as possible and confines his efforts to obtaining subbids, collecting money under the general contract, paying subcontractors, and collecting what he hopes will be 10 percent or more profit for work done by others. He tries to place the responsibility of settling disputes between subcontractors upon the architect's representative, and he depends upon the specifications writer to divide the work in such a manner that the entire job can be performed with none of the responsibility falling to him. If the architect wishes to avoid this type of contractor and the possible loss of coordination of the work, he must investigate the contractor's organization carefully and include in the agreement a statement explaining what he will expect from the contractor. The minimum work force that most architects feel is essential, on most jobs, consists of a contractor's full-time superintendent or foreman and a crew of carpenters and laborers.

Subcontractors and General Contractors. Most contractors sublet portions of the work to specialists. These specialists are considered his employees, whether they are paid by the hour, piece, or job. As employees of the general contractor, they are mentioned in the specifications only through the instructions to the general contractor, if at all. Each general contractor may have a different method of breaking down the work to be done on a project. How he will sublet any portions of it is his decision. The architect may include in the contract documents a form of subcontract that the bidder must use. However, this is more for the protection of the contractor than of the owner. The general contractor will be responsible for the acts or omissions of his employees regardless of the type of contractual relation that may exists between them.

Relation of Owner and Subcontractor. There is no contractual relation between the owner and a subcontractor. If the architect wishes to give directions to a subcontractor, either in the specifications or on the job, it must be through the general contractor with whom the owner has a written agreement. If a subcontractor wishes to register a complaint against another subcontractor, this must be settled by the general contractor. An instance such as this would be considered the same as an argument between two of the general contractor's employees. The general contractor has agreed to furnish a complete job. How he breaks down his work and how he deals with his employees are not the architect's responsibility.

OTHER PRIME CONTRACTORS

In many instances, the owner wishes to have

more than one general or prime contractor perform work on a project, and he then enters into contracts with more than one prime contractor. Some governmental agencies require that certain parts of the work, such as plumbing, heating and ventilation, and electrical work, be let on an individual basis. It is sometimes advantageous for a private owner to let portions of the work to specialists. Items of work such as structural-steel erection require specialized equipment, crews, and skills which have become the specialty of some contractors. This method, when carried to an extreme, is called letting the job on a "segregated contract" basis.

SEGREGATED CONTRACTS

The administration of a project on a segregated basis imposes a great deal more responsibility on the architect. He, in effect, must now act as the general contractor and coordinate the work. This does give him closer control over the project but involves the expenditure of more time. For this extra work, he usually receives a larger fee, which tends to balance any savings the owner might realize from eliminating the prime contractor. Another reason that segregated contracts seldom result in any savings is that each subcontractor who now becomes a prime contractor, usually adds to his bid to guard himself against possible delays or controversies that may stem from the division of authority on the job.

COORDINATION BETWEEN CONTRACTORS

When more than one prime contractor is to work on a project, it is very important that the work, authority, and responsibility of each be carefully spelled out in the specifications. This is comparatively simple when the breakdown of the work is such that only one prime contractor is performing work during a certain period of time. If one prime contractor is performing the rough grading, he will usually be finished before the steel erector comes on the site. The structural-steel frame may be completed before the carpenters or masons have proceeded very far. The major portions of the structures will be complete when the landscape contractor arrives on the job site. There are very few contractors who do not object strenuously to another contractor performing work on the project at the same time. The construction of a complex modern building requires that each part be installed on a pre-

cise time schedule. The boilers and condensers for heating and air conditioning must be attached to the structural frame. Piping and ducts pierce structural members and must be covered with finish material. Lighting must be integrated with ceilings. The coordination of the installation of these many times is extremely important.

MATERIALS STORAGE

The storage of materials on many projects can create problems. Someone must designate storage areas for each of the prime contractors. If the site is limited, this storage space can be critical. The storage areas must be in locations where the materials of one contractor will not interfere with the work of another. If the work is under the direction of a single prime contractor, this is his responsibility. If it is under several, the areas designated for storage must be allocated and limited by the specifications. The manner in which material is received and stored can effect job costs. Certain materials must be protected from the weather, while provisions for covering others would entail needless expense. Some items may be checked onto the job by a simple glance, while others must be checked, item by item, against the contract documents. Some items must be protected from vandalism or theft, while others need not be. In considering what measures should be taken when receiving and storing materials on the job, the following questions should be asked:
1. What can be done to make sure we receive everything we sign for and that it is correct?
2. Is it easy to steal?
3. Is it worth stealing?
4. Can the weather hurt it?
5. Does the risk of loss justify the cost of protection?

CONFLICTS BETWEEN PRIME CONTRACTORS

If the work is let to one prime contractor, it is his responsibility to settle any disputes that arise between his subcontractors or employees. If several prime contractors are on the job, this is the responsibility of the architect or his representative. Notices may be included in the specifications requiring the various contractors to cooperate. The responsibilities of each must be carefully spelled out. However, conflicts may arise in the interpretations of the documents, and it will require the use of all the knowledge, diplomacy, and tact we spoke of earlier on the part of the architect's representative to keep the job running smoothly.

MATERIALS DEALERS

The materials dealers chosen to furnish the material for the project are the responsibility of the contractor or subcontractors. However, the delivery of these materials and their storage become the responsibility of the prime contractor. On a limited site, the schedule of deliveries must be set up well in advance of need. This schedule is then kept up to date and revised to coincide with any changes of production schedules. A close check must be kept by the architect's superintendent. In many cases, payment to the contractor may be due when certain materials are delivered to the job site. The architect's superintendent must insist that those items that are to be delivered in their original containers or packages and marked in a certain manner be received as specified. He must check samples and test reports that accompany the materials. He must see that they are stored in the designated areas.

BARRIERS

Barriers or barricades may be needed on many job sites to protect the public or workmen on the job. If the project is large, these barricades may be detailed on the drawings or described in the specifications. In other instances, the type and location of barriers may be left to the contractor's judgment. The specifications may simply state that barriers shall be erected and maintained where necessary to protect the public or workmen. Many municipalities require certain barriers where the work borders a public thoroughfare. The Industrial Accident Commission requires that certain safeguards be maintained. Insurance companies have rulings on safety precautions to be observed. These barriers are extremely important when a project, such as an addition to a school plant, is under construction during the time children are in school. In some instances, the construction activity must be screened visually as well as physically to prevent it from becoming an attractive nuisance. The protection of materials from theft and the work from vandalism requires special barriers in some areas. The exclusion of unauthorized

persons from a building project is required by insurance companies because of the added risk to them. Gates attended by guards may be required. Signs, peepholes for "sidewalk superintendents," and temporary lighting under covered barricades must be considered. The construction and maintenance of barricades can involve considerable cost and must be figured carefully by the architect, the engineer, and the contractor.

MATERIALS LIFTS AND SCAFFOLDING

Materials and personnel lifts, hoists, and special rigging devices must be provided for all work to be done on the job. Each separate trade will not, in most cases, provide individual facilites for vertical movement of its materials on the project. The provision, maintenance, and coordination of the use of lifts are usually the responsibility of the prime contractor. Scaffolding, if it is extensive and is to be used for an appreciable length of time by several trades, will usually be furnished by the prime contractor. Some specifications state that scaffolding, hoists, and similar facilities must be provided by one trade and left for the use of another. These are matters with which the architect should not be burdened. The design of lifts, hoists, and scaffolding must meet the requirements of the Industrial Accident Commission, which will send inspectors onto the job to see that its regulations are carried out. The costs of lifts and scaffolding must be considered by the prime contractor, and he must check on proposals submitted by his subcontractors to determine whether they have included these costs in their bid or will expect the scaffolding to be furnished for them and be in place when they arrive on the job.

JOB OFFICE

Job offices vary greatly with the size and location of the job. The job office may be a relatively large building or a simple shed to store tools and house a telephone and desk. The contractor may have a mobile office that he moves from job to job. If the architect is to have a full-time employee on the site, he must have a desk, drawing board, and layout table for the drawings. Storage for samples and materials to be tested must be provided. Facilities such as telephones, heat, light, and toilet must be considered. The responsibility for furnishing these facilities is the contractor's, but thought should be given to such items

as temporary power, lights, and sanitary facilities. The general contractor does not usually have electricians or plumbers on his own
crew. Possibly the description and installation of these services should be placed in the
sections of the specifications dealing with the
electrical and plumbing work.

TEMPORARY HEAT

In many parts of the country, if construction
is to proceed throughout the entire year provisions must be made to heat the work areas.
This is necessary for the comfort of the workmen and also to maintain the constant temperatures that are needed during the installation
of certain materials. The overall heating of
a project during certain phases of construction
is not feasible. In many instances, this heat
for small areas is furnished by the particular
crew working there. The general rule is that
the prime contractor furnishes this heat and
shelter when several trades are working in an
area that can be heated. In several areas in
the Western desert regions, where summer
temperatures become unbearable, contractors have had to install temporary air-conditioning or cooling equipment to keep men on
the job.

COLD-WEATHER CONSTRUCTION

Where temperatures may drop below 40°,
protection of certain materials, both before
and after they are incorporated in a building,
is an absolute necessity. The comprehensive
strength of mortars may be reduced by as much
as 90 percent if they are frozen prior to har-
dening. Masonry units coated with ice will not
bond to mortar. Temperatures below 40°
necessitate special protection of masonry and
concrete in place. The chemical reaction of
water and portland cement is greatly retarded
by lowered temperatures, and concrete must
be kept above 40° for periods of forty-eight
to seventy-two hours after pouring. These
periods may be shortened by the additions of
admixtures or by the use of a higher cement
content in the mix. The specifications writer
and the contractor must anticipate the need for
special provisions that may be necessary.
Construction projects vary greatly in size,
design, and location. The most economical
method of providing protection to workmen and
materials can be determined only after a detailed study of that particular project.

The heating of enclosed spaces during cold-
weather construction presents another problem, that of ventilation. The use of plastic
sheet material to enclose working areas can
prevent the escape of moisture and cause
many problems not present when a material
such as muslin or cheesecloth is used. A
1,000-sq-ft concrete slab may release as
much as 2 tons of water into the air during the
setting period. Other materials, such as
gypsum plaster, may release a proportionate
amount of water. The products of combustion
from unvented area heaters add water to the
atmosphere. Unless this moisture in the air
is exhausted by proper ventilation, considerable damage can be caused to structural and
finish materials in such an area.

SHOP DRAWINGS

It is seldom possible for the architect or
engineer to detail exact construction methods
to be followed in subassemblies to be delivered
to the job by subcontractors or furnished by
materials dealers. Shop practices vary, and
there may be several acceptable methods of
fabrication for a given product. The architect
or engineer will require that the fabricator
furnish shop drawings showing details of what
he intends to fabricate and install. These
drawings will be presented for approval through
the prime contractor only. They must be
signed by the prime contractor in order to be
considered. The shop drawings will show
actual field measurements of work in place
and will show how the product will fit into adjoining work. The architect or engineer must
check these shop drawings to make certain
that the installation or material complies with
the intent of the drawings and specifications.
This checking must be done with extreme care
to see that the fabricator has correctly interpreted the architect's or the engineer's drawings.

Value of Shop Drawings. If a portion of
the work is to be fabricated in a shop away
from the job site, the fabricator must make
drawings for his workmen to follow. These
will detail each individual part to be fabricated.
The checking, done by the architect or engineer, is a service to the fabricator or subcontractor. It can be very costly for him to
rework an item after it has been installed, and
it is better to know whether his product will
be accepted before manufacture. If there are
differences of opinion on the method of fabrica-

tion or installation between a subcontractor and the contractor, agreement can be reached before fabrication and installation. Therefore, the prime contractor must check all shop drawings. Shop drawings should be submitted far enough in advance to allow time for a meeting of minds among the architect, the engineer, the prime contractor, the subcontractor, and the materials dealer before manufacture.

Submission of Shop Drawings. It has been stressed above that shop drawings must be submitted before installation. In order that there will be time for adequate checking of the various shop drawings required by the specifications, the prime contractor must set up a production schedule. On this production schedule, which must be constantly revised if delays or speedups are encountered, the contractor must schedule a date for submission of shop drawings. This date must be far enough ahead of the start of fabrication to allow the shop drawings to be checked thoroughly. The architect's superintendent must see that these are delivered as scheduled. A late submission of drawings may delay construction. It is usually permissible to withhold payments to the prime contractor if these drawings are not presented on schedule. The late submission of shop drawings, if this delays the work, cannot be used as a valid excuse by the prime contractor for not completing the contract on schedule.

Approval of Shop Drawings. Most projects require that four or more copies of the shop drawings be submitted for approval. These are checked by the prime contractor, the architect's superintendent, the architect, and the engineer. Notations are made by each of these, and the drawings are returned in order for the fabricator to correct his original drawings. The fabricator will then resubmit prints of his corrected shop drawings for an approval stamp by the architect. Personnel in the architect's office must recheck the drawings to make sure that all corrections have been made and, when satisfied that they are correct, stamp the drawings "APPROVED" and return them to the contractor. Although the architect has checked the shop drawings, he will not be held for errors discovered at a later date. He is offering a service to the fabricator, who alone is responsible for the correctness of his installation. It must be realized that the architect gives only a qualified approval. Quantity and dimensions are not verified by

him, nor does his approval relieve the contractor of responsibility for the strength or sufficiency of bracing, shoring, or other engineering work designed by the contractor. The stamp of approval used by the architect usually indicates the limitations pertaining to approval of the drawings.

ARCHITECT'S LARGE-SCALE DETAILS

The architect is often called upon to furnish additional details or instructions as the work progresses. It is not always possible for the architect to foresee and solve all problems that may arise in a complicated project, and he does not always have time to detail minor items before the drawings are made available for bidding. The contractor must then bid on the basis of drawings in which all details have not been shown. He does this with the understanding that the architect will furnish these missing instructions or large-scale details as they are needed. The contractor submits his bid with the understanding, also, that the details furnished by the architect will not appreciably change or modify the contract documents. It is the responsibility of the architect to be sure that the large-scale details are furnished when needed and that they do not add to or change items included in the contractor's estimate. The only purpose of issuing these details after work has started is to save time and clarify the contract documents.

CHANGE ORDERS

If, during construction, the owner wishes to make changes that will affect the cost of the project or require more or less work by the contractor, he must issue, through the architect, a "change order." If unforeseeable conditions arise that will affect the contractor's cost, the architect must issue a written change order in order for the contractor to collect for the extra work. Even though borings, test pits, and soil analyses have been made, conditions encountered underground may give rise to legitimate claims by the contractor. Large construction projects have become so intricate that even an expert cannot foresee and describe exactly every item that will be needed. Improvements in design, construction methods, or materials may occur to the architect or the engineer during construction. The owner may change his mind. With the owner's permission, the architect will write a change order. The value of work added to, or eliminated

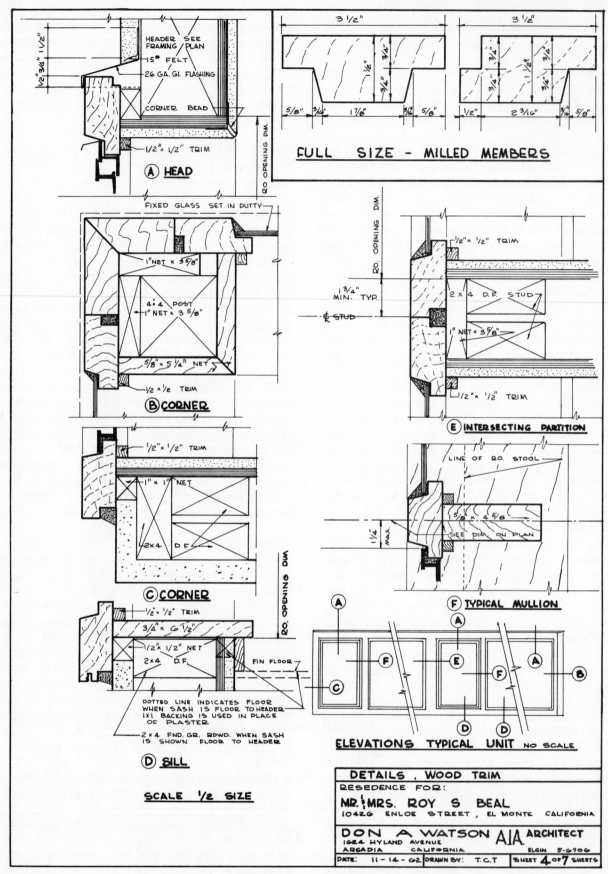

Fig. 4-4. Full-sized detail—exterior trim.

40

from, the contract by a change order is usually determined in one or more of the following ways:

1. By estimate and acceptance of a lump sum
2. By unit prices agreed upon or named in the contract
3. By cost and percentage or by cost and a fixed fee

Form of Change Order. The American Institute of Architects (AIA) publishes a form that can be used for change orders (G-701), or each office may develop its own. The form illustrated in Fig. 4-5 was developed by a large architect-engineer's firm for use in school construction. This form is filled in and distributed to the specifications department, the project engineer, the project architect, the job captain, the inspection department, and the owner. The contractor acknowledges the receipt of the change order and replies stating the amount this work will increase or decrease the total contract. If the amount of increase or decrease is satisfactory to the owner, the architect then orders the contractor to proceed. The change order and its approval then become a part of the contract documents.

Emergencies. The owner is not financially responsible for any change that would increase the cost of the project unless this change is ordered by a valid change order or the contractor has acted in an emergency. The architect or the owner cannot be on the job at all times, and emergencies may arise where there is not time to process a written change order. The contractor, through his experience and his constant presence on the job, should be able to recognize when an emergency exists and take appropriate action to protect the safety of employees. The contractor may be protected by liability insurance, but he must prove that he took all reasonable steps to protect workmen on the job or the public. If the action taken by the contractor involves extra costs for work of an emergency nature that was not included in the original contract, the amount of additional money paid must be settled by agreement or arbitration. This is the only instance where the contractor can collect extra money for additional work without a written change order.

PROTECTION OF ARCHITECT'S DRAWINGS

A large construction project will require many drawings that must be referred to constantly. A set of specifications that may approach the size of a large telephone book must be kept on hand in the job construction office at all times for the use of inspectors who will come onto the job from time to time. When the sets of drawings are submitted to the governmental agency for checking and a building permit is issued, the governmental agency which has authority over this particular project stamps each page of drawings and returns this set to the contractor. This becomes the official set and must be on the job site at all times. Other sets must be provided for use by tradesmen on the job. It is extremely important that the contractor provide means to preserve these drawings. Racks are usually constructed in the construction office where they will be convenient for all. These drawings that are used on the job must be protected from direct sunlight, or they will soon fade to the point where they can no longer be read. They must be protected from splashing of construction materials such as concrete, plaster, and paint. The replacement of a large set of drawings can be very expensive.

Keeping Drawings up to Date. It is the architect's superintendent's job to see that any changes made on the project are entered on the drawings. These notations or changes on the drawings should be accompanied by a date and the number of the change order responsible for the change. If sheets are revised, he must see that all sets on the job include the revised sheet. Copies of change orders must be distributed, attached to all sets of specifications or drawings, and filed for future reference. Shop drawings must be included in the contract drawings as they are approved.

As-built Drawings. During the course of construction of an involved project, many changes may be made. The building may be located at a slightly different place from that shown on the plot plan. Piping buried underground may follow a different path from the one shown on the mechanical plans or be located at a different depth. Electric wiring and duct work may have to be relocated from originally planned routes. Errors in framing, discovered during construction, may necessitate moving structural members. Change orders may alter many items that will later be covered by finish materials. While these changes may be noted on the official job drawings as they are made, many times it becomes almost impossible for anyone who was not intimately connected with the project under con-

REQUEST FOR CONSTRUCTION CHANGE

TO: (1) Section Head R. Whitley   Approved: _BW_ Date: _1-20-63_

      (2) Project Manager S. Ford   Approved: _SF_ Date: _1-22-63_

      (3) ( ) Supervision for action (Change Orders or Instruction Notices)

         (X) Chief Architectural Draftsman for action (Addenda)

FROM: __Electrical__ Department or Section

      Prepared by __B. Wells__

SUBJECT: ( ) Addendum   (X) Change Order   ( ) Instruction Notice

      Job Name __Wilson Bus Maintenance Garage__ Job No. __30-8-2__

Reason: (X) A conflict with drawings or specs.   ( ) An omission

           ( ) Owner request   ( ) Other _____

Reference: Drawing No. __E 1__   Detail $\frac{A}{E\ 1}$

           Specification Section _____ Paragraph _____

Requirements:

    ( ) Drawing   ( ) Specification   (X) Written information
                                            only

    ( ) Delete   ( ) Add   ( ) Change

Comments:

Delete the word "Relocate" from the notes at Power Poles #8600Y,

W 9002Y and W 9003Y. Add to note at pole 1173326E, "Relocate

anchor to avoid interference with fence and gate".

_____

_____

_____

_____

Fig. 4-5. Sample of change order.

PRESCOTT & WHALLEY A.I.A. ARCHITECTS & ASSOCIATES

JOB MEMO

Project   GATES STREET SCHOOL   Date   28 March 62

Persons involved: ☐ Telephone

        Inspector   – Geo. Dawson   ☐ Correspondence
        Contractor – John Miller

Information for record: ☒ Conference

      Authority granted to re-roof entire area that was originally intended to be patched only. The additional cost agreed for this is $590.00

Fig. 4-6. Owner's authority to change. (By permission of Prescott & Whalley.)

struction to decipher them after the completion of the project. If the owner wishes to have a record of exactly what was installed, and where, for purposes of future maintenance and alterations, he will insist on a set of "as-built drawings." The contractor may be required to furnish the architect with two neat, legible copies of completed as-built drawings. These drawings must be approved by the architect before he will issue a final certificate of payment.

SAMPLES

The submission of many samples for approval is required during the progress of the job. These may vary from a small swatch of colors to several sections of masonry walls laid up for the architect's or engineer's approval. Each sample must be of a specified size and have a label indicating the materials represented, its place of origin, the names of the producer and the contractor, and the building or work for which the material is intended. The sample should also be marked to indicate where the materials represented are required on the drawings and in the specifications. When a sample has been approved, the architect's superintendent must store it on the job site in a protected location and use it as a reference as the work progresses. Space is usually provided in the construction office,

under the control of the architect's superintendent, for this locked storage area. Certain approved samples of items such as hardware may, under certain conditions, be suitably marked for identification and later incorporated into the work. Large samples, such as walls, must be demolished and removed by the contractor.

MATERIALS TESTING

Certain materials that will be installed on the project must be tested before, during, or after construction. The amount of testing will be governed by the specifications. Some items delivered to the job must be accompanied by test reports. Premixed concrete delivered in a transit-mix truck may be accompanied by a report showing exactly what was put into the mix. Certain owners require that an inspector be employed, at the owner's expense, to certify each load as it is placed in the trucks for transportation to the job site. When bulk materials for mixing concrete are delivered to the job, the specifications may state that cement must be accompanied by certification from a test laboratory as to its chemical and physical properties. The American Society for Testing and Materials (ASTM) is a national organization composed of persons interested in setting up national standards for materials and testing procedures. This group publishes many volumes of standards widely used by all industry. These will be described in detail in Chap. 6, References and Source Material. Each test is given a letter and number designation which can be referred to in the organization's published standard.

Testing Concrete. The testing of concrete is probably the most expensive testing program on a construction project and is usually done under rules set up by the ASTM. The architect's superintendent may take samples of the cement, the aggregate, and the reinforcing bar that will go into the concrete, but the testing of these samples must be done in a testing laboratory. The water may be tested for impurities; the aggregate may be tested for strength, for the presence of dirt or other materials, and for size; and the steel reinforcing may be analyzed for composition and strength. The sampling of these materials must follow exactly the procedures set up by the ASTM if the tests are to be valid. As concrete is poured, samples are taken from the mixer and cast into prescribed test cylinders. The number of test cylinders will be governed by the specifications, for example: "At least three test cylinders shall be taken in accordance with ASTM G-31 for each 100 cu yd or portion thereof poured each day. One cylinder shall be tested at seven days and one at twenty-eight days, and the third shall be stored at the site until after the twenty-eight-day test has been performed. Tests shall be made in accordance with ASTM C-39. "

The specification continues with a description of other tests to be performed. A slump test, which tests the stiffness of the mixture, may be taken. In this test, the fresh concrete is poured into a bottomless container of a certain size and shape. The container is then lifted from a base leaving a column of fresh cement standing alone. The amount this wet concrete column sags is said to be its "slump. " This process, as well as the container, is designated by ASTM C-143. The architect's superintendent must see that these test cylinders are made and stored in a proper manner.

Testing Concrete in Place. The strength of the cylinders of concrete that have been made during the pouring operation cannot be finally determined until they have cured for a certain period of time. While they are curing, construction is proceeding, and many cubic yards of concrete may be poured before it can be determined whether the concrete is satisfactory. If, at the end of the seven- or twenty-eight-day period, the samples indicate defective concrete, what steps must the architect or engineer take? A core drill or saw is then used to remove a sample of the concrete in question, and this is then tested. The sample cylinder prepared when the concrete was being poured may have been defective, and the core removed from the partially cured concrete structure may indicate that the concrete in place is actually up to the quality desired or necessary. If the core cut from the structure proves to be defective, the structural-concrete work must be removed and replaced or adequately strengthened in a manner acceptable to the owner as well as to the architect or engineer.

Testing Other Materials. Bricks and concrete blocks may be tested for their ability to absorb water or for their strength. Cores may be cut from masonry walls to test the strength of the masonry units and the mortar that is holding them together. A section of roofing material may be removed from the finished roof of a building for testing. Each required

Fig. 4-7. Taking a concrete core sample.

test is designated in the specifications. The decision of how many tests will be taken, and from where, cannot be left up to the contractor, the architect, or the engineer.

Who Pays for Tests. A predetermined sum of money should be incorporated into the specifications, to be paid by the owner, for all tests to be performed. The owner, the architect, or the engineer selects the laboratory which is to perform the tests. The contractor does not have to pay for any of the testing if no defective work is discovered, but he must bear the costs of removing defective work and the cost of the additional tests caused by these defects. The cost of repairing or filling holes made by tests is usually paid for, and carried out by, the contractor.

PAY REQUESTS

Most construction contracts make provisions for periodic payments to be made to the contractor. The contractor will, in most instances, have to prepare papers requesting payment for work done or material delivered. In some instances, the requests for payment may be made by the architect's superintendent. Certain Federal agencies require that the contracting officer prepare these forms. In most cases, the contractor prepares the request, which is checked for accuracy by the architect's superintendent. The architect's superintendent then forwards it to the architect, noting whether the work has been done and the material delivered and what, if anything, is lacking.

Payment Based on Labor and Materials. The payment due the contractor and the basis on which he will be paid are governed by the type of contract which has been entered into by the owner and the contractor. In one type of contract, the contractor is paid monthly for material delivered on the job site, the cost of labor paid by him, and the actual amount he has expended on subcontractors' work. In this submittal the contractor would include his overhead and a percentage of his profit.

Payment Based on Percentage of Completion. The payments due the contractor may be based on the percentage of completion. The contractor must calculate what percentage of the total cost is represented by the work that is now in place. This would include all work done by his subcontractors as well as that done by his own forces. The contractor, from his production schedule and from a survey of

Fig. 4-8. Testing a brick masonry core. (By permission of the Associated Brick Manufacturers of Southern California.)

the work in place, estimates the percentage of completion of work his crews are handling. He must then add to this a percentage of work completed by his subcontractors based upon invoices they have presented to him.

UNIT-PRICE CONTRACTS

The contract may be set upon a "unit-price" basis. In this case, the payments will be based on field measurements of work actually in place. The units may be cubic yards of concrete, square feet of concrete or asphaltic concrete, cubic yards of excavation or fill, lineal feet of pipe installed, or any other units that may have been set up in the contract. It is simply a matter of measuring the units in place and multiplying by the price per unit.

SPECIFIC STEP PAYMENTS

The contract may be broken down into specific steps of construction. This is done mostly on small projects and residences. The project may be broken down into five steps:

1. Foundation poured
2. Rough framing and roof complete
3. Plumbing and electrical work complete and tested
4. Plastering complete
5. Final notice of completion filed

This breakdown parallels somewhat the points of inspection as made by building departments. A payment would then be due the contractor after that portion of the work had been inspected and passed by the building department and approved by the architect.

RETAINED PERCENTAGES

When the contractor prepares a request for payment, regardless of the type of contract, he must expect a percentage of this money to be withheld from the payment due him. This retained percentage, held by the owner, has a dual purpose: (1) It is an incentive for the contractor to complete the job as soon as possible and so get his final payment, and (2) it provides funds that can be used by the owner to cover the costs of any defects in the work if the contractor refuses to make good under his contract. The general contractor usually withholds a percentage from the money due his subcontractors for the same reasons. This percentage to be withheld is usually 10 percent of the value of the work that has been completed. At the completion of the job, this 10 percent of the total contract is retained for a given period, usually thirty days but sometimes as long as ninety days. This percentage retained by the owner covers the period in which materials dealers, subcontractors, workmen, and the general contractor may file a lien against the property.

LIENS

A lien is defined, in part, as a charge upon real or personal property for the satisfaction of some debt or duty. A lien is in the nature of a mortgage. The holder of a lien may start court proceedings of foreclosure on the property if not paid. A lien is given to secure compensation for those who have supplied materials or labor for the improvement of real property. Each state has its own lien laws. These vary in minor points, but in general they have the same provisions. It is the architect's responsibility to know the law of the locality in which he is operating. If the architect or the contractor has any doubts, he should consult a competent attorney to investigate and report the exact terms of the statutes governing this point. Included in the lien laws of most states are construction, alteration, demolition, and addition to, or repair of, any building or other structure including railroads, wharves, bridges, ditches, flumes, wells, tunnels, fences, roads, and mines. Most lien laws also cover the grading or improving of any lot or the streets or sidewalks in front of, or adjoining, such a plot of land. The land, property, building, structure, or improvement upon which work was done, together with as much land as is necessary for the convenient use and occupation of the structure or the improvement, is subject to a lien. A mechanic's lien takes precedence over any mortgage or deed of trust which may later be put on a property. In effect, the charge is put against the property and must be satisfied before a clear title can be granted for a piece of property.

Responsibility for Liens. Work done on a piece of property with the knowledge of the owner, whether or not he personally ordered it, is subject to these regulations, and a lien may be had. Title insurance companies or lending institutions are very strict on this point. If there is evidence of work of any nature being performed on a piece of property, they will hold up escrow proceedings until such time as the period in which a lien may be filed has expired. The owner may hurry the process of clearing title to his land if he posts a notice on his property, within ten days after he obtains knowledge of the work, that he is not responsible for the work done. He must also file a copy of this notice with the county recorder. If a lien has been filed against the property, the private owner may withhold, and the public owner must withhold, from the original contractor an amount equal to the claim made. A lien may not be filed against a public body, but a claim, which in effect is the same, may be. The contractor is required, as are his subcontractors in the agreement, to furnish evidence that he has satisfied all claims that may be leveled against the building.

Time for Filing Liens. Notice of a claim for services or material may be given by a workman, a material dealer, or a subcontractor at any time after the claimant has ceased to perform labor or furnish material and until thirty days after the completion of the work. This means after the entire job is finished, not the particular workman's portion of it. The percentages retained throughout a job that is in construction for a long time may be needed to protect the owner from claims filed by a workman several years after he has performed work on the project. A contractor who has a contract with the owner, called variously the "original contractor" or the "prime contractor," has sixty days in which to file a lien.

Architects' and Engineers' Liens. In most states, architects and engineers who prepare plans for, and supervise the construction of, buildings and other structures are entitled to a mechanics lien under the laws that define a lien in general terms for material or labor furnished in the erection of a building. Several states have held that an architect or engineer who does not supervise the work but only prepares the drawings and specifications is not entitled to a lien.

Time Limitations of Liens. In most states a lien is binding for only ninety days after filing. At the end of ninety days, it automatically expires unless (1) foreclosure proceedings have been commenced in the proper court or (2) a credit has been given against the lien. The giving of credit extends the lien claim for ninety days, but extensions due to the giving of credits may never be longer than one year from the time the work was completed. No credit extends a lien unless notice of the credit is recorded in the county records within the original ninety-day period.

CERTIFICATE OF PAYMENT

When the contractor has presented a request for payment under the contract for work completed and the architect has checked the work and the request and found both to be satisfactory, the architect must, within a reasonable period of time, issue a "certificate of payment." The architect or his representative on the job measures the work in place or checks the contractor's invoices, which the contractor includes with his request, to see that the money is due. The architect will, in some instances, insist on a "labor and material release" being submitted at the same time as the request for payment. This is a document signed by everyone who worked on the project or delivered material to the site stating that they have been paid in full. This release may be simply a signed statement by the contractor that he had paid all bills and that he agrees to settle all liens that may be filed against the property. The architect, when he has assured

himself that the work has been done, that the workmen have been paid, and that materials delivered are free from claims, deducts the agreed-upon percentage to be retained and writes a certificate of payment. The architect must issue this certificate within a certain period of time or by a certain day of the month, as called for in the agreement. The contractor then presents the certificate of payment to the owner, who must pay the contractor. This certificate of payment must be issued before the contractor can receive his money. The architect's judgment is final in most instances unless fraud can be proved or unless it is proved that a gross error has been made. It should be stressed in the agreement that the certificate of payment is not an approval of work done to this point. It is simply a statement that a certain percentage of the total money on the contract is now due to be paid to the contractor.

PROJECT COMPLETION

Before the architect can issue a final certificate of payment to the contractor, he must establish the time of completion and exactly what will be considered completion under the contract documents. The time of completion must be set in order that the period during which liens may be filed will have been defined. The architect must be very certain that the owner's rights have been protected.

Cessation of Work. If work on the project has been stopped for a period of thirty days, this is equivalent, for the purpose of filing liens, to completion. In this instance, all persons claiming liens have ninety days after this cessation of work to file a lien. If the contractor has not completed the work to the satisfaction of the architect, the owner may withhold payment due the contractor until the work has been completed. The architect must, however, notify the contractor that he considers that labor has ceased on the project.

Substantial Completion. A definition of the term "substantial completion" is essential because this determines the date on which, according to most agreements, the next to the last certificate of payment is issued. This also determines the date from which all guaranties and warranties of work performed are figures. The words "substantially completed" are used here in order that the architect may use his judgment in the issuance of the certificate. At this point, there may be some minor items to be corrected or finished, but all major portions of the work have been completed. If the architect feels that, according to his best judgment, the contractor has conscientiously endeavored to complete the contract and has substantially performed what was expected of him, he issues the next to the final certificate. The owner will still be protected by the percentages retained throughout the duration of the contract.

Use of Completed Portions by Owner. Most agreements, general conditions, or special conditions of the contract documents make some provisions for the owner's right to take possession of and use any completed portions of the work, even though the time for completing the entire work has not expired. This taking of possession cannot be considered acceptance of any work or evidence of completion. If the use by the owner of portions of the work increases costs or delays the work, the contractor is entitled to such extra compensation or extension of time as the architect may determine.

CORRECTION OF WORK BEFORE FINAL PAYMENT

The contractor must remove from the site all work condemned by the architect or engineer as failing to conform to the contract, whether it is incorporated into the project or not. If more than one prime contractor has done work on the site, each is responsible for repairing damage he may have caused to the other contractor's work. If the contractor does not remove work that is bad or material left on the site, the owner may have such work removed or material stored at the contractor's expense. If the contractor does not pay the expense of this removal or storage, the owner may, ten days after written notice, sell the material and deduct the cost from what has been retained from the final payment.

FINAL INSPECTION

When the work is substantially completed, the contractor notifies the architect that the work will be ready for final inspection or test on a definite date. As noted before, "substantial completion" implies that all major portions of the work are completed and that only minor items are still unfinished. This notice to the architect must usually be given at least ten days before final inspection. The architect and the owner usually make the final

inspection together, noting points to be picked up or finished. If the architect finds only minor items to be finished or corrected and the contractor agrees to these corrections, the architect may issue a semifinal certificate of payment to the contractor and make out a notice of completion.

NOTICE OF COMPLETION

The "notice of completion" is filed by the owner, usually through the architect, in the office of the county recorder. It sets forth the date labor ceased or work was completed, the location of the property, the nature of the project or improvement, and the names of the owner, the architect, and the contractor. The date of this filing establishes the time for filing liens and the start of the period covered by warranties or guaranties that may be required of the contractor. The filing of the notice of completion or the issuance of the final certificate of payment does not indicate the approval of work done by the contractor, nor does it relieve the contractor of the responsibility for faulty work discovered at a later date.

GUARANTY OF THE WORK

The contractor is usually required to furnish a warranty that all his work was in conformance with the contract documents and to guarantee to repair any deficiencies or defects that appear during a period of one year from the date of the filing of the notice of completion. During this one-year warranty period he will be required to pay for any damage to other work resulting from defects in his work. For certain portions of the work, the contractor is required by the specifications to furnish a guaranty which will be in effect for a longer period of time. In these instances, the prime contractor has to furnish the guaranties. Even though a portion of the work was performed under a subcontract and a guaranty has been made by him, it is the prime contractor who will be held for repairing and paying for any future damage. If the contractor has been required to furnish a performance bond at the start of the project, this bond will usually cover the one-year period after the project is completed. If the performance bond does not cover this warranty period, the contractor may be asked to furnish a maintenance bond. Many contractors, even after the expiration of the warranty period, find it advisable, from a public relations standpoint, to correct deficiencies voluntarily.

PROJECT ANALYSIS

Throughout the progress of the project, the architect has been keeping records of progress and costs on a daily, weekly, or monthly basis. Many of these details of construction are of value only at the time the work is being done or until that particular phase of the work has been completed. However, many of these reports, charts, and pieces of correspondence will be valuable in the future if put in a form in which they will be readily available for reference when a similar project is being designed, estimated, or constructed. A report should be made summarizing all problems encountered during construction for use by the specifications writer and job captain in the architect's office. Permanent records showing the costs of the work are valuable as an aid to future preliminary estimates. These overall cost figures should be broken down into units of work. Areas, volumes, and quantities of materials should be related to costs. Square footage or cubic content figures should be calculated, and the actual cost should be compared with the estimated costs. A list of all persons, with their addresses, performing work on a project should be kept. This may prove convenient later when questions arise that make it desirable to contact someone who performed some important part of the work.

The architect should summarize his costs connected with the work. Each office should develop the forms that will best suit its particular organization. Was the project successful? Were there problems caused by poorly written specifications or inaccurate drawings? What steps must the architect, the engineer, the draftsman, or the specifications writer take to assure a successful project next time around?

QUESTIONS

1. Name six types of government agencies or departments from which it may be necessary to have approval before a project may be started?
2. What is a bid bond?
3. How should telephone requests for information from materials dealers during the bidding period be handled?
4. Discuss the advantages and disadvantages to architects of incorporation.
5. Discuss the relationship of specifications consultants and architects.
6. What is a prime contractor?
7. What information must accompany samples submitted to the architect?
8. Define a mechanic's lien.

CHAPTER 5   The Drawings

Needless to say, the specifications writer must be able to read and interpret working drawings in order to write specifications. In small offices, he may assist in the preparation of these working drawings. The draftsman who wishes to become a specifications writer may be familiar with only a certain portion of working drawings. The engineering draftsman may not be familiar with the preparation of drawings in an architect's office. The architectural draftsman must be able to interpret structural and mechanical drawings. Procedures vary from one office to another and from one section of the country to another. This chapter will cover, in a general way, the preparation and interpretation of the many drawings needed for a modern construction project.

PLANS OR DRAWINGS

Persons in the construction industry have for many years used the word "plans" when they mean "drawings." We must be exact in the use of words. In a construction drawing, a plan is a horizontal section. A floor plan would show a building as though the walls were cut off, usually 4'-0" above the floor, looking down. The plans, then, are only a part of a set of construction drawings. If the specifications writer means all the construction drawings, he should not use the word "plans."

RELATION TO OTHER CONSTRUCTION DOCUMENTS

The drawings are a part of the contract documents. They are a representation of the elements of a project that can best be shown pictorially or graphically. They show items that cannot be adequately described in words. It is very difficult, if not impossible, to draw a picture of quality. This is left to the specifications writer. The drawings and the specifications are complementary, and they must not overlap. What is shown or described in one must not be repeated in the other. The danger of "twice-told tales" is always present when information is given both in picture form and as a word description. If the picture and the word description were identical all that would be involved would be the additional cost of preparing the documents. However, the chance of error is greatly increased when an item is described twice, and the question of which will govern may then arise.

CONFLICTS BETWEEN DRAWINGS AND SPECIFICATIONS

No mention is made in the general conditions or the agreement as published by the AIA of which will govern in case of a discrepancy between the specifications and the drawings. Many architects place a statement in their general conditions or, if they are using the AIA form, in the special conditions stating: "In case of discrepancies between the contract documents, the specifications shall take precedence over the drawings."

INFORMATION INCLUDED IN DRAWINGS

The drawings, in most cases, should contain the extent, size, shape, and location of the component parts of the project and should designate the basic materials to be used. The qualities, trade names, methods of installation, and finishes of these component parts should then be described in detail in the specification trade section. In addition to the confusion resulting from the inclusion of statements defining quality on the drawings, another factor should be considered. It is simple to make a change, by addendum or change order, in installation procedures or in the designation of materials when the description is included in the specifications. It may be difficult to change original drawings and reproduce them for reissue. Unfortunately, in many instances the drawings are completed and reproduced before the specifications are written. The specifications writer, when analyzing drawings indicating quality or a specific trade name, may notice conflicting requirements that cannot be easily remedied by the architect at this point. Quantities and dimensions left to be included in the specifications can easily be overlooked when the drawings are made and so may not be included in either the drawings or the specifications. Notes on the drawings such as "see specs," or notes in the specifications such as "as shown on the drawings" should be very carefully checked to make sure that the information actually is shown or specified. It is much better to eliminate both these notes. Establish a consistent office policy that can be followed by the entire office staff. If each person knows what type of material is to be shown on the drawings, these notes are not needed and embarrassing mistakes will be avoided.

OMISSIONS

A consistent office policy and a guide or checklist to follow during preparation of the drawings will result in fewer costly omissions. The draftsman, in following such a guide, will know what is expected to be included in the drawings. The specifications writer will know what he must cover. One result of omissions from the drawings or specifications is a greater cost to the owner. The subcontractor may include the cost of an item in his bid as a matter of trade practice. During construction, he makes a more detailed inspection of the drawings and discovers it has been omitted. He may claim an extra, and thus the owner pays for the item twice.

SYMBOLS AND ABBREVIATIONS

Unfortunately, the symbols and abbreviations used in drawings are not uniform throughout the country. Because of this, it is necessary that any symbol or abbreviation used on a drawing be identified by a legend. This can be in the form of a schedule on the drawings or, in some instances, in the specifications. As an example of the confusion that exists, consider the abbreviation "A.C." In plastering, A.C. may indicate "acoustical plaster." In the mechanical section, A.C. may indicate "air conditioning." The symbol "∅" in the electrical drawings may indicate "phase," and in structural drawings or in concrete reinforcing it may indicate "round." The mechanical drawings, the electrical drawings, and the structural and architectural drawings each may be prepared in a different office, and each office may have a different meaning for the same symbol.

HATCHING ON DRAWINGS

Many hours are spent by draftsmen covering large areas of drawings with dots and diagonal lines. Since these symbols are not universally recognized, a legend must be placed on the drawings indicating exactly what is meant. Figure 5-1 shows a portion of a legend as one architect has developed it. These symbols representing materials are of questionable value except possibly where several materials join. If, when the drawings are nearly complete, a change of materials is necessary, many more hours must be spent correcting the hatching. The exact material to be used in each portion of the work can be covered in the specifications. Then, if a change is made, a simple addendum or the alteration of a line of typing in the specifications is all that is necessary to accomplish the change.

NOTES ON DRAWINGS

Many architects make a practice of including notes on the drawings. The hand-lettering of many notes on the drawings is an expensive process. Many notes also tend to clutter up the drawings and make them more difficult to interpret. In most instances, the notes could more easily be included in the specifications. If we accept the premise that the drawings include only instructions that are more easily drawn than written, only enough lettering is needed on the drawings to identify or clarify the graphic representation. There is also the matter of precedence to be considered. The specifications will take precedence over notes on the drawings, so why not include the notes only in the specifications and state in the general conditions or the special conditions, as discussed before, what the specifications govern? There is also the matter of the ease of changing specifications.

DIMENSIONS

All drawings must be dimensioned in such a way that there can be no question of the location or the size of the various elements of the building. It is not always possible to show the exact limits of dimensions as shown on 1/8" to 1'-0" or 1/4" to 1'-0" floor plans. In wood-stud construction as shown in Fig. 5-2, the dimensions are to the outside of the wood-stud walls, as indicated in the upper right-hand side of the drawing. Dimensions of doors and windows are to the center line of the window or door. In this type of construction, it would be difficult to dimension to the outside of the openings because this dimension varies

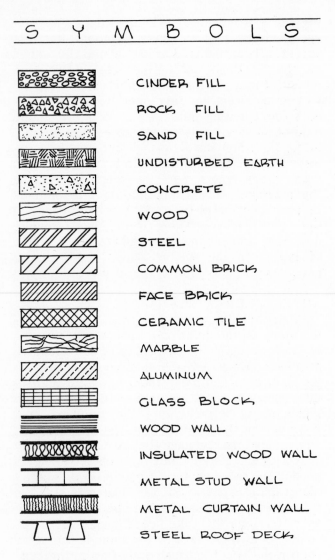

S Y M B O L S

CINDER FILL

ROCK FILL

SAND FILL

UNDISTURBED EARTH

CONCRETE

WOOD

STEEL

COMMON BRICK

FACE BRICK

CERAMIC TILE

MARBLE

ALUMINUM

GLASS BLOCK

WOOD WALL

INSULATED WOOD WALL

METAL STUD WALL

METAL CURTAIN WALL

STEEL ROOF DECK

Fig. 5-1. A portion of a legend indicating symbols.

with the type of window or door. A window which will be classed as a 4'-0" wide window may actually need an opening of 4'-2-1/4". Therefore, the center line of the opening is given on the floor plan, and the large-scale window details will show the exact size of the openings. If a masonry building is being dimensioned, the openings in the walls would be dimensioned and noted as rough openings. The draftsman must then check the masonry material for size of units. The openings in a masonry wall should be placed in such a manner that a minimum of cutting of masonry units is necessary.

SCALE

In drawings of larger buildings, the entire floor plan may be presented at a scale of 1/16" or 1/8" to 1'-0". This would be followed by drawings of individual buildings or parts of buildings at a scale of 1/4" to 1'-0'. Sections or portions of these areas then may be reproduced for clarity at scales of 3/4", 1-1/2", or 3" to 1'-0". Extremely critical or complicated sections may even be shown at full scale. Thus as the parts are shown in more detail, the scale is enlarged. The scales normally used on construction drawings are 1/16" to 1'-0", 1/8" to 1'-0", 1/4" to 1'-0", 1/2" to 1'-0", 3/4" to 1'-0", 1-1/2" to 1'-0", and 3" to 1'-0". The use of scales such as 3/16" to 1'-0", 3/8" to 1'-0", or 1" to 1'-0" is discouraged. The workman on the job usually carries a scale divided into halves, quarters, eighths, and sixteenths of an inch, and it is difficult for him to convert these scales into full-sized dimensions. This conversion can be the cause of many errors on the job. The drawings should be prepared as accurately as possible to scale. If there is a difference between a scaled drawing and a written dimension, the written dimension will govern.

ENGINEER'S SCALE

Most civil engineers and surveyors use an engineer's scale. This scale is divided into tenths rather than twelfths, as is the architect's scale. The dimensions given on plot plans and maps prepared by the surveyors are usually in feet and hundredths of a foot. The scale will vary from 1"-100' to 1"-20'. This must be converted to an architectural scale by the draftsman in placing a building on the plot. The elevations of the site are also given in feet and hundredths of a foot. The architectural draftsman and structural draftsman must convert this into feet and inches in designing the building.

REFERENCING

A large set of construction drawings which includes many details must also include a uniform system of referencing. The construction details may be spread over many sheets—some architectural, some electrical, and some mechanical—and the system of referencing must be such that construction methods and materials to be used may be located quickly.

It is not possible or desirable to indicate all materials or methods of joining or reinforcing on small-scale drawings. Therefore a set of symbols and lines is used to indicate where construction details may be found. Each office will establish a system of symbols. The system shown in Figs. 5-2 to 5-6 has been found to work successfully.

NUMBERING OF DRAWINGS

It is seldom possible to number a set of drawings consecutively. The architectural or structural draftsman does not know, when he starts, how many drawings will be needed for each portion of the work. Therefore he numbers only those that are being worked on in his office so that he may include references as the drawings are being prepared. The usual practice is to use both letters and numbers in the drawing titles, such as:

A—Architectural drawings
C—Civil drawings
S—Structural drawings
E—Electrical drawings
M—Mechanical drawings
P—Plumbing drawings

Not all these designations may be used on every job, and in certain projects having large sections of work involving specialties other letters may be used.

FLOOR PLANS

The portion of the floor plan shown in Fig. 5-2 (a floor plan of a motel, drawn at 1/4" to 1'-0") has one type of symbol to indicate the location of details. This type of symbol indicates in the lower half of the circle the sheet number on which the details will be found and in the upper half indicates the letter designation of the detail. The second type of symbol is used to identify a particular wall as shown on the sheets containing interior elevations of each room.

SECTIONS

The reference symbol shown in Fig. 5-2 indicates where the details of the concrete-block wall and the fascia will be found. It indicates that the wall will be shown in section, looking toward the left.

Structural Sections. Figure 5-5, taken from a structural drawing, indicates the structural members and construction methods to be used in the wall construction. This section does not indicate all materials that will be involved.

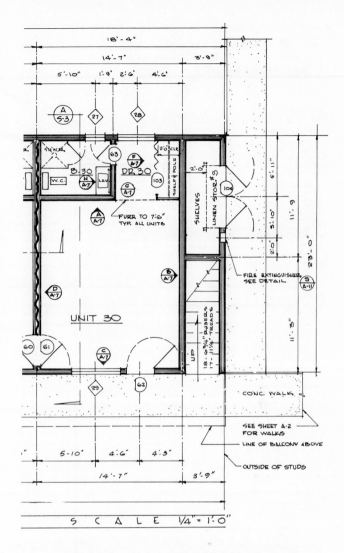

Fig. 5-2. A portion of a floor plan.

Note that the finish materials are not shown on the structural sections. Only the line of the finish material is shown, while the structural members are detailed. To find further details of the wall section at this point, the reader is referred to architectural sheets. This section is drawn at 3/4" to 1'-0".

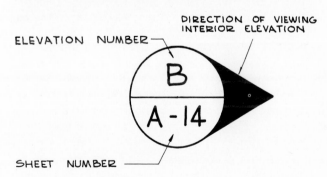

Fig. 5-3. Reference to interior elevation.

53

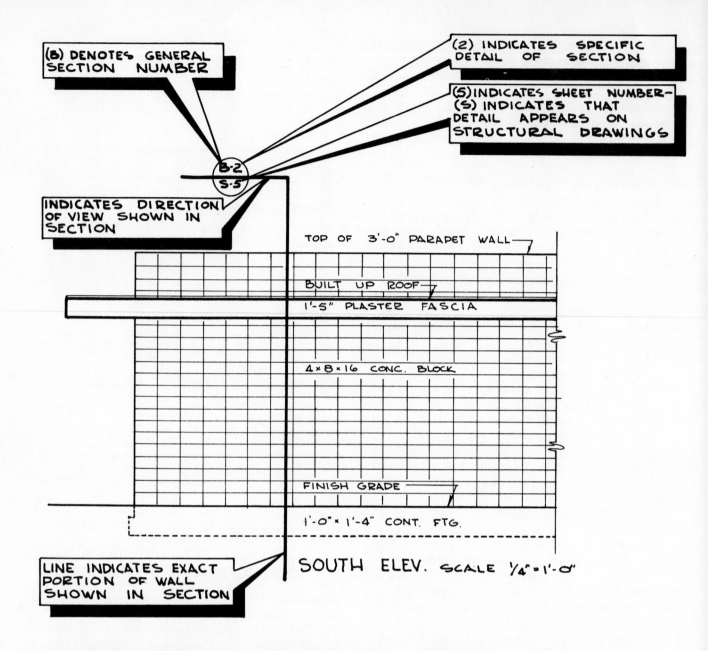

(B) DENOTES GENERAL SECTION NUMBER

(2) INDICATES SPECIFIC DETAIL OF SECTION

(S) INDICATES SHEET NUMBER- (S) INDICATES THAT DETAIL APPEARS ON STRUCTURAL DRAWINGS

B-2
S-5

INDICATES DIRECTION OF VIEW SHOWN IN SECTION

TOP OF 3'-0" PARAPET WALL

BUILT UP ROOF

1'-5" PLASTER FASCIA

4 × 8 × 16 CONC. BLOCK

FINISH GRADE

1'-0" × 1'-4" CONT. FTG.

SOUTH ELEV. SCALE ¼" = 1'-0"

LINE INDICATES EXACT PORTION OF WALL SHOWN IN SECTION

SECTION LINE AS INDICATED ON ELEVATIONS SHEET A-4

Fig. 5-4. A portion of an elevation.

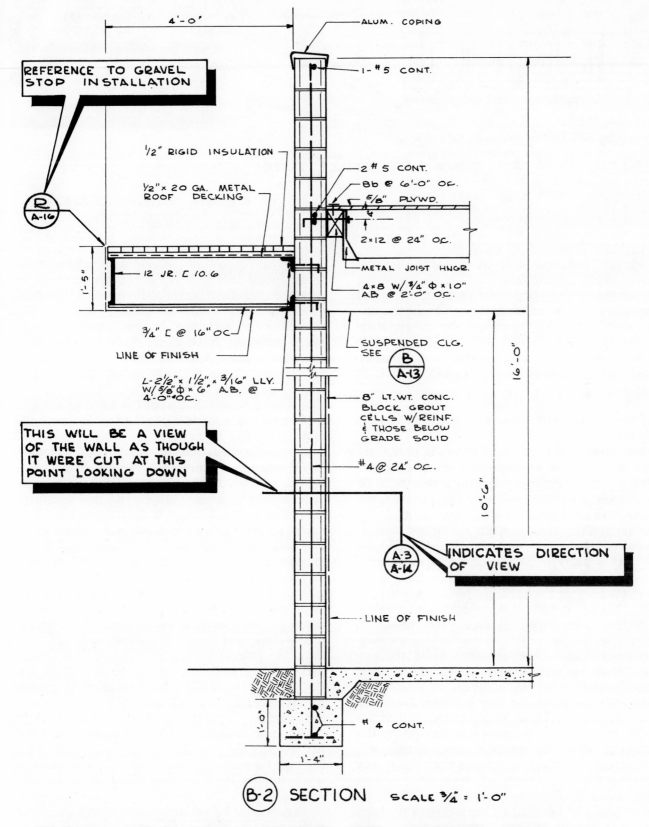

REFERENCE TO GRAVEL STOP INSTALLATION

4'-0"

ALUM. COPING

1-#5 CONT.

½" RIGID INSULATION

½" × 20 GA. METAL ROOF DECKING

R
A-16

2 #5 CONT.

8b @ 6'-0" O.C.

⅝" PLYWD.

2 × 12 @ 24" O.C.

METAL JOIST HNGR.

12 JR. C 10.6

1'-5"

4 × 8 W/ ¾" Φ × 10" A.B. @ 2'-0" O.C.

SUSPENDED CLG. SEE

B
A-13

16'-0"

¾" C @ 16" O.C.

LINE OF FINISH

L-2½" × 1½" × 3/16" LLY. W/ ⅝" Φ × 6" A.B. @ 4'-0" O.C.

8" LT. WT. CONC. BLOCK GROUT CELLS W/ REINF. & THOSE BELOW GRADE SOLID

#4 @ 24" O.C.

THIS WILL BE A VIEW OF THE WALL AS THOUGH IT WERE CUT AT THIS POINT LOOKING DOWN

10'-6"

A-3
A-14

INDICATES DIRECTION OF VIEW

LINE OF FINISH

1'-0"

4 CONT.

1'-4"

B-2 SECTION   SCALE ¾" = 1'-0"

DETAIL B-2 AS SHOWN ON SHEET S-5

Fig. 5-5. A structural section.

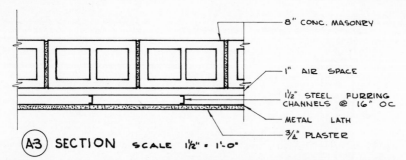

8" CONC. MASONRY

1" AIR SPACE

1½" STEEL FURRING
CHANNELS @ 16" OC

METAL LATH

¾" PLASTER

(A3) SECTION   SCALE 1½" = 1'-0"

DETAIL B-3 AS SHOWN ON SHEET A-14

Fig. 5-6. Large-scale architectural drawing.

ARCHITECTURAL DETAILS

Figure 5-6, taken from an architectural sheet, shows additional details of construction not shown on the structural section. It is not necessary on this horizontal section in the architectural drawings to repeat any information on reinforcing or structural materials. The nonstructural furring channels and plaster finish are indicated here at a scale of 1-1/2" to 1'-0".

LARGE-SCALE ARCHITECTURAL DRAWINGS

Because of the press of time, it is not always possible or feasible to complete all the detailed architectural drawings that will be needed on a project before the contractor starts work. These large-scale details are prepared after the contract is signed and as they are needed for construction. A schedule, which is usually prepared jointly by the architect and the contractor, fixes the date when detailed drawings will be needed for construction. These detailed drawings, at a large scale or sometimes full size, are meant to amplify and clarify the methods of construction to be used. The architect must prepare these drawings with extreme care. They must be consistent with the contract drawings and be of such a nature that they are clarifications of the drawings, not additions to them. Large-scale drawings or instructions issued by the architect after the contract has been signed, indicating construction details not reasonably inferred from the contract drawings, can be considered by the contractor to be a change order and can be used as the basis of a claim for extra money. These details must be prepared and issued as they are needed, or they may result in disputes that may cause delays on the job and additional expense.

SCHEDULES

Certain types of information which must be included in the contract documents can be grouped together in the form of schedules. The schedules would be either placed on the drawings or included in the specifications. Many attempts have been made to eliminate hand-lettered schedules from the drawings, but few have been entirely successful. If they are to be included in the specifications, the question of where they would be located arises. A schedule of room finishes gives information that is needed by several trades. A door and window schedule that includes wood windows, metal windows, hardware, wood doors, fire doors, cabinet doors, and painting may involve carpenters, masons, glaziers, and caulking specialists. Each trade will be concerned with some of the facts presented in a schedule. If the schedule is placed on the drawings, it can be used by all as a quick and easy reference.

Need for Schedules. A set of drawings for a modern building project is very complex and often becomes difficult to read because of the amount of information which must be included. If the size and type of each window and door must be placed on the floor plan, it becomes extremely confusing. If all the materials and finishes for the walls and ceilings are included in the interior elevations, they may become unreadable. A simple symbol placed in a door or window opening or the assigning of a number to each door or window frees the floor plan for other necessary information. The door or window may then be described in detail in a schedule.

Structural Schedules. Structural drawings make use of schedules indicating details of structural elements when they can be easily identified. The plans and elevations would simply identify each structural beam or column by number or letter, and the schedule would give the full information on each member. Details may be shown of a typical reinforced-concrete beam. The placement of the reinforcement would be shown, but the number and size of the reinforcing bars for each beam would be placed in a schedule. Steel columns or beams would be given a number and size. The type of connections of each column would be placed in a schedule for quick reference.

Typed Schedules. Several types of schedules have been developed in an attempt to simplify schedules or to cut down the time spent in their preparation. Some of the larger offices have special typewriters that will receive a full sheet of vellum. It is then possible to type the schedule on a standard sheet. The making of the schedule can then be left to a typist. Other offices have a schedule typed on a regular 8-1/2" by 11" sheet of vellum and then insert this into a sheet of drawings. After a trial period, many have gone back to the hand-lettered schedule on the drawing. The draftsman must make out the original, even in this system, and can usually save time by putting it on the drawing in the first place. A change that may be necessary after the schedule is complete is easily made by the draftsman when the drawing is on the board.

Window Schedules. Figure 5-7 shows one type of window schedule. In this instance, the schedule was used for a large residence. The first column indicates the exact window involved. Each window in the project was given a number, and the number, preceded by a "W," was then placed on the floor plan at the window opening. The size and type were listed next. The catalog number refers to a standard type of window as designated by the Metal Window Manufacturers Association. Special features or details that should be noted are included in the "remarks" column. The abbreviations used in the schedule are included in a legend under the schedule. The practice of numbering each window in a large project that may include many hundreds of windows of a similar type is not always advisable. In this situation, each different window TYPE would be placed in the schedule, and the windows as shown on the drawings would be identified by type and not numbered consecutively. It is sometimes desirable to include small elevations such as shown in Fig. 5-9 when the size, shape, and arrangement of the individual lights in the windows are difficult to indicate in the schedule.

Door Schedules. Figure 5-8 is a residential door schedule following a form similar to the window schedule. Each door in the project was numbered, and this number, preceded by a "D," was placed in the door opening on the drawings. Figure 5-9, an industrial door schedule, includes a small elevation of each door type in the schedule. In an industrial building such as this, where the walls were of brick masonry, steel panels, and wood studs and the floor construction varied from room to room, it was necessary to identify the conditions that would be encountered at the head, jamb, and threshold. These notations refer to details on the architectural drawings.

Room Finish Schedules. Room finish schedules can be very simple or extremely complex. In Fig. 5-10 the rooms are named and, in a commercial building, would also be numbered. Information is then given on type and finish material to be used on the floor, walls, and ceiling. Simple abbreviations are used to identify each material to be used. The specifications spell out the quality of each type of construction. This schedule, taken from a set of working drawings of a particular residence, does not include all items that might be required for commercial or industrial buildings.

Figure 5-11, taken from a portion of a set of drawings from a school, illustrates a widely used type of schedule. This same type of schedule could be used for door and window schedules. Here, all finishes that will be used on the project are placed in the headings of the vertical columns, and the rooms are identified on the left. It is then necessary only to make an "X" or a dot, as shown here, under the appropriate column. This saves time in making the schedule. However, there are problems involved in the use of this type of schedule. First, there is a greater possibility of error. In a large, complex schedule of this sort, it is necessary to follow the columns with absolute exactness, or an error will be made. Secondly, there is difficulty in making certain changes after the schedule is completed. Under the column labeled "Keene's cement ceilings," there is no dot. Was this eliminated from the job, or has an error been made? If, after this schedule is complete, it is found advisable to use vinyl tile on the floor on one room and there is no column for this material, where is the information placed?

INTERMEDIATES

In order to simplify the work of the con-

WDW. NO.	SIZE	TYPE	CAT. NO.	MATERIAL	GLASS	SCREEN	REMARKS
	W I N D O W				S C H E D U L E		
W-1	SEE ELEV.	FIXED		WOOD STOPS	DSB	NO	SEE SHEET # 6
W-2	2'-8"± x 4'-2"±	FIXED		WOOD STOPS	DSB	NO	CHECK DIM. ON JOB
W-3	2'-8"± x 4'-2"±	FIXED		WOOD STOPS	DSB	NO	" " " " "
W-4	2'-8"± x 4'-2"±	FIXED		WOOD STOPS	DSB	NO	" " " "
W-5	2'-8"± x 4'-2"±	FIXED		WOOD STOPS	DSB	NO	" " " "
W-6	SEE ELEV.	FIXED		WOOD STOPS	DSB	NO	SEE SHEET #6
W-7	SEE ELEV.	FIXED		WOOD STOPS	DSB	NO	SEE SHEET #6
W-8	SEE ELEV.	FIXED		WOOD STOPS	DSB	NO	SEE SHEET #7
W-9	4'-2⅝" x 6'-8	FIXED	4400 X	ALUM.	DSB	NO	NO MUNTINS
W-10	4'-7"± x 8'-9"±	FIXED		WOOD STOPS	¼" GRAY Pr	NO	SEE DETAIL ⊖/4
W-11	4'-7"± x 8'-9'±	FIXED		WOOD STOPS	¼" GRAY Pr	NO	SEE DETAIL ⊖/4
W-12	4'-7"± x 8'-9"±	FIXED		WOOD STOPS	¼" GRAY Pr	NO	SEE DETAIL ⊖/4
W-13	5'-8"± x 6'-10"	FIXED		WOOD STOPS	¼" Pr	NO	SEE DETAIL ⊖/4
W-14	5'-8"± x 6'-10"	FIXED		WOOD STOPS	¼" Pr	NO	SEE DETAIL ⊖/4
W-15	5'-4" x 3'-2⅜"	CSMT	4313 N	ALUM.	DSB	YES	
W-16	4'-0" x 3'-2⅜"	CSMT	2313 XWL	ALUM.	DSB	YES	
W-17	4'-0" x 3'-2⅜"	CSMT	2313 XWL	ALUM.	DSB	YES	
W-18	4'-0" x 2'-2⅜"	CSMT	2212 XWL	ALUM.	DSB	YES	
W-19	4'-0" x 2'-2⅜"	CSMT	2212 XWL	ALUM.	DSB	YES	
W-20	2'-8" x 2'-0"	ARCH. PROJ.		ALUM.	SSB	YES	
W-21	2'-8" x 2'-0"	ARCH. PROJ.		ALUM.	SSB	YES	

A B B R E V I A T I O N S

SSB	- SINGLE STRENGTH B GRADE WINDOW GLASS
DSB	- DOUBLE STRENGTH B GRADE WINDOW GLASS
¼" Pr	- ¼" POLISHED PLATE GLASS
¼" GRAY Pr	- ¼" HEAT ABSORBING GRAY TWIN GROUND PLATE GLASS
CSMT	- CASEMENT
ARCH. PROJ.	- ARCHITECTURAL PROJECTED

Fig. 5-7. Window schedule.

sultants and engineers in the preparation of their drawings and to help avoid discrepancies in the size of areas in the building or project, the architect sometimes furnishes intermediate copies, or "transparencies," of partially completed drawings. The main outlines, plans or elevations are roughed out on transparent paper or cloth by draftsmen in the architect's office, and these sheets are reproduced. This type of intermediate print may be produced by several methods. Two common methods are the ozalid process, which uses ammonia vapor for developing the image, and the whiteprint process, which uses a chemical bath. The engineer can complete the sheet so reproduced, showing only those portions of the work that pertain to his specialty on the drawings. The job captain cannot go too far in finishing his architectural drawings until the structural and mechanical problems have been solved. During this phase of the planning process, it is essential that the architect and the engineer work together closely. What each does is affected by the work of the other.

DOOR NO.	SIZE	TYPE	THICKNESS	MATERIAL	THRESH.	FRAME	TRIM	REMARKS
D-1	3'-0" x 6'-8"	SC	1 3/4"	HRDWD	ALUM	RWD	HRDWD	
D-2	2'-8" x 6'-8"	SC	1 3/4"	HRDWD	ALUM	METAL	METAL	FIXED SASH
D-3	2'-6" x 6'-8"	SC	1 3/8"	HRDWD	NONE	METAL	METAL	
D-4	PR 5'-8 x 6'-8"	SC	1 3/4"	PG	NONE	METAL	METAL	FULL WOOD LOUVERS
D-5	2'-6" x 6'-8"	HC	1 3/8"	HRDWD	NONE	D.F.	HRDWD.	
D-6	2'-6" x 6'-8"	HC	1 3/8"	HRDWD	NONE	D.F.	HRDWD	
D-7	2'-0" x 6'-8"	HC	1 3/8"	HRDWD	NONE	DF	DF	
D-8	2'-8" x 6'-8"	HC	1 3/8"	HRDWD	NONE	DF	DF	
D-9	2'-8" x 6'-8"	HC	1 3/8"	HRDWD	NONE	METAL	METAL	
D-10	2'-8" x 6'-8"	HC	1 3/8"	HRDWD	NONE	METAL	METAL	
D-11	2'-6" x 6'-8"	HC	1 3/8"	HRDWD	NONE	METAL	METAL	
D-12	2'-0" x 6'-8"	HC	1 3/8"	HRDWD	NONE	HRDWD	NONE	
D-13	2'-0" x 6'-8"	SC	1 3/4"	PG	NONE	METAL	METAL	
D-14	1'-6 x 6'-8"	CAB	3/4"	PB	NONE	NONE	NONE	
D-15	PR 5'-0" x 6'-8"	CAB	3/4"	PB	NONE	NONE	NONE	FOLDING
D-16	2'-8" x 6'-8"	H.C.	1 3/8"	PG	NONE	D.F.	D.F.	
D-17	2'-0" x 6'-0"							PLASTIC GLAZED SHOWER DOOR
D-18	5'-0" x 6'-0"							PLASTIC GLAZED TUB ENCLOSURE
D-19	4'-6" x 6'-0"							PLASTIC GLAZED SHWR. PARTITION & DOOR
D-20	3'-0" x 6'-8"	SC	1 3/4"	PG	NONE	METAL	METAL	DRESSING ROOM
D-21	3'-0" x 6'-8"	HC	1 3/8"	PG	NONE	METAL	METAL	" "
D-22	PR 3'-0" x 6'-8"	CAB	3/4	PB	NONE	NONE	NONE	" "
D-23	2'-6" x 6'-8"	HC	1 3/8	PG	NONE	METAL	METAL	" "
D-24	2'-0" x 6'-0"	CAB	3/4"	D.F. PLY.	NONE	NONE	NONE	" "
D-25	2'-0 x 6'-0"	CAB	3/4"	DF PLY	NONE	NONE	NONE	" "
D-26	PR 5'-0" x 6'-0"	CAB	3/4"	PB	NONE	NONE	NONE	CAR PORT
D-27	9'-0"± x 6'-10"	SL	GLAZED	ALUM.	ALUM.	ALUM.	NONE	CHECK SIZE ON JOB, 1/4" PL GLASS

D O O R   S C H E D U L E

A B B R E V I A T I O N S

S.C. - SOLID CORE	P.G.	PAINT GRADE
HC - HOLLOW CORE	S.L	SLIDING
HRDWD - HARDWOOD	P.B.	PARTICLE BOARD
D.F. - DOUGLAS FIR	ALUM.	EXTRUDED ALUMINUM
D.F. PLY - DOUGLAS FIR PLYWOOD		
CAB - FLUSH CABINET DOORS		

Fig. 5-8. Door schedule A.

DOOR SCHEDULE

DOOR	TYPE	SIZE	THICKNESS	THRE'SHOLD	HEAD	JAMB	GLASS	REMARKS	RM.
1	A	3'-2" x 7'-0"	1 3/4"	A3-6	A1-6	A2-6	CLR. WIRE	ENTRANCE — FLR. CLOSER	101
2	B	3'-2" x 7'-0"	1 3/4"		K1-6	K1-6	CLR WIRE		102
3	B	3'-2" x 7'-0"	1 3/4"		K1-6	K1-6	CLR. WIRE		103
4	B	3'-2" x 7'-0"	1 3/4"		K1-6	K1-6	CLR. WIRE		104
5	D	3'-2" x 7'-0"	1 3/4"		K1-6	K1-6	CLR WIRE		105
6	D	3'-2" x 7'-0"	1 3/4"		K1-6	K1-6	CLR. WIRE		106
7	E	3'-2" x 7'-0"	1 3/4"	H2-6	H1-6	H1-6			107
8	E	3'-6" x 7'-0"	1 3/4"	H2-6	H1-6	H1-6			107
9	E	3'-2" x 7'-0"	1 3/4"	H3-6	H1-6	H1-6		CLASS "C" FIRE DOOR	108
10	E	3'-2" x 7'-0"	1 3/4"		H1-6	H1-6		CLASS "A" FIRE DOOR	109
11	E	3'-6" x 7'-0"	1 3/4"	H3-6	H1-6	H1-6		CLASS "A" FIRE DOOR	110
12	E	3'-6" x 7'-0"	1 3/4"	E3-6"	E1-6	E2-6		WEATHERSTRIP	106
13	C	3'-2" x 7'-0"	1 3/4"	K3-6	K2-6	K1-6			111
14	B	2'-8 x 7'-0"	1 3/4"	K3-6	K2-6	K1-6	OBSC. WIRE		115
15	B	2'-8" x 7'-0"	1 3/4"	K3-6	K2-6	K1-6	OBSC. WIRE		114
16	E	3'-2" x 7'-0	1 3/4"	J3-6	J2-6	J1-6		LOUVER TRANSOM	109
17	C	3'-6" x 7'-0"	1 3/4"	C2-6	C1-6	C1-6		WEATHERSTRIP	116
18	F	PR.5'-6" x 7'-0"	1 3/4	E3-6	E1-6	E2-6		WEATHERSTRIP	105

DOOR TYPES - ELEVATIONS NO SCALE

Fig. 5-9. Door schedule B.

ORDER OF DRAWINGS

The order in which the individual sheets of a set of construction drawings is arranged will vary from office to office. The generally accepted practice is to arrange the drawings in the order in which they will be needed on the construction project. The title page, index, and drawings pertaining to existing buildings, demolition, plot plans, and general site information would thus be placed at the first of the set of drawings. This group of drawings is classed as the "civil drawings" by some offices and may be prepared by a consultant retained by the architect, by employees of the architect, or by a separate department in larger architectural offices. The foundation plan or plans pertaining to subsurface structures may be included in the structural, civil, or architectural drawings.

Location of Detail Sheets. Information should be arranged not only in the order of which it is to be used but also in such a way as to give those interested (1) an overall picture of the project, (2) a closer look at the individual parts, and (3) detailed instructions as to how each part is to be constructed. Some architects and engineers feel that all details should be grouped together at the back of a set of drawings. This practice, however, may make drawings more difficult to interpret. The man on the job must turn through, in many cases, a large number of sheets and search

ROOMS FINISH SCHEDULE

Fig. 5-10. Room finish schedule A.

ROOMS	FLOORS ROUGH	FLOORS FINISH	FLOORS BASE	WAINSCOT MATERIAL	WAINSCOT HEIGHT	WALLS MATERIAL	CEILING MATERIAL	CEILING HEIGHT	SOFFIT MATERIAL	SOFFIT HEIGHT	REMARKS
FRONT ENTRY HALL	CONC.	SLATE	HARDWOOD			CONC. BLOCK	HRDWD PLY	7'-2"			SEE ELEVATIONS FOR SCREEN
LIVING ROOM	CONC.	CARPET	HARDWOOD			CONC. BLOCK	T&G RAND.	SLOPING			SEE ELEVATIONS FOR PANELING
FAMILY ROOM	CONC.	VINYL ASB.	HARDWOOD			BLOCK & HRDWD	T&G RAND.	SLOPING	HARDWOOD	7'-2"	
BEDROOM #1	CONC.	CARPET	D.F.			CONC. BLOCK	T&G RAND.	SLOPING			
BEDROOM #2	CONC.	CARPET	D.F.			CONC. BLOCK	T&G RAND.	SLOPING			
BEDROOM #3	CONC.	CARPET	D.F.			CONC. BLOCK	AC PLAST.	8'-0"			
BATHROOM #1	CONC.	CER. TILE	CER. TILE	CER. TILE	6'-8"	BLOCK & HRDWD	T&G RAND.	SLOPING	HARDWOOD	6'-8"	SEE ELEVATIONS
BATHROOM #2	CONC.	CER. TILE	CER. TILE	CER. TILE	6'-8"	BLOCK & PLAST.	T&G RAND.	SLOPING			
PASSAGE	CONC.	CARPET	D.F.			CONC. BLOCK	AC PLAST.	7'-6"			
LAUNDRY AREA	5/8 PLWD	ASPH. TILE	TOP SET			CONC. BLOCK	PLAST.	8'-0"	PLAST.	7'-2"	
KITCHEN	CONC.	VINYL ASB.	COVE			CONC. BLOCK	PLAST.	8'-0"			NATURAL FINISH CABINETS
HEATER	5/8 PLWD	ASPH. TILE	TOP SET			CONC. BLOCK	PLAST.	8'-0"			
STORAGE AREA	5/8 PLWD	ASPH. TILE	TOP SET			CONC. BLOCK	PLAST.	8'-0"			
WOOD STORAGE	CONC.	CONC.	NONE			CONC. BLOCK	NONE				
DRESSING ROOMS	CONC.	CONC.	NONE			CONC. BLOCK	NONE				
CAR PORT	CONC.	CONC.	NONE			CONC. BLOCK	NONE				
BATHROOM #3	CONC.	CEMENT	CEMENT	CER. TILE	7'-4"	CEM. PLAST.	PLAST.	8'-0"			SEE ELEVATIONS

FINISH SCHEDULE BLDG. "C" FIRST FLOOR

Fig. 5-11. Room finish schedule B.

RM NO.	LOCATION	FLOORS ASPH TILE	FLOORS TILE	FLOORS CEM.	BASE WOOD	BASE TILE	BASE CEM.	WALLS PLASTER SAND	WALLS PLASTER SMOOTH	WALLS PLASTER KEEN'S CEM.	WALLS ACUST TILE	WALLS PAINT ENAML	WALLS PAINT WHITE WASH	WALLS PAINT LEAD & OIL W.W.	WALLS TILE WSCT	CEILING PLASTER SAND	CEILING PLASTER SMOOTH	CEILING PLASTER KEEN'S CEM.	CEILING ACUST TILE	CEILING PAINT ENAML	CEILING PAINT WHITE WASH
1	CLASS ROOM	●						●											●		
2	KITCHEN		●		●				●			●					●			●	
3	STORAGE		●		●				●			●					●			●	
4	TOILET			●		●				●		●			●		●			●	
5	GARBAGE ROOM			●			●			●		●						●			
6	HALL	●			●				●			●					●			●	
7	WAITING ROOM	●			●				●			●					●			●	
8	SHOWER			●		●				●			●		●				●		●
9	TOILET			●		●				●			●		●				●		●
10	TEACHERS REST RM	●				●	●			●		●					●			●	
11	CHAIR STORAGE			●		●	●	●				●							●		●
12	JANITOR'S CLOSET			●		●	●	●				●							●		●
13	NURSES ROOM	●							●			●					●			●	

61

through innumerable details to find the information he desires. The closer the details of specific items can be placed to the drawings, which show the overall picture, the less wear and tear there will be on the set of drawings. A large set of construction drawings being used on a project site for an extended period of time may become mutilated to the point where they are difficult to read. Any device that tends to cut down on the constant turning of pages will be a help. It is expensive to replace a large set of construction drawings.

Location of Schedules. The proper placement of many items of information concerning the size and type of doors and windows and the location and finish of different types of paneling, flooring materials, and wall finishes and similar information which is indicated in tabular form is a controversial matter. Again, some architects prefer to place these schedules at the end of a set of drawings, and others feel that the schedules should be placed as near as possible to the floor plan or drawing to which they refer, for quick and easy reference.

STRUCTURAL DRAWINGS

The structural drawings are sometimes prepared by a civil or structural engineer and are started as soon as possible after, or even before, the architectural drawings. When the floor plans, elevations, and sections are roughed out, the engineer is called in for a conference and given check prints of the roughed-out architectural drawings. Many architects prefer to furnish all those who will be preparing drawings of a portion of the project with standard-sized sheets of vellum matching those to be used for the architectural drawings. These may have printed title blocks and borders, or these titles and borders may be drawn by the draftsmen in the architect's office. This assures a uniform appearance of all sheets in the complete set of construction drawings.

Checking Structural Drawings. Checking structural drawings is usually the responsibility of the job captain or project architect. He may assign portions of the work to several draftsmen, and each draftsman may therefore be familiar with only one part of the project. The job captain or project architect, who is responsible for the coordination of the entire project, will be able to visualize the effect of each small part and how it fits into the whole.

The architect has designed a building that will work for the client. He also desires to create certain aesthetic effects. The structural engineer will be striving to make this effect possible by designating materials and construction methods that will accomplish this. The job captain must carefully check all items to be certain that the structural frame designed by the engineer fits the concept expressed by the preliminary studies which have been approved by the owner. The job captain must check the architectural plans carefully for items that do not conform to the finished structural drawings. Has he located openings in the structure that will be blocked by a necessary beam or column? Has he shown finish materials surrounding a member that the engineer has had to enlarge to take a particular stress? Has he shown finish materials attached to a structural member that has been eliminated because it was not needed? These and other items must be carefully checked if the completed drawings are to reflect the conditions that will actually be present when the project is under construction.

MECHANICAL DRAWINGS

Mechanical drawings, which vary greatly from job to job and also in various sections of the country, must be carefully checked by the job captain and the specifications writer. These drawings usually cover those items calculated or designed by a mechanical engineer. They could include, among other things, storm-water drainage systems, water sources, sewage- and waste-disposal systems, hot- and cold-water piping and fixtures, gas and fuel-oil piping, boilers, pumps, valves, regulators, compressed-air or oxygen piping, and similar distribution systems. The above items are sometimes grouped together and designated as "plumbing." Heating, air conditioning, and ventilation and the necessary furnaces, boilers, cooling towers, condensers, refrigeration units, ducts, grilles, registers, controls, and thermostats make up a large part of the mechanical drawings. The design of other portions of the project such as escalators, elevators, hoists, kitchen equipment, and similar items is sometimes included in the mechanical drawings, although these may be classed as specialties and placed in separate sections.

Checking Mechanical Drawings. The checking of mechanical drawings must be thorough.

These drawings are usually being prepared on the basis of unfinished architectural drawings furnished by the architect. The mechanical, as well as the structural and electrical, drawings are usually in preparation over the same period of time. The job captain must coordinate this preparation to assure that allowances are made by all persons concerned for equipment to be used or any changes that may be necessary. A change in the size of ducts or air-conditioning equipment may necessitate a change in the finish material covering the structure. Holes cut through structural members for pipes may necessitate a change or redesign by the structural engineer. Additional grading required by the civil engineer may alter the location of plumbing lines. Towers or enclosures may alter the appearance of the building as shown in the exterior elevations of the architectural drawings. This coordination makes necessary constant exchange of the latest information, as it is prepared, between all involved.

ELECTRICAL DRAWINGS

Electrical drawings may be prepared by the architect or an electrical engineer. The person who prepares this section of the drawings must take into consideration the electrical requirements of all equipment that will be installed on the entire project. The type, size, and location of the heating and air-conditioning equipment, as well as the necessary electrical connections, must be shown in order for the electrical engineer to design his electrical systems and connections. Electrical panels, boxes, transformers, and conduits may be attached to the structural frame. Lighting systems must be coordinated with heating and air-conditioning grilles, ducts, and registers. The size and placement of the electrical fixtures may vary with materials, textures, and color of finish materials indicated on architectural drawings.

READING WORKING DRAWINGS

The preparation or reading of working drawings requires considerable experience. Unfortunately, most graduates of architectural schools in the United States have not had adequate training in this phase of the design profession. A good specifications writer must have had considerable experience either in the preparation of working drawings or in their interpretation under actual on-the-job conditions. The draftsman must be able to visualize the finished product as he draws the details. He must be able to place himself in the position of the contractor who will interpret the drawings. Has he shown everything the contractor will need to know in order to do his job? Has he repeated details or included some that could have been eliminated? The specifications writer must be able to analyze quickly the intent of the designer and, through a careful study of the details, visualize exactly how each individual part of a project fits into the whole.

QUESTIONS

1. What criteria are used when deciding whether information is to be placed in the specifications or the drawings?
2. Describe a method that can be used to help eliminate omissions in the drawings.
3. Sketch and describe a reference symbol.
4. Define the following and list briefly what would be included in each: a. Plot plan b. Foundation plan c. Floor plan d. Roof plan e. Reflected ceiling plan f. Structural section g. Architectural section.
5. Describe four types of schedules used on drawings.
6. What is the most widely used filing system for manufacturers' literature?

CHAPTER 6

References and Source Material

BUILDING CODES

Sooner or later in the practice of his chosen profession the structural engineer, the architect, or anyone concerned with building construction is confronted with a set of rules and regulations which constitute the building code of the city or area of his operations. These have been set up to guard the health and safety of the community and each person living or trading in that community. In most work, the specifications writer must consider these rules his prime reference. He must first determine which code or codes he will be working under and then thoroughly familiarize himself with the contents. He must then keep copies of all codes which will apply close at hand for constant reference. During the design and construction of a large hotel in a big city, the architect found that he must conform to twenty-one different city, county, and state codes and that more than two hundred appeals for modification had to be made.

City Building Codes. Many cities have passed ordinances referred to as "building codes." These codes usually cover all types of occupancies and all alterations to be made or new buildings to be constructed in a city. Most cities either adopt new codes or modify their codes every three to five years. In addition to these periodic modifications, the designer and the specifications writer must check to see whether any modifications have been made of the current edition. There usually are regulations administered by various city departments, such as those for fire and health, which supplement the city building code.

County and Township Codes. Some counties and townships have codes which govern work done outside incorporated cities. The specifications writer must check to see whether such a code exists when he has a project to be carried out in a rural area. These usually follow the form and substance of the municipal codes, and, in most instances, if the designer follows good construction practice, he need not be concerned except about zoning and fire regulations peculiar to the area.

State Codes. Most states have regulations which apply to buildings of a particular type of construction or use. Many of these regulations affect primarily the design of multiple dwellings, hotels, and places of public assembly. Only a very few states have these regulations gathered together in the form of a code which can be easily used as a reference. If the statutes, laws, regulations, and interpretations have not been gathered together into one code, the specifications writer must obtain them and cross-index and summarize the contents in order to know the limits within which he must work. Unfortunately, these local and state regulations do not always agree, and he often must have them interpreted in order to be able to proceed.

National Building Codes. At the present time, there is no national building code in the United States. Buildings erected on Federal property are not subject to the requirements of local codes. Work executed for Federal agencies must comply with the regulations of that particular agency. The National Board of Fire Underwriters publishes, from time to time, a suggested national building code which may be adopted by communities for use as a local code. In 1956, this code had been adopted by approximately one thousand cities throughout the United States. A group of building officials representing cities in all parts of the United States have published a recommended code entitled The Building Officials Conference of America Basic Code, which can be adopted by municipalities as a local code.

Regional Building-officials' Groups. In addition to the two organizations of national scope, there are several regional building-officials' groups that have prepared recommended building codes, such as the New England Building Officials Conference, the Southern Building Code Congress, and the Pacific Coast Building Officials Conference. These organizations have published uniform building codes that are regional in nature for adoption by cities in their region. Revisions of these suggested codes are made periodically. The uniform building code published by the Pacific Coast Building Officials Conference is published every third year.

Adoption of Codes by Cities. Many cities have passed ordinances adopting one of the suggested national or regional codes. This code then, by reference, becomes the local code. In most instances, the city adopts a particular edition of this code, and this edition remains the official code of the city until a new resolution is passed adopting a later edition. Because of this situation, one city may operate under, say, the 1955 edition of a particular uniform building code, while an adjacent city operates under the 1964 edition of the same code. Many cities adopt the basic code with modifications that they feel are necessary in their locality. The designer must determine four points: (1) which basic code to follow, (2) what edition of that code is in effect, (3) what modifications have been made in that particular area, and (4) what other agencies will be concerned with this particular project.

Specialized Codes. Most city and regional building codes do not cover the plumbing and electrical work. Cities may adopt separate codes for these sections. Some cities have codes for grading, elevators, and other specialties. A city may publish its own building code and adopt, by reference, the National Plumbing Code as published by the National Board of Fire Underwriters. The design of buildings to be used for specific purposes is usually governed by national, state, or local codes. Hospitals, schools, homes for the aged, nurseries, auditoriums, and similar buildings must conform to these specific codes.

Safety Codes. Most states have established safety codes that apply to construction. These codes cover a wide range of subjects such as fire protection, wall openings, scaffoldings, lifts, electrical hazards, and protection of the public. The designer must be sure that his building conforms to the requirements of the safety codes in force in that particular area. The specifications writer must have the safety rules on hand to make sure this work will be carried out in the manner required. He may write these rules in the specifications by reference. The specifications writer must use caution in this type of reference. In a recent court case, the reference to the Industrial Safety Code in the specifications was not allowed because that code states that the enforcing agency will be the Industrial Safety Organ-

ization, and the specifications stated that the architect would enforce the regulations.

Need for Uniformity. The number of codes in use and their varying requirements lead to confusion and inconsistency. There are locations where an apartment house on the side of a street may be designed for a live load of 40 psf, while across the street (in another borough, city, or political subdivision) an apartment house must be designed to resist 75 psf. It is difficult to understand why a particular type and grade of wood will support 1,800 psi in one location but will support only 1,600 psi across a political subdivision. Some progress has been made, but it will be many years before the specifications writer or designer can depend on a uniform building code to give him all the answers and resolve all conflicts.

BUILDING-CODE STANDARDS

In order to reduce the bulk of a building code, many cities have set up standards to which they refer in their regularly published codes. These standards are published in a separate volume. As an example, the Uniform Building Code, 1958 edition, of the Pacific Coast Building Officials Conference, in referring to the quality of portland cement, gives the designation as "U.B.C. 26-1-58." To find the exact specifications for portland cement referred to, the specifications writer must locate 26-1-58 in the Uniform Building Code Standards, 1958 edition. This, he will find, is an excerpt from Standard Specifications C150—153 of the ASTM. In order for this reference to be legal, the city must keep on file copies of all reference documents. This is done by publishing a set of standards which give the complete specifications of the materials referred to.

AMERICAN SOCIETY FOR TESTING AND MATERIALS (ASTM)

This organization was incorporated in 1902 for the purpose of "promotion of knowledge of materials of Engineering, and the standardization of specifications and the method of testing." ASTM has over ninety committees made up of producers and consumers from industry who are studying new materials, new applications, and new testing methods for the use of industry. The ASTM publishes a book of ASTM standards which presently consists of eleven volumes and over seventeen thousand pages and which contains about three thousand standards for materials. Most large architectural or engineering offices have copies of these standards. Every office should have a copy of ASTM Standards in Building Codes, which is a special compilation of standards adopted by reference in the major nationally known codes of the United States and Canada. The ASTM also has for sale, at nominal prices, copies of separate standards for individual materials or testing methods. The annual index of ASTM standards is very convenient in locating any specification or testing procedure. Single copies are available on request without charge from the American Society for Testing and Materials, 1916 Race Street, Philadelphia 3, Pa. Quantities may be purchased at special prices.

<u>Use of ASTM Standards</u>. It is possible for the specifications writer to save much time and effort by referring to an ASTM standard, for example: "Reinforcing steel shall be intermediate-grade billet steel conforming to ASTM A15-58T," "Slump tests shall be made in accordance with ASTM C143-52," and "Sewer pipe shall be laid according to ASTM C12-58T."

In the above, the letter "C" refers to the general classification; the number "12" indicates the specific standard; and the number "58" designates the year adopted or the date of the latest revision. If these numbers are followed by a letter "T," this is a tentative standard which may, after a period of use, become a standard. The ASTM recommends processes, such as that cited above (ASTM C12-58T), only in instances where proper installation is of paramount importance and where correct practice is not followed as often as it might be. Each of these letters and numbers must be used when referring to an ASTM standard. ASTM standards are constantly being revised in the light of experience with a product. ASTM C114-51T, which describes the chemical composition of portland cement, contains information that was deleted entirely in ASTM C114-56. The specifications writer should have the standard at hand and must know its contents before he can include it in his specification by reference.

AMERICAN STANDARDS ASSOCIATION (ASA)

The ASA was founded in 1918 as the American Engineer Standards Committee. Following expansion of the program to embrace standards of all types as well as engineering standards, the association was reorganized in 1928 as the present ASA. It is now a federation of 138 trade associations, professional and technical societies, insurance groups, and other national organizations. It also has more than two thousand company members. The functions and purposes of the ASA are clearly stated in its constitutional objective:[1]

1. To provide systematic means by which organizations concerned with standardization work may cooperate in establishing American Standards, to the end that duplication of work and the promulgation of conflicting standards may be avoided.
2. To stimulate the work of existing committees and other organizations competent to formulate standards suitable for approval as American Standards, and to bring about the establishment of committees or organizations for the purpose where they do not already exist, but not to formulate standards.
3. To serve as a clearinghouse for information on standardization work in the United States and foreign countries.
4. To further the standardization movement as a means of advancing national economy and to promote a knowledge of and the use of approved standards.
5. To act as the authoritative American channel in international cooperation in standardization work, except in those fields adequately provided for by existing international organizations.

The ASA thus is the national standards coordinating body. It is not a technical society or other form of organization in that it does not itself formulate standards. Instead it provides the means by which all other organizations, including the governmental departments and agencies, may cooperate in the establishment of a single consistent set of national standards. It operates on the basic principle that "an American Standard implies a consensus of those substantially concerned with its work under the procedure of the Association, to the method of work to be followed, and to the final approval of the standard." The ASA also serves as the United States member

[1]By permission of the American Standards Association.

AMERICAN SOCIETY FOR TESTING AND MATERIALS
1916 Race St., Philadelphia 3, Pa.

Reprinted from Copyrighted Book of ASTM Standards, Part 5.

Tentative Recommended Practice for
INSTALLING VITRIFIED CLAY SEWER PIPE[1]

ASTM Designation: C 12 – 58 T
ISSUED, 1958.[2]

This Tentative Recommended Practice has been approved by the sponsoring committee and accepted by the Society in accordance with established procedures, for use pending adoption as standard. Suggestions for revisions should be addressed to the Society at 1916 Race St., Philadelphia 3, Pa

Scope

1. This recommended practice is intended to define proper methods of installing vitrified clay sewer pipe in order to develop and utilize the structural properties of such pipe to their fullest advantage.

NOTE.—Attention is called to the Specifications for Standard Strength Clay Sewer Pipe (ASTM Designation: C 13),[3] Specifications for Extra Strength Clay Pipe (ASTM Designation: C 200),[3] Specifications for Standard and Extra Strength Perforated Clay Pipe (ASTM Designation: C 211),[3] Specifications for Standard Strength Unglazed Clay Pipe (ASTM Designation: C 261),[3] and Specifications for Extra Strength Unglazed Clay Pipe (ASTM Designation: C 278).[3]

Strength Classification

2. (a) The strength classification of the pipe shall be such that pipe of the proposed dimensions will have structural strength in excess of the prospective total load.

(b) Any determination of the prospective load on the pipe shall be based upon adequate acknowledgement of live loads and dead loads as they may be affected by such factors as unit weight of backfill, moisture content, kind of soil, depth of cover over the pipe top, width of trench at the level of the top of pipe, dimensions of the pipe, and manner of support for the bottom of the pipe.

(c) In determining the strength classification of pipe and its prospective structural strength, there shall be recognition of the effect on structural strength due to variation in the manner of bedding the lower quadrant of pipe barrel. No bedding shall be considered adequate unless it provides satisfactory uniform bearing for the entire bottom quadrant of exposed pipe barrel.

---

[1] Under the standardization procedure of the Society, this recommended practice is under the jurisdiction of the ASTM Committee C-4 on Clay Pipe.

[2] Reverted to tentative and revised by action of the Administrative Committee on Standards, September 9, 1958.

Prior to its present publication as tentative, this recommended practice was published as tentative from 1915 to 1919, being revised in 1916 and 1917. It was published as standard from 1919 to 1951. It was revised and reverted to tentative in 1951 and published as tentative from 1951 to 1954. It was adopted in 1954 and published as standard from 1954 to 1958.

[3] Appears in this publication, see Contents in Numeric Sequence of ASTM Designations at front of book.

Fig. 6-1. An ASTM standard. (By permission of the American Society for Testing and Materials.)

ASTM SPECIFICATIONS
for
STEEL BARS FOR
CONCRETE REINFORCEMENT

I N T R O D U C T I O N

For many years there has been wide acceptance and use of the Standard Specifications for Steel Bars for Concrete Reinforcement (ASTM Designations: A 15, A 16, and A 160) providing for both plain and deformed bars. No requirements are contained in these specifications for the deformations of deformed bars. Investigations over the past few years have shown the desirability under certain design conditions of improving the bonding properties of deformed bars and, accordingly, in 1947 the Tentative Specifications for Minimum Requirements for the Deformations of Deformed Steel Bars for Concrete Reinforcement (ASTM Designation: A 305) were issued and subsequently adopted as standard in 1949 to provide requirements for deformations on bars. In December, 1950, several pending and newly proposed revisions of the basic reinforcing bar Specifications A 15, A 16, and A 160 were incorporated and cross references between each of these basic specifications and Specifications A 305 were established, the requirements consolidated in a clearer and more useful manner for the purposes of both manufacturer and purchaser. It will be observed for one example, that a deformed bar furnished under these tentative specifications must conform to the requirements of Specifications A 305 - 56 T. In order that a uniform designation date apply to all four specifications and to assure the orderly process of standardization of these developments, all four specifications are being published as tentative and appear in this pamphlet.

In 1957 Specifications A 408 were published to cover special large size deformed reinforcing bars. Specifications A 431 were published in 1958, and Specification A 432 in 1959.

Specifications for:

OCTOBER, 1961

Authorized Reprint from Copyrighted Publications of the

AMERICAN SOCIETY FOR TESTING AND MATERIALS

1916 Race St., Philadelphia 3, Pa.

Fig. 6-2. An ASTM standard. (By permission of the American Society for Testing and Materials.)

of the International Organization for Standardization (ISO), the International Electrotechnical Commission (IEC), and the Comité Panamericano de Normas Técnicas (CPANT) (Pan American Standards Committee). In this capacity the ASA serves as the channel through which United States industry and other interests may cooperate with their counterparts from other countries in the development of international standards.

The association maintains a standards library containing all the American standards, all the Federal and military specifications and standards, most of the standards developed and published by other organizations, and most of the national standards of other countries throughout the world which have standardization programs. The more than two thousand American standards approved to date are available for purchase from the ASA individually, as a complete set, or in sets relating to particular industries such as civil engineering and construction. A catalog of these standards is available free of charge, and the catalog lists other publications of interest in connection with standards and standardization such as How American Standards Are Made, Dollar Savings through Standards, Proceedings of the National Conferences on Standards, and numerous others. The association also publishes a monthly magazine, The Magazine of Standards. Publications and other information can be obtained by addressing the American Standards Association, 10 East 40th Street, New York 16, N.Y.

COMMODITY STANDARDS

The U.S. Department of Commerce issues two series of standards classed (1) commercial standards and (2) simplified practice recommendations. Commercial standards were set up to establish definite quality levels for certain commercial products as a means of promoting sound commercial practices in their manufacture, marketing, and application. Simplified practice recommendations establish sizes and types of products that are in greatest demand. They were designed to simplify manufacturing, distribution, and installation and to reduce the waste resulting from the great variety of products that manufacturers kept on hand to meet the demands of consumers.

As an example, softwood plywoods are manufactured and graded in accordance with Commercial Standards CS-45, CS-157, and CS-122. These standards cover the technical requirements of manufacturing and testing and should be referred to for complete information on plywood grades.

FEDERAL HOUSING ADMINISTRATION (FHA)

In residential work, the FHA Minimum Housing Requirements is a good reference. These requirements apply only to property which is offered or proposed to be offered to the FHA as security for an insured mortgage loan. The FHA mentions thirty-nine commercial standards in its Minimum Property Requirements issued in 1958.

FEDERAL STATUTES

Certain projects, such as schools built adjacent to government bases and other projects that are built with, or assisted by, Federal funds, must comply with Federal statutes and certain rulings of the Secretary of Labor, the Housing and Home Finance Agency, and others. These statutes—Title 18 U.S.C., Section 874; Title 40 U.S.C., Section 276C; and the Copeland Act, 29A CFR 5.5, 29 CFR, Part 3—cover working conditions, pay scales, subcontracts, and other such items. Notice that the contractor must comply with these sections must be included in the specifications. The contractor must be notified as to what reports will be required of him, and when. This information can be obtained from the local office of the U.S. Department of Labor. Any designer or specifications writer who is doing work on a project that is Federally financed, in whole or in part, must have this information on hand as a reference.

VETERANS ADMINISTRATION (VA)

The VA has regulations that must be followed when work is being done under its auspices. A set of standards is published by the VA entitled Construction Service Standard Specifications. It is obtainable at local VA offices.

FEDERAL SPECIFICATIONS

In 1949 an act of Congress set up a procedure to authorize the General Services Administration (GSA) to prescribe standard specifications for purchases made by Federal governmental agencies. One of the purposes of the agency is to establish standards and procedures that would result in maximum value

Commercial Standards

Classified List Revised to June 1, 1962

COMMODITY STANDARDS DIVISION

Commercial standards are specifications that establish quality levels for manufactured products in accordance with the principal demands of the trade. They give technical requirements for materials, construction, dimensions, tolerances, testing, grading, marking, labeling, or other details, so as to promote sound commercial practices in the manufacture, marketing and application of the products. The standards are developed by voluntary cò-operation among manufacturers, distributors, consumers and other interests, upon the initiative of any of these groups, through regular procedures of the Commodity Standards Division. A statement of the procedures is obtainable gratis from the Commodity Standards Division, Office of Technical Services, Washington 25, D. C.

Prices in this catalog apply as of the date of issue, and are subject to change. A discount of 25 percent will be allowed on orders for 100 or more printed copies of one title. Unless otherwise indicated, mail your order with remittance to the Superintendent of Documents, Government Printing Office, Washington 25, D. C. Prices include delivery to addresses in the U. S. and its possessions, and to other countries extending the franking privilege.

Where the price is not shown, the following notes apply, as indicated in the price column:

"T"--Printed copies were temporarily unavailable when this price list was issued, but reproduced typewritten copies of the standard or proposed revision will be supplied gratis, in limited quantities, by the Commodity Standards Division until printed copies are again in stock.

"M"--Printed copies are no longer available, but mimeographed or other forms of copy are supplied in limited numbers by the Commodity Standards Division.

"LC"--No printed copies are available for distribution in any form; they may be consulted in many public libraries, or microfilm or photo copies may be obtained from the Library of Congress. Information concerning them will be furnished by the Commodity Standards Division upon request.

Supplement. Standards in preparation are given in a supplement on the last page of this list. They are in various stages of development, and copies may or may not be available upon request. Inquiries regarding them may be held, if necessary, until copies become available. They will be furnished without charge.

Simplified Practice Recommendations. Lists of staple sizes, kinds and types of certain commodities that are produced and stocked in greatest quantity, or methods applicable to them, which are utilized most effectively to keep variety to a minimum. Price list mailed on request to the Office of Technical Services, Commodity Standards Division, Washington 25, D. C.

A BUSINESS REPORT of the U.S. DEPARTMENT OF COMMERCE
Luther H. Hodges, Secretary
OFFICE OF TECHNICAL SERVICES
John C. Green, Director

Fig. 6-3. Commercial standards list. (By permission of the U.S. Department of Commerce.)

Simplified Practice Recommendations

Classified List Revised July 1, 1962

COMMODITY STANDARDS DIVISION

Catalog No. 979

Simplified Practice Recommendations give the sizes, kinds, and types of specific manufactured articles that are produced and stocked for the trade in greatest quantity, or methods applicable to them, which may be used most effectively to keep variety to a minimum. Facilities for production and marketing of the recommended varieties, and their application by users, are the most fully developed and most widely adapted to current needs, according to surveys of industry practices. General utilization wherever practicable of the varieties or methods described avoids wasteful overdiversification, and enables producers and suppliers to give better service to customers.

The Recommendations are developed voluntarily by manufacturers, distributors, and users, upon the initiative of an industry organization, in cooperation with the Commodity Standards Division. Information on the method of their development is obtainable from the Commodity Standards Division, Office of Technical Services, U. S. Department of Commerce, Washington 25, D. C.

This classified list includes the recommendations of current interest, which are available in printed form at the prices shown herein. Orders should be mailed with remittance to the Superintendent of Documents, Government Printing Office, Washington 25, D. C. Prices include delivery to addresses in the United States and its possessions, and to other countries extending the franking privilege. One-fourth of the list price should be added for delivery to other countries. A discount of 25 percent will be allowed on orders for 100 or more copies of one title. Prices apply as of the date of this catalog and are subject to change.

This list also includes certain recommendations which are not available in printed form, but due to a continued limited trade interest are maintained by the Commodity Standards Division in mimeographed or other form of copy. They are marked "M" in the price column and are available in limited numbers without charge from the Division at the address given in the second paragraph above. A numerical list is also available from the Division giving the complete list of Simplified Practice Recommendations, including those now out of print, many of which are available for reference in public and college libraries. Photocopies and micro-reproductions may be secured by arrangement with the Division, when needed copies are not otherwise obtainable.

Commercial Standards establish standard quality requirements, methods of test, rating, certification, and labeling of commodities, to promote sound commercial practices in their manufacture, marketing and application. A list will be mailed on request to the Commodity Standards Division, Office of Technical Services, U. S. Department of Commerce, Washington 25, D. C.

A BUSINESS REPORT of the U. S. DEPARTMENT OF COMMERCE
Luther H. Hodges, Secretary

OFFICE OF TECHNICAL SERVICES
John C. Green, Director

Fig. 6-4. Simplified practice recommendations list. (By permission of the U. S. Department of Commerce.)

being received for the public funds expended. Many state, county, and municipal governments and some institutional and educational bodies require the use of these standards in their construction specifications. The National Association of State Purchasing Officials, as a result of a nationwide survey, has indicated that over sixteen hundred Federal specifications have been approved and recommended for use in state purchasing operations. Materials producers are, for the most part, familiar with the requirements of Federal specifications (sometimes referred to as "Fed. specs."). In some instances, the material producer is required to have his material pretested in order to qualify it for purchase by governmental agencies. If a material meets or conforms to a Federal specification, the specifier has some assurance that the product being specified has the quality and characteristics, price being a factor, that will best satisfy the intended user. These specifications are developed through the cooperation of Federal agencies and representative segments of industry.

Use of Federal Specifications. Even for a project that does not require the use of Federal specifications, the specifications writer will find these standards of great value to him as a reference. They will be recognized by most producers and can be included in a trade section of the specifications by reference, for example: "Mineral surfaced cap sheet shall conform to Federal Specification SS-R-521, Type 1." This reference would be sufficient to identify the material required. However, a reference such as this should never be included in a specification unless the specifications writer has a copy of the particular specification at hand. Federal specifications are constantly being revised, and manufacturers must keep abreast of revisions or changes and possibly alter their products to conform to the latest Federal specification. The description of a material as given in one Federal specification may be entirely different from that given in a revised version of the same specification. For further details and descriptions of Federal specifications and their use, see Chap. 13, Specifications for Governmental Agencies.

SWEET'S CATALOG SERVICE

This large collection of manufacturers' literature, published annually, is of great value as a reference to the specifications writer. Several types of sets are published. For those who are concerned with residential or light construction, a small set is published that is limited in scope. As an aid to easy reference, each volume has, in the front, a complete index for the entire set. This index is divided into three sections. The first section lists all the literature under firm names. If the specifications writer knows only the manufacturer's company name, he can use this index. The second section is arranged under product headings, for example:

ejectors....................30
electrical insulation.........32
elevators...................24

The third index is a listing of all trade names, proprietary names, or trademarks, for example:

L & S (structural bolts)$\frac{2d}{LA}$

LAPODOLITH (concrete hardeners)$\frac{9}{SI}$

LARCO (watercolors)$\frac{30d}{Ce}$

Sweet's Catalog Numbering System. Products have been divided up into sections, and each general classification has been given a number. Thus "Foundations—1"; "Structural Systems—2"; "Curtain walls—3"; "Masonry—4"; etc. These divisions appear on the back cover of the catalog in which they are included. The main headings are further broken down as 2a, 2b, 2c, 2d, etc. The subheadings are in turn broken down by individual manufacturers or distributors as Fe, Le, Mat, Te, etc. The entire heading could then be $\frac{2i}{Inl}$ or $\frac{3b}{Jo}$.

Availability. These catalogs are available, free of charge, from Sweet's Catalog Service, McGraw-Hill Book Company, 330 West 42nd Street, New York 36, N.Y.

As the reproduction and distribution of these catalogs are governed by contracts with the manufacturers, copies are sent only to those doing a given volume of business. The McGraw-Hill Book Company will send applications on request, which the architect must return requesting the catalog service.

Use of Sweet's Catalog. Sweet's Catalog

File does not solve all problems of the specifications writer. This file is made up of literature from companies throughout the United States. If an item cannot be found in this file, it does not mean that it is not available. Many companies, both large and small, choose other forms of advertising and are not included. The second caution in its use is that many products advertised in the catalog are not readily available in all parts of the country. The specifications writer should make sure there is a local distributor or representative before specifying an item. Most manufacturers list their distributors on the last page of their literature. If there is no distributor in or near the area of the project, it is necessary to proceed with extreme caution and to check to see whether the product can be furnished when it will be needed for construction.

AIA BUILDING PRODUCTS REGISTER

The AIA Building Products Register is the only reference which directly compares the physical characteristics and performance criteria of building products. Specifically, the register describes a product, gives its technical characteristics, and tells who makes it, what it is called, how long it has been made, how it should and should not be used, what it is made of, what sizes and finishes are available, what additional treatment it needs, what accessories are furnished with it, and what standards it conforms to. The register does not replace the manufacturer's product literature. In point of fact, the user is encouraged to refer to other sources such as Sweet's Catalog File and the AIA Standard Filing System and Alphabetical Index Document No. E-301. The register often makes other literature more useful by narrowing the search for the kind of supplemental information needed.

Use of Building Products Register. The register was first published in 1960 after ten years of professional study by a committee of the AIA. It contains 1,700 individual product listings published in twenty-four product categories. The reader should refer to the pages of the register shown in Figs. 6-5 and 6-6, which concern category 3—"Curtain walls"; subcategory 3.01—"Systems and frames"; and sidehead A—"Framing, window, and panel assemblies." In addition to the information shown in the figures, at the end of each section is a bibliography listing further reference material on the products covered by the particular section. This is broken down into the following: abstracts of standard documents, Federal specifications, military specifications, U.S. Department of Commerce commercial standards, summaries of association literature, and reference material.

A-E-C WESTERN CATALOG FILE

Distances to Eastern points which adversely affect freight rates, delivery schedules, and service facilities have predisposed Western architects and engineers to use the building products of manufacturers who warehouse or maintain distributor stocks in the West. The Times-Mirror Press, whose main offices are located at 1115 South Boyle, Los Angeles 23, Calif., publishes annually the A-E-C Western Catalog File, a clothbound volume of prefiled catalogs of building products available from these manufacturers. To receive the A-E-C Western Catalog File, one must be qualified as an architect, engineer, contractor, or designer, recognized and active in specifying products for use in construction in the West. The specifier must be in private practice or in the employment of a governmental agency or corporation involved in the planning and construction of buildings in the thirteen Western states. This growing catalog service has become a valuable aid to Western architects and engineers in preparing specifications. The A-E-C is affiliated with the California Council of the AIA. The use of the AIA Standard Filing System together with the A-E-C Western Catalog File makes for quick and easy cross-referencing.

CONSTRUCTION SPECIFICATIONS INSTITUTE (CSI)

This organization of interested specifications writers, architects, engineers, manufacturers' representatives, contractors, building officials, and others is doing constant research in all fields of the construction industry. The results of this research are published, as technical reports, in the institute's national monthly magazine, The Construction Specifier. These technical reports are not guides to be copied but are extremely valuable reference sources on the various phases of manufacture, supply, installation, and use of building products. These publications also contain interesting articles on specifications writing and other materials of value to the

CURTAIN WALLS — Systems & Frames — 3.01

62

KEY TO STANDARDS, SPECIFICATIONS & TESTS		
Key No.	Standard	Category & Abstract No.
M1.	ASA A94.3 – 1955	3-A 2
M2.	ASTM A 93-59 T	2-A 9
M3.	ASTM A 167-58 T	2-A 5
M4.	ASTM A 415-58 T	2-A20
M5.	ASTM A 366-58 T	2-A24
M6.	ASTM A 415-58 T	2-A29
M7.	ASTM B 103-60	3-A 9
M8.	ASTM B 169-55	3-A11
M9.	ASTM B 209-60 T	3-A12
M10.	ASTM B 210-60 T	3-A13
M11.	ASTM B 221-60 T	3-A14
M12.	ASTM B 235-60 T	3-A15
M13.	ASTM B 308-60 T	3-A16
M14.	ASTM B 313-60 T	3-A17
M15.	ASTM C 208-60 T	3-A19
M16.	ASTM C 352-56 T	10-A14
M17.	ASTM C 378-60 T	10-A16
M18.	Fed Spec HH-1-525	10-A30
M19.	Fed Spec HH-1-526a	10-A31
M20.	Fed Spec HH-1-562(1)	10-A37
M21.	Fed Spec HH-1-00575	10-A41
M22.	Fed Spec QQ-A-274	3-A23
M23.	Fed Spec QQ-A-359d	3-A24
M24.	Fed Spec QQ-A-620	3-A25
M25.	Fed Spec QQ-1-716(3)	cncl
M26.	Fed Spec QQ-S-00640	2-A94
M27.	Fed Spec QQ-S-692b	2-A95

Side Heading: A — ASSEMBLIES

1 COMPANY NAME, STREET ADDRESS, CITY & STATE	2 PRODUCT BRAND OR TRADE NAME / YEARS IN PRODUCTION	3a AIA FILE NO.	3b SWEET'S 1962 ARCH FILE NO.	3c MFR'S CATALOG TITLE, NO. & DATE	3d MFR'S CATALOG INCLUDES	4 MFR'S ASSN	5a USES RECOMMENDED	5b NOT RECOMMENDED	6a WHERE OBTAINABLE	6b DISTRIBUTION BY MFR	6c METHOD OF SUPPLY	7a PRODUCT (YRS)	7b INSTALLATION (YRS)	8a INSTALLATION BY	8b INSPECTION BY	9a MATERIAL	9b CONFORMS TO STD SPEC	9c STANDARD TEST METHOD	9d TESTING LABORATORY	9e CONFORMS TO MODULAR BUILDING STANDARDS
Aluma-Vue Company, 10325 Highland Road, Milford 2, Michigan	ALUMA-VUE (style Tech Motelwall) 1	17-A		Aluma-Vue CW-6261-1 2-61	des info, product spec, illustrations		commercial		mfr or dist	nation-wide, foreign	std mfd to order, custom	curtain wall warr 5	NA	lic instal, contractor	mfr, lic instal, contractor	aluminum extrusions	M11		not tested	no
American Art Metals Co., Box 7188, Station "C", Atlanta 9, Georgia	TRIMLINE 808, AMAR-TITE® 7	17-A	3a Am	Entrances, Store Fronts, Curtain Walls, 1961	des info, product spec, instal det, illustrations	PC, MBSA	commercial, industrial		thru dist	nation-wide				mfr, lic instal	mfr, lic instal	aluminum	M11			yes
Artex Corporation, 120 Industrial Rd., Summerville, S. C.	---	16-E	3a Ar	Artex Alum Windows, CW, 1962	des info, product spec, instal det, illustrations	AWMA	commercial, industrial		mfr or dist	nation-wide	std mfd to order, custom	materials, 1; workman-ship, 1		mfr, lic instal, contractor	mfr, lic instal, contractor	alum*	AWMA standards	AWMA window tests	Univ. window of Miami tests	as req
Brown & Grist, Inc., 25 Tyler Ave, Newport News, Va.	BROWN & GRIST 15	17-A	3a Br	Brown & Grist Alum Panel Walls, 1962	des info, product spec, instal det		residential, commercial, ind, schools		mfr or dist	limited area	std mfd	1	1	lic instal, contractor	mfr, lic instal		M11			no
Ceco Steel Products Corp., 6501 West 26 Street, Chicago 50, Ill.	CECO curtain walls 6	17-A	3a Ce	Ceco Alum, St CW, 1069-E, 1961	des info, product spec, instal det	AWMA, SWI	commercial, institutional, industrial		dir from mfr, thru dist	nation-wide	std mfd to order, custom			mfr, lic instal	mfr, lic instal	alum 6063-T5	M11			yes
Flintridge Corporation, 668 E. Huron River Drive, Belleville, Mich.	FLINTRIDGE PAN-O-WALL	17-A					residential, commercial, industrial		dir from mfr, thru dist	nation-wide, foreign	std mfd, custom			lic instal	mfr, lic instal		M11			yes
Geyser, E. K. Company, 915 McArdle Rdwy., Pittsburgh 3, Pa.	GEYSER (Grid series 3600) 22	17-A		Geyser Grid System, 1960	des info, product spec, illustrations	BRI	commercial, institutional		mfr or dist	limited area	custom	1		mfr, lic instal	mfr	alum	M11			yes

1 Who makes it, what is it called, and how much experience has he had?

2 What literature is available and what does it include? Where can I find it quickly?

3 To what manufacturers or trade associations does the company belong and subscribe?

4 What uses for the product are recommended? Which ones are not recommended by the company?

5 Can the product be obtained locally and from whom?

6 What kind of guarantees does the product carry with it and for how many years?

7 Will the manufacturer install and inspect his product?

8 To what standards do the materials conform? Does the product conform to modular building standards?

Note: The illustrations here are only partial pages from the building products register.

Fig. 6-5. Page from Building Products Register AIA. (By permission of the American Institute of Architects.)

3.01   Side Heading: **A**   FR

10 FRAMING							11 MAXIMUM SPACINGS				12 WINDOWS				13 PANELS								14 FINISHES				15 COMPONENTS REQUIRED					16 INSTALLATION				ADDITIONAL INFORMATION
a FRAMING DIRECTION	b CONSTRUCTION	c METAL & ALLOY	d SHAPE	e DIMENSIONS (Min./Max.)	f WEIGHT (Lbs) (Min./Max.)	g SECT MODULUS (Min./Max.)	a VERT MEMBERS (Ft)	b HORIZ MEMBERS (Ft)	c VERT MEM SUPPORT (Ft)	d HORIZ MEM SUPPORT (Ft)	a TYPE	b METAL AND ALLOY	c MAXIMUM WIDTH (Inches)	d MAXIMUM HEIGHT (Inches)	a TYPE	b EXTERIOR FACING	c INTERIOR FACING	d CORE MATERIAL	e THERMAL CONDUC (Min./Max.)	f MAXIMUM WIDTH (Inches)	g MAXIMUM HEIGHT (Inches)	h THICKNESS (Inches)	a FRAMING METAL	b WINDOW METAL	c EXTERIOR PANEL FACING	d INTERIOR PANEL FACING	a VAPOR BARRIER	b DRAINAGE WEEP HOLES	c AIR VENTS	d FURRING STRIPS	e INSULATION	a METHOD	b FASTENERS FURNISHED	c ACCESSORIES FURNISHED	d SEALANT RECOMMENDED	
vert, hor	extru	alum 6063-T5	our des	2" 12"	40 250	1' 12'	12	12	12	6	fixed, sliding	alum 6063-T5	144	72	varies per spec	varies per spec	varies per spec	varies per spec	var per spec	72	48	1/4 to 2	mill	mill	varies per spec	varies per spec	no	no	no	no	no	preasmb fr, windows, panels	anchors, etc	none	compound, tape, Thio	we do not mfr panels but will furnish them as required
vert, hor	extru	alum 6063-T	des	12"	—	—	—	—	—	—	fixed, proj, revrs	alum 6063-T5	—	—	open pan, sandw	as spec	as spec	as spec	—	60	—	—	204 A1 or as spec	204 A1 or as spec	as spec	as spec	no	no	no	no	no	preasmb fr, windows, panels	no	(15)	—	polybutene, polybutene tape 2 part Thiokol
vert	extru, formed	alum 6063-T5, 5005	var per spec	var w wall type	var w wall type	var w wall type	varies with wall type	—	—	—	all types per spec	alum 6063-T5	var w wdw type	var w wdw type	sandw	porc, ceramic tile	steel, cement asb bd	foamglas, styrofoam	.20 .25	—	96	1-1/2, 1-5/8	mill, anodize	mill, anodize	porc & tile patt spec	paintgrip primer	no	yes	no	no	yes	preasmb fr, windows, panels	curtain wall to structure	curtain wall protection material	compound, tape, gasket	*product custom adapted to std, variety of matl & sys available
vert	extru	alum 6063-T6		var w wall type	var w wall type		6	—	—	—	fixed, awning, hopper-in	alum 6063-T6	51	360	sandw	as spec	as spec	as spec	—	48	368	—	as spec	as spec	as spec	as spec	no	yes	no	no	yes	preasmb fr, windows, panels	as required	stools, trim	as spec	(16)
vert, grid	extru, rolled	—							vary		fixed, dbl-hung	alum 6063-T5 steel	vary	vary	skin, sandw	porc, steel, alum*	alum, steel	—	—	—	vary	—	paint, caustic etch, alum	paint, caustic etch, alum	optional	optional	no	no	if req		yes	dep on des & type of curtain wall	as required	stools, casg, trim, sills, gravel stops	consult w sealant mfr	*alum ceramic
hor, vert, grid	extru	alum 6063-T5					var		var		proj, hor, gliding	alum 6063-T5	vary	vary			alum, steel			vary	vary		mill, anodize	mill, anodize	optional	(13)	no	no	no		no	preasmb fr, windows, panels	optional		met to met Thio, met to msnry*	*use butyl tape
vert	extru	alum 6063	I H X	3-5/8 4-1/4 in.	1' .986 2.154	1.11 3.16	8 and 10	8 and 10	8 and 10	8	fixed, proj, revrs	alum 6063	72	48	sandw	P.E. alum, tile, others	steel, others	plastic, fbrglas, foamglas(U)	.07 1.07	72 x 120 P.E.	var face mat	3/8 3-5/8	P.E. anodize C-3 clr, colr	C-3 anod clr, colr	galv, paint, anodize	galv, paint, anodize	var per spec	var per spec	var per spec	var per spec	var per spec	site asmb max 28' x 28'	yes	protection material	gasket	construction is equally applicable to projected window use

(9) Of what material are the framing members made and in what size can they be obtained?

(10) How far apart must the vertical and horizontal framing members be spaced?

(11) What types, kinds and sizes of windows can the manufacturer furnish?

(12) What types and sizes of panels does he furnish including exterior and interior facing, cores and thermal conductance properties?

(13) What types of finishes are available for each component of the assembly?

(14) What other items are required to make a complete package?

(15) Are the units assembled at the site or pre-assembled? What fasteners and accessories are furnished? What sealant is recommended for installation?

(16) What additional information about the product should I know?

Fig. 6-6. Page from Building Products Register AIA. (By permission of the American Institute of Architects.)

• ARCHITECTS • ENGINEERS • CONTRACTORS

C.C.A.I.A. DOCUMENT NO. 401-63

AE C WESTERN CATALOG FILE •

1963

★ *Affiliated with California Council, The American Institute of Architects*

FILED ACCORDING TO A.I.A. STANDARD FILING SYSTEM

3. PREPARATION OF SITE AND PRELIMINARY WORK

4. CONCRETE AND MONOLITHIC CONSTRUCTION

5. BRICK MASONRY

7. WATERPROOFING AND DAMPPROOFING

8. STONE WORK

10. MASONRY UNIT CONSTRUCTION, HOLLOW AND SOLID

11. ROADS, PAVING, SURFACING, CURBS, GUTTERS, SIDEWALKS, VAULT LIGHTS

12. ROOFING AND SIDING (OTHER THAN WOOD), INCLUDING GYPSUM, FIBER, ETC., SHEET METAL AND SKYLIGHTS

13. STRUCTURAL METALS

14. MISCELLANEOUS METAL WORK

15. ORNAMENTAL METAL WORK AND METALS IN GENERAL

16. DOORS, WINDOWS, FRAMES, TRIM AND ACCESSORIES

17. PREFABRICATED BUILDINGS AND MATERIALS USED IN COMBINATION

18. VAULTS AND SAFES

19. CARPENTRY, LUMBER—EXTERIOR COVERINGS—AND MILL-WORK

20. FURRING AND LATHING

21. PLASTERING

22. MARBLE AND OTHER NATURAL STONES

23. TILE, TERRAZZO, WALL BOARDS, AND MISCELLANEOUS FLOOR AND WALL FINISHES

24. PLASTICS

25. PAINT, PAINTING AND FINISHING

26. GLASS AND GLAZING

27. HARDWARE

28. FURNISHINGS AND INTERIOR DECORATION

29. PLUMBING

30. HEATING, VENTILATING, AIR CONDITIONING AND REFRIGERATION

31. ELECTRICAL

33. ELEVATORS, MOVING STAIRWAYS, DUMBWAITERS AND ACCESSORIES

35. EQUIPMENT

37. INSULATION

38. LANDSCAPE WORK

39. ACOUSTICS

A-E-C's new look for 1963. This preview of A-E-C's new cover heralds a completely changed file. The contents will be filed in strict accordance with the A.I.A. Standard Filing System and thoroughly cross-indexed for quick reference. It will eliminate reference to another index when going from A-E-C to loose files or vice versa. In addition, standard specification material in various divisions will be included when available, as in the current edition. For products readily available in the West, see A-E-C. A-E-C is exclusively Western. Published by Times-Mirror Press, 1115 So. Boyle, Los Angeles 23.

Fig. 6-7. A-E-C Western Catalog File. (By permission of the Times-Mirror Press.)

Fig. 6-8. Panel discussion—CSI. (Photography by Charles Schoenberg.)

specifications writer. Valuable information on new and improved techniques is presented to members by panels of experts from industry in monthly chapter meetings throughout the United States. Information on the CSI and its publications may be obtained by writing to the Construction Specifications Institute, 632 DuPont Circle Building, Washington 6, D.C.

MANUFACTURERS' LITERATURE

Literature produced by manufacturers must be evaluated carefully by the specifications writer. The advertising appearing in established publications and trade magazines, and even much which reaches the architect or engineer through the mail, tends to present eye-catching photography of pretty girls holding items such as cast-iron sewer pipe or a sheet of aluminum. Catch phrases and tricky wording are used repeatedly to influence the public. A large percentage of this type of literature reaches the architect's or specifications writer's desk every day, to pause for just a moment before it lands in the wastebasket. Manufacturers' literature can be placed in three classes: (1) promotional literature, (2) general technical information on the products of one manufacturer, and (3) basic data on design, application, and specifications of a basic product or process.

Promotional Literature. Very well done, straightforward, colorful promotional literature of a nontechnical nature can be of use to the designer. Clients may have to be sold on a product when they cannot visualize how it will appear in a finished project. The client may wish to choose from several products that are presented in promotional literature of this sort. Through promotional literature, examples can be shown, photographically, of buildings, citing the architects and engineers as references.

General Information on Manufacturers' Products. Most large manufacturers prepare and distribute to architects and engineers catalogs which give information on all their products. These may be bound in a hard cover and indexed in such a manner that any product manufactured by the company can be easily located. As the material becomes out of date or is superseded by new products, new catalogs are distributed. Some manufacturers distribute hardback ring binders which their architectural representatives keep up to date for the architect or engineer. The catalogs describing materials used regularly by the specifications writer are kept on shelves for quick reference.

Basic Design Data. It is not feasible for companies who handle only a few products to issue catalogs. The specifications writer needs this information in such a form that it can be handily filed. This technical data, if it is to be of value, must give all the information the designer needs to know on quality, availability, and price range. It is obviously impossible to list exact prices of installed products, but a comparison should be made with alternative materials or products of comparable quality on a percentage or some other similar basis. Not only should the use of the product be described, but its limitations should be noted. The draftsman should have enough graphical information to detail how the the product will fit into adjacent construction. The specifications writer should have reports of testing that has been done and standards which the product meets. Sample specifications are sometimes included in the technical literature. However, these sample specifications are of questionable value. If the specifications writer has all the necessary data, he will prepare the specifications in accordance with his particular office practice.

ARCHITECTURAL REPRESENTATIVES

Most manufacturers or distributors of building products employ men whose job it is to assist architects and engineers in the use of the company's products. These men, in most instances, are not salesmen primarily but are interested in promotion of the products. The specifications writer should feel free to call on these men for advice on particular products. The representative will call at the architect's office and give suggestions on quality selection, show samples, and assist in the preparation of specifications. The specifications writer will soon learn which representatives can be depended upon to give honest advice on the adaptability of their products. The conscientious company representative knows that if he oversells his product or recommends its use for applications in which it is likely to fail, it will not be included in the specifications again. The representative should know the limitations of his product and realize that when his company does not have a product that will do a satisfactory job, the recommendation of a competitor's product may, in the long run, benefit his own company.

AIA FILING SYSTEM AND ALPHABETICAL INDEX

The problem of where and how to file the many needed catalogs and individual sheets of reference material so that they will be available for quick reference by the specifications writer must be considered. This has been greatly simplified by the use of the AIA Standard Filing System, established in 1920 by a committee of the AIA. New editions of an alphabetical index are published from time to time in order to incorporate new developments and products of the construction industry. Manufacturers are requested to include the AIA file number on their literature in such a manner that each piece of literature can be properly filed, even by a person who has no special knowledge of building processes. A copy of this Standard Filing System and Alphabetical Index, AIA Document No. E-301, may be purchased for a nominal sum from the Division of Professional Services, the American Institute of Architects, 1735 New York Avenue, N.W., Washington 6, D.C.

ASSOCIATIONS

Various groups composed of manufacturers, applicators, or contractors have joined together in order to promote jointly their basic products or services. These associations, bureaus, institutes, councils, societies, or producers, as they may be called, are essential to the specifications writer. They are formed to better their particular segment of the industry by setting standards of quality, size, or application methods.

Association Standards. Many of these associations issue suggested specifications or standards that can be utilized by the specifications writer. The standard specifications as published by the associations are sometimes included in the specifications by reference, for example: "Ceramic tile shall be installed in accordance with Standard Specifications for Installation of Ceramic Tile with Water Resistant Organic Adhesives, released 1961, as published by the Ceramic Tile Institute, 3415 West 8th Street, Los Angeles 5, Calif." This particular standard specification also notes items which the specifications writer must include in other sections (concrete, carpentry, lathing, plastering, plumbing). The specifications writer should never include such a reference in his specifications unless he has the current issue on hand and has checked it carefully to see that it is exactly what he wants. Some association standards may list several qualities of materials or methods of application. To refer to their standards without qualifying this reference can be the same as allowing the contractor to furnish whatever he wishes in the way of materials or workmanship. The specifications writer should further check and make certain that the practices recommended are appropriate, are not in conflict with regional union or trade practices, and will not violate local codes.

Association Consultants. As associations usually represent several manufacturers or distributors who may or may not be competitors, the specifications writer can usually get an unbiased opinion on at least a basic group of products by calling or writing to an association. Associations are interested in seeing that their basic products are used in the right places and installed correctly, and in most cases they have expert consultants to help the architect or engineer. In some instances, they will inspect, grade-mark, or stamp their approval on work installed.

List of Associations. When a specifications writer wishes to obtain information on products or methods of application, he can usually obtain help from one of the associations listed in Appendix B. This is only a partial list of the hundreds of such associations, but those given will help the specifications writer obtain information on many products. Some of these associations are nationwide and some of local interest only. Many of the associations listed as national have local chapters or representatives in local areas. Many of these organiza-

AIA Document No. E-301

(Formerly 172)

Standard Filing System
and Alphabetical Index

issued by

THE AMERICAN INSTITUTE OF ARCHITECTS 1962

AIA Document No. E-301

(Formerly 172)

Fig. 6-9. AIA Standard Filing System and Alphabetical Index. (By permission of the American Institute of Architects.)

STANDARD SPECIFICATIONS
FOR INSTALLATION OF
CERAMIC TILE

WITH WATER RESISTANT ORGANIC ADHESIVES
INCLUDING REQUIREMENTS OF
RELATED DIVISIONS

CERAMIC TILE INSTITUTE
3415 WEST 8th STREET
LOS ANGELES 5, CALIF.

Released 1961

 III

A.I.A. 23A and 23P

Fig. 6-10. An associations standard. (By permission of the Ceramic Tile Institute.)

tions publish literature of general interest regarding their services or products. Others furnish technical help, reference material, and suggested standard specifications. Many of these organizations are identified in specifications and otherwise by the first letter of each work in the association name. Thus the American Institute of Architect's becomes the AIA; the American Society of Heating, Refrigerating and Air-Conditioning Engineers, Inc., becomes ASHRAE; and the Underwriters Laboratories, Inc., becomes UL.

QUESTIONS

1. What are association standards, and how can they be used by the specifications writer?
2. Are all the products shown in Sweet's Catalog Service available on a nationwide basis? Why?
3. What is the CSI and how can it be of help to the specifications writer and architect-engineer?
4. How can a manufacturer's representative help the specifications writer?
5. What is the advantage of using an association representative rather than a manufacturer's representative?

CHAPTER 7

Assembly and Reproduction of Specifications

Specifications are seldom, if ever, written entirely anew for each project. Many sources of reference material available to the specifications writer have been described in previous chapters. However, one source of reference material was not covered. Copies of specifications produced for similar projects can be used as a starting point and reference for new projects. No two projects are ever identical, nor do the words used by another specifications writer ever seem to fit exactly. Even specifications written by the same writer need careful inspection to determine whether what was written several years, or even months, ago is exactly what is wanted on the present project. The preparation of specifications may then be considered a process of editing in addition to the original writing necessary to adapt reference material to a particular project. This repeated editing of material used successfully for previous projects should, in time, produce perfect specifications. Theoretically, these could then be copied word for word from that point on. If construction techniques did not change; if no new materials were developed; if the same building were duplicated in the same location, by the same contractor, for the same client, then this might be so. Copies of previously written specifications must be considered only a starting point.

OLD SPECIFICATIONS

If we use old specifications as a starting point for the preparation of new specifications, realizing that careful editing will be necessary before they can be so used, several methods may be followed. If a set of specifications for a project can be located that parallels the present project, the specifications writer may be able to use this set and prepare the new specifications by simply crossing out material not applicable to the present project and adding paragraphs and phrases where they are needed. By the use of this method, material found to be good through previous use may be reproduced without the laborious process of copying in longhand what will be needed. There are several drawbacks to this method. Typographical errors which occurred in the old set of specifications may be repeated in the new. Materials or methods appearing in the old set may not belong in the new. A detailed description included in a set of specifications of a material which is not to be used in that particular project can cause considerable confusion. References made in the old set may have to be changed. Page numbers of sheets may be altered by the deletion of unwanted information, and the addition of new material may cause references to page numbers or sections to be inaccurate. The sometimes cramped notes written between the lines of typing make it difficult for the specifications writer to be sure that he has produced an easily read, smooth-flowing description of exactly what he wants.

CUT-AND-CLIP METHOD

A variation of the technique of using old specifications can be described as the "cut-and-clip method." The old set of specifications is taken apart, and sentences, paragraphs, or sections are cut out and pasted, stapled, or attached with rubber cement to blank sheets of paper. The specifications writer then writes transitional sentences or adds new material in longhand where necessary. By this method, information may be taken from several old sets of specifications and used where it applies. Portions of manufacturers' standard printed specifications may be used where they are needed. The specifications writer can then turn the pasted-up sheets over to the typist for final typing.

PARAGRAPH METHOD

A third method may be used by the specifications writer. Paragraphs relating to a particular item are typed on 3" x 5" cards or 8-1/2" x 11" sheets to fit in a loose-leaf binder, and the cards or sheets are filed according to sections or materials for future use. These paragraphs or sheets would then be arranged in the desired order and handed to the typist for final typing. After typing, the cards would be refiled for future use. After several projects have been completed and the cards have been filed in a common file, the specifications writer, by selecting the proper cards and writing new ones only for new materials or methods of construction, may, with a minimum expenditure of time, prepare a set of specifications for a new project. One problem is the time necessary to prepare such a system. Once the files are set up and cards prepared to cover all variables, the system should work well. However, few specifications writers have the time to prepare such a system. Another drawback of the card system is that the finished specification tends to lack the continuity of thought necessary for intelligent interpretation and becomes merely a series of uncoordinated instructions grouped in a haphazard manner. Unless information is included on each card as to the type of project for which the original paragraph was prepared, the use of an isolated paragraph—for example, one on installation methods—can be dangerous.

Problems of Paragraph Method. There are several other problems related to the paragraph method. Unless the paragraph files are maintained in perfect order, preferably by one person, it is simpler to write new paragraphs than to find cards that must be filed under several sections to be effective. If the specifications for two projects are being written at the same time, duplicates must be filed. The time spent in returning file cards to their proper places and removing unwanted material tends to offset some of the apparent gains of the system. A scope paragraph must usually be written for each section even though pretyped paragraphs are used.

NECESSITY FOR REVIEW

Specifications writers must constantly review the material they are using as a basis for their specifications. Are they perpetuating language or wording that has become obsolete or now has other meanings? Have trade practices or union regulations made certain practices uneconomical or controversial? Have new methods of testing or measuring been developed that are more reliable than those used in the past? Have new materials been introduced by industry that will do the job better or more economically? The numbering system and the method of indicating headings and subheadings must be checked to determine whether they will fit into present office practices. The use of old specifications as a base for the new is standard practice, and if proper caution and careful reading and evaluation of the material to be used are carried out each time the old specifications are used, they can be a great help to the specifications writer.

GUIDE SPECIFICATIONS

As a time-saving device, and in an effort to eliminate some of the problems involved in writing over old specifications or of cutting and pasting, guide specifications have been developed. A guide specification consists of a series of partially completed specifications sections with blanks left in appropriate places to be filled in by the specifications writer. Another type has several choices of materials and methods, one of which may be selected to make the completed specification paragraph. Some guides have the blanks to be filled in and also offer choices of methods and materials.

Published Guide Specifications. The most comprehensive set of guide specifications was developed by Sleeper.[1] This rather large volume covers most situations that would be encountered in a building-construction project and is arranged in such a manner that the specifications writer can fill in blanks, circle desired information, or cross out unwanted information in soft pencil. The entire book would then be turned over to a typist for final typing. As Sleeper admits, the use of this book as a guide specification is valuable only to one who has a thorough knowledge of local practices. The wide variances in local laws, rulings, and customs make it extremely difficult, if not impossible, to prepare a guide specification which will be adequate under all conditions in all parts of the country. Another problem that occurs in the use of published guide specifications is the speed at which they become obsolete. Unless the material is constantly revised in the light of the latest materials and methods universally used in construction, it is of little value. However, as a reference, this book is extremely valuable.

Specification Work Sheets. Ben H. Dyer, of the AIA, has prepared a set of specification

[1] H. R. Sleeper, "Architectural Specifications," John Wiley & Sons, Inc., New York, 1940.

work sheets for use by the specifications writer.[2] This set of guide specifications consists of perforated 8-1/2" x 11" sheets under sixty-eight trade divisions. The specifications writer starts with a new set of work sheets for each project. He may then remove those sheets which apply, fill in the blanks, cross out material not desired, and add information not included in the guide. The sheets are then turned over to a typist, who prepares the final copy of the specifications. The use of these work sheets can save the specifications writer time and be of assistance to him in preparing specifications. However, as with Sleeper's work, the material must be checked with extreme care to see that it is applicable and follows local practice.

ASSEMBLING INFORMATION

The major portion of the specifications writer's time is spent in the assembling of information from reference books, industry standards, government specifications, company representatives, and specifications of other projects. He should have all this material in such a form and filed in such a manner that it is available for instant reference. If old specifications are to be used in the preparation of new, extra copies should be reproduced and a specification file set up. This specification file should be set up in two sections: one of complete specifications filed by job types and a second broken down into sections. Several copies of each section of each job should be filed so they may be used as needed. As projects are completed and as more material accumulates in the section files, care must be taken to avoid unnecessary duplication, and all outdated or unsatisfactory material must be removed. Unless these files are kept up to date, they soon become unmanageable.

References on Hand. Before the specifications writer can start the preparation of the final specifications, he must have all possible information at hand. Records of conferences which took place during the preliminary phases of design should be available. Outline specifications prepared at the completion of preliminary studies and the cost estimates based on these preliminary outlines are important.

[2] B. H. Dyer, "Specification Work Sheets," American Institute of Architects, Washington, D.C., 1951.

Checklists used by draftsmen and copies of office-practice manuals indicating items to be included in the drawings and in the specifications must be at hand for reference. Draftsmen using a checklist in the preparation of the drawings should make notes on materials to be used or note any questions that they may have on specific items. These checklists with draftsmen's notations can be used by the specifications writer.

Notes on Drawings. As the draftsman is preparing the drawings, he should make notes on margins to call the specifications writer's attention to items that may be in doubt. Check prints will be made of the drawings when they are approximately 20 percent completed, and the specifications writer can start to rough out the trade sections. He must proceed with caution at this point because changes will probably be made and major decisions reached. The specifications writer, in many instances, will be able to answer draftsmen's questions and make a preliminary check of the partially completed drawings.

SPECIFICATION BRIEFS

Until the working drawings, both architectural and engineering, are well under way, it is not possible to proceed very far with the specifications. The outline specifications have been prepared as a part of the preliminary design, but changes will probably be made during the preparation of the working drawings. Some offices follow the practice of starting the preparation of what they call "specification briefs." When the working drawings are approximately 20 percent completed, check prints are made of all working drawings, both architectural and engineering, and the specifications writer takes all information he can from these check prints, preliminary studies, and notes of conferences and determines the section headings for the specifications. These specification briefs list the scope of each section of the work and cover, in a general way, items that must be considered. If there are questions in the mind of the specifications writer on materials or processes to be used, he will note them in the brief. This brief is then duplicated and, in the larger offices, sent to each department for checking and comments. As the preparation of the working drawings continues, draftsmen, job captains, project architects, and engineers keep the briefs beside them for reference and make notes in spaces left in the briefs for this purpose.

STANDARD SPECIFICATIONS

Many architects would like to see standard specifications developed that could be used unchanged for all their projects. A large number of these standard specifications could then be printed and used on all projects. The production cost of specifications would be reduced, and the contents of the standard specifications would become familiar to contractors, resulting in lowered construction costs. Any change could be made by a simple amendment. The development and use of standard specifications could be of value only if many projects of a similar nature were being designed. Even then, the amendments that are necessary to keep the standard up to date tend to become more numerous and lengthy with each project. A point is reached where there are amendments of amendments and the continuity and advantages of the standard specifications are lost entirely. It then becomes a matter of cutting, pasting, and retypings, as in the use of old specifications.

TIME TO START FINAL SPECIFICATIONS

Whether the specifications will be written by employees or by a specifications consultant, many offices schedule the final preparation of specifications to start when the working drawings are approximately 80 percent completed. Time must be allowed not only for the actual writing but for answers to questions to arrive by mail, manufacturers' representatives to appear, products to be tested, and final typing, proofreading, and reproduction to be done. The time necessary for the preparation of specifications will vary with several factors. The complexity of the project—more than the mere size, cost or fee—will affect the time required to prepare a set of specifications. The similarity or availability of information on projects completed by a particular office will alter the time required. Many public agencies furnish, and insist on the use of, standards they have prepared for insertion into specifications. This can reduce the time spent in the architect's office in preparing the specifications. On the other hand, clients may insist on the use of certain forms or methods to be followed in writing specifications, that can complicate and extend the time

necessary to prepare a portion of the contract documents.

ARRANGEMENT OF MATERIAL

The technical material to be presented in the specifications must be arranged in such a manner that individual items of information may be located easily and quickly. Work performed by a single trade should be described in one location. The division of the work should follow local practices. Each part would then include only work that is normally included in one subcontract. The work should be arranged, as closely as possible, in the same sequence that will be followed during the actual construction process. The title given to such groupings of information varies greatly among specifications writers. The groups may be called "articles," "divisions," or "sections." In order to avoid confusion, the term "trade section" will be used here when referring to the work usually performed by one trade or one subcontractor.

Grouping of Information. It would simplify the writing of specifications if a comprehensive list of materials and processes could be prepared noting the particular trade section into which each item of information should be incorporated. A recognized, universally accepted standard list of trade-section headings under which each item of information would always appear would be of assistance. Mention has been made of specification checklists and guide specifications that have been developed, which attempt to group the information necessary for a construction project. The development of such a list or guide that would be valid in all sections of the country, for all projects, is doubtful. Each section of the country has different trade practices and trade jurisdictions. State licensing laws which limit the work of subcontractors must be considered. The work to be performed by contractors holding these specialty contractors licenses should be included in only one section. As an illustration, in some states the installation of general plumbing systems requires a different license from the one required for the installation of sprinkler systems even though both systems may be installed by plumbers. Each project may require a particular grouping. Each specifications writer has a preferred method of arranging material to be presented. There is no substitute for a thorough knowledge of local construction practices and a careful takeoff of the materials noted on the working drawings.

Information for the Estimator. In establishing a system for organizing material into trade sections, the needs of the persons who will actually be using the information must be considered. The builder's estimator will be the first to use the specifications during the preparation of a bid. He must be able to find quickly any item of information he needs. Individual portions of the work must be segregated so that estimates may be made on each individual item as he takes off quantities of materials or work from the drawings. If all information on a particular item is to be found in only one place, there will be less chance of missing items that will affect costs. The estimator must be able to separate work that will be done by the general contractor from that which will be let out on a subcontract basis. All work that will be handled by one subcontractor should then be covered by one section.

Information for Project Superintendent. The contractor's or architect's superintendent would like the specifications to be arranged in the order in which the work will be done. Each trade section could then be checked in order as tradesmen appeared on the job. A simple building on a flat lot that is free from obstructions may require an entirely different sequence of operations from that required by a more complicated project to be built on a difficult site. Excavators and carpenters to build forms may be the first to appear on the simple project, while the other may require wreckers, house movers, or contractors who will install pilings or caissons before the concrete forms are constructed. If the building is to be constructed on a concrete slab on grade, electrical, plumbing, air-conditioning, and other work to be placed under the slab must be completed before the foundations are placed. A structural-steel frame may be completed before the masons come on the project to install masonry filler walls. Electricians and plumbers may have to install conduits and piping systems as walls are erected in a reinforced-masonry building. Metal door and window frames may be required before walls are erected in a tilt-up building.

Segregated Contracts. Certain cities and governmental agencies require that portions of the work be performed under separate contracts. Electrical work and plumbing work may be let to separate contractors and all the work of all trades required under each contract must be grouped together. Owners may wish to remove portions of the work from the general contract and let this work on a segregated basis to specialty contractors. This will require a different grouping of material to be presented in the trade sections. The entire project may be performed on a segregated basis under the control of the architect. The work of several trades may then appear in several sections to allow portions of the work to be performed by designated contractors.

Dual Systems. Several municipalities, school districts, and governmental agencies require the use of specifications that are divided into two parts. One part consists in a schedule which is made up of standard requirements of materials, and the other consists of the workmanship to be required of each trade on any project. These schedules are printed by the agency and furnished to the architect for inclusion in his specifications. The architect writes a portion of the specifications and refers to particular items in the schedule that are applicable to the individual project. The contractor is then directed to ignore those items of information included in the schedule which are not specifically referred to.

It should be apparent from the above discussion of the variables that are encountered that any arrangement of the material to be included in a trade section and the arrangement of these trade sections in the specifications must be a compromise. It is not possible to arrange the material to the entire satisfaction of the estimator. Neither is it possible to arrange the material in the exact order in which the work will be performed, nor will it be possible to establish a satisfactory sequence of operations on all projects.

PUBLISHED LISTS OF TRADE SECTIONS

Several lists of trade sections with suggestions as to what information could be included in each have been published. These lists are helpful as a starting point in the organization of material into trade sections.[3] The references given divide the work to be done on a construction project into from seventeen to sixty-six sections. Each such reference used must be evaluated carefully as to its adaptability to the local regional practices and the requirements of each project being designed.

THE CSI FORMAT FOR BUILDING SPECIFICATIONS

In 1963 the CSI, as the result of many meetings throughout the United States and comments and criticism by members of the construction industry, adopted the CSI Format for Building Specifications. This system of arranging the content of specifications was also adopted by the AIA.

Basically, this format is a proposed arrangement of the information to be included in the specifications into divisions and sections. The division headings and numbers would be identical in every set of specifications written throughout the country. The work of a single trade, the work done under a single contractor, or a basic unit of work is grouped into a technical section or trade section. Several trade sections are grouped under a division, and each division includes one or more trade sections that can be grouped into commonly understood categories. The following divisions have been established by the CSI for building specifications:[4]

[3]H. R. Sleeper, "Architectural Specifications," John Wiley & Sons, Inc., New York, 1940.

B. H. Dyer, "Specification Work Sheets," American Institute of Architects, Washington, D.C., 1951.

H. G. Edwards, "Specifications," 2d ed., D. Van Nostrand Company, Inc., Princeton, N.J., 1961.

D. W. Gale, "Specifying Building Construction," Reinhold Publishing Corporation, New York, 1961.

B. J. Small, "Streamlined Specifications Standards," vol. I, Reinhold Publishing Corporation, New York, 1956.

[4]By permission of the Construction Specifications Institute.

The CSI Format for Building Specifications

Bidding requirements
Contract forms
General conditions (and supplementary general conditions)
Specifications
  Division 1—General requirements
  Division 2—Site work
  Division 3—Concrete
  Division 4—Masonry
  Division 5—Metals: structural and miscellaneous
  Division 6—Carpentry
  Division 7—Moisture protection
  Division 8—Doors, windows, and glass
  Division 9—Finishes
  Division 10—Specialties
  Division 11—Equipment
  Division 12—Furnishings
  Division 13—Special construction
  Division 14—Conveying systems
  Division 15—Mechanical
  Division 16—Electrical

The first three items in the CSI format—bidding requirements, contract forms, and general conditions—are contract documents that may or may not be bound with the specifications. The present trend is to bind these documents in the book of specifications. Many architects and engineers feel that for reference purposes samples of these documents should accompany the trade sections, even though separate bidding documents may be furnished to the contractor.

While the division headings and numbering always remain the same, the individual subjects or sections under each division will vary with each project. A sample book of specifications which follows the CSI format has been included as Appendix D. These specifications were used on a project costing approximately $140,000. On a more involved project, each division may include many more sections than are used here. On smaller projects, several sections may be grouped together under an appropriate section heading. In an effort to preserve uniformity in the use of the CSI format, the divisions retain the same name and number, and, if a division heading is not needed, this is so noted in the index.

SYSTEMS OF IDENTIFYING TRADE SECTIONS

Several systems have been devised and used in the numbering or identifying of information.

Some specifications writers simply name the section heading and list the page where that section occurs in an index. By this method, sections may be added or deleted by simply changing the index. Each section may be identified by a letter, and individual portions or paragraphs of a particular section may be identified by a number:

Section B—Concrete
   B-1—General
   B-2—Work included in this section
   B-3—Work not included in this section
   B-4—Materials

By the use of this method, individual paragraphs may be located quickly when references are to be made to specific items of information. This system, however, is limited to twenty-six sections unless double letters are used. In order to avoid the use of double letters, some specifications writers prefer to use Roman numerals. However, XIV or XVIII tends to become meaningless to the workman on the job.

Extremely complicated systems can be set up by the use of hyphens, Roman numerals, capital letters, small letters, and decimal systems. By the use of such systems, every sentence in a set of specifications could be identified. As numbering systems become more complex, the chance of typographical error becomes greater. It is questionable whether the additional time that must be spent in following such a complicated system is justified.

TITLE PAGES AND COVERS

Architects should consider the impact of a first impression when considering the makeup of a title page or cover to be used on a set of specifications. A good-looking well-organized set of working drawings which is accompanied by a book of documents that lacks organization and is covered by a thin sheet of paper on which a title has been typed in whatever manner a typist has desired tends to create an impression that the architect does not consider the specifications important enough to justify spending some time designing an attractive, well-thought-out cover. The number of sets of specifications that will be distributed and the volume of work produced by the office will, of course, affect the type of cover to be used. The additional cost of lithographing or printing

a good-looking sturdy cover is minor compared with the cost of preparing and reproducing a large set of specifications. These specifications are legal documents that will be seen and used by many persons before the project is completed. The appearance of a cover tends to be taken as an indication of the architect's competence, technical qualifications, and business ability.

The information to be included on the cover or title page should be brief. The following information should be included:

Contents—Are all the contract documents, except the drawings, to be included between these covers, or only the specifications? If more than the general conditions and the trade sections is included, the title must not be "Specifications."

Project description—Building use and address.

Owner—Name and address.

Date—This could be the date the specifications are completed or the date they are issued for the first time.

Prepared by—Architect's name, address, and sometimes telephone number.

Set number—A space is usually left for numbering those sets that are issued to bidders, contractors, or owners. It is important to keep a record of sets issued if addenda or changes are made after the original specifications are issued.

TABLE OF CONTENTS

It is well to give an overall picture of what is included in the book. The table of contents should list the documents that are included and, in some instances, the number of pages in each. A table of contents does not give page numbers where information will be found. It will act as a quick reference, and if it becomes too long or involved, it loses its value. If individual sections, subjects, or paragraphs and the page on which each appears are included, it becomes an index.

INDEX

The value of a detailed alphabetical index to a set of specifications is doubtful. A tremendous amount of time must be taken to prepare such a listing of paragraphs and subject matter. The estimator who is preparing a bid or the superintendent on the job wants to make sure that no sheets have been removed from a trade section. If the index notes the

TABLE OF CONTENTS

DIVISION I - GENERAL INSTRUCTIONS

DIVISION II - TRADE SECTIONS

MUSIC BUILDING - UNIVERSITY OF RENO   INDEX
NEVADA NORTHERN REGIONAL BRANCH   PAGE 1 only

Fig. 7-1. A table of contents.

number of pages included in a trade section, he can quickly check to be sure he has the complete section.

STYLE OF TYPING

There are a number of methods widely used by different offices in the organization of the typed pages which comprise the various trade sections. While the specifications will vary within a single office, depending upon the size and complexity of a project, each office generally adopts a style, or format, to be used on all specifications. Which style is selected will depend to a certain extent on the office organization. Another factor in choosing the style of typing is the importance the architect places on clear, concise, and easily read specifications. If the specifications are to be sent out to be typed and the masters typed and reproduced at a page rate, the architect may want as much information on each page as possible in order to lower the cost of typing and reproduction. His book of specifications then includes fewer pages and seems shorter. If the typing is to be done by the hour, the number of pages to be used will not greatly affect the cost.

Block System. Figure 7-2 shows an extreme form of the block system. The individual paragraphs are formed in blocks with no titles, numbers, or letters to identify a particular paragraph. There is no doubt that this form of the block system saves space, and as no paragraphs or headings are numbered, it is simple to use these paragraphs again in other specifications or to add or delete paragraphs. However, it is very difficult to find specific information at a glance. If addenda or changes are made after the specifications are completed, how will the architect be able to identify specific instructions that must be changed? The texts of the section may be read as easily and smoothly as a book; however, a trade section is actually a series of detailed instructions, each pertaining to a specific part of the work.

Indented System. The system shown in Fig. 7-3 could be called the "indented system." The saving of space is again the prime consideration. It is an improvement over the block system shown in Fig. 7-2 in that the headings are underlined and identified by numbers or letters. However, the text is still difficult to read, and the possibility of typographical errors is greatly increased because of the different indendations used in each paragraph.

Modified Block System. The style shown in Fig. 7-4 is the easiest to read and presents information in such a way that the estimator in the contractor's office and the superintendent on the job can quickly and easily recognize at a glance the topics for which they are searching. The section heading and page number are shown in the bottom right-hand corner. The specifications writer's and the typist's initials and the job number are in the lower left. Each main heading is identified by a number easily located, and the subject is capitalized and underlined. Subheadings and subsubheadings are identified by small letters and numbers in parentheses. The body of the paragraph is then placed in block form. If a change is to be made at a later date, specific items of information are quickly identified by section number, heading number, and paragraph number. An addendum or a change can refer to a specific paragraph to be deleted, and a new paragraph can be inserted in its place.

REPRODUCTION

When the specifications have been written, they must be reproduced for distribution to those who will need them. The number of sets that must be reproduced will vary greatly. The number of sets of drawings and specifications for the small project to be built by a preselected contractor is much smaller than the number needed for a large involved project let out for public bidding. The method used in this reproduction will vary with the size of the set of specifications and the number of sets needed. The specifications writer must realize that even in the simplest project a number of sets of specifications will be needed. Building departments usually demand two sets, and lending institutions require one or two sets. The owner should have one set for reference. A contractor will need several sets if he is to ask for subbids, and the architect must keep one set for reference.

Carbon Copies. If not more than a maximum of eight copies of a set of specifications will ever be needed, onionskin paper with carbon-paper inserts may be used. The last two or three sets will be rather hard to read. If it is found that more sets are needed during the construction phase, the specifications must then be retyped in order to furnish the additional copies. If the first sheet is back-car-

90

WORKMANSHIP: All interior wood finish, cabinet and casework shall be smoothly dressed, well sanded, and thoroughly cleaned before priming until surfaces are smooth and all defacements are entirely removed. All material showing machinery, sandpaper, or other defacing marks will be rejected. No interior wood finish or cabinet work will be permitted in the buildings before the plaster in that section in which the material is to be used is reasonably dry and approved by the representative of the architect.

All interior wood finish, doors, frames, and other cabinet work or fixed wooden equipment shall be properly installed, level, plumb and true. Members shall be neatly and accurately scribed in place, maintaining full width of end members where possible. All trim shall be put on in full lengths without piecing, except where the use of single lengths would be impractical or impossible, and then, if jointed, butt joints shall be beveled. All exterior angles shall be mitered, and interior angles of the molded parts shall be coped. All nails shall be set for putty. In all instances where wood finish adjoins other finished materials, a neat, tight joint shall be made.

All cabinet and casework shall be accurately scribed to contacting surfaces and shall be straight, plumb, level, and in true alignment, closely fitted and rigidly fastened in place.

All trim shall be set in full lengths without piecing, except where the use of single lengths would be impractical. Pieces shall be bevel jointed, not butt jointed, where joints are unavoidable. All exterior angles shall be mitered, and interior angles and moulded parts coped.

Paneling in Business Men's Lounge and Young Adult Lounge shall be applied to strip backing as shown by the drawings, using the high frequency glue weld process. Glue strips, 2" wide, shall be applied to the strips. After finish plywood is placed in position over the glue, apply the welding device to face of finish plywood at approximately 12" o.c. vertically over all glue strips except edge where the next sheet or panel is to be applied and leave for the prescribed time necessary to set up the glue.

PRIMING AND BACKPAINTING: All interior wood finish, millwork, case and cabinet work shall have been thoroughly primed and backpainted before erection and installation. Such priming and backpainting is specified in the "Painting" section, and is to be performed immediately following the delivery of such

RWR:jp
#54-21
10/10/55

Fig. 7-2. Block system of typing.

(3) Color Hardener: To concrete floor surfaces which will remain exposed and are scheduled to receive color, apply color hardener where indicated on the finish schedule. Finished surface to be uniform in appearance. Wax cure as specified.

(4) Troweling and Marking: Unless otherwise directed or specified shall be smooth-hand-troweled with steel trowels and of uniform natural color throughout.

a. Troweling: Three (3) separate operations with steel hand trowel. Do not use long-handled or "Fresno" trowel. Do not start second troweling operation until cement finish will support operator upon knee boards, laid flat on surface. Do not start last operation until topping has set sufficiently to permit burnishing.

b. Mark cement finished slabs and stops only in areas designated by drawings. Make markings with commonly used V-type or edging tools struck to straight lines and at spacing as indicated.

(5) Non-Slip Aggregate Finish: Cement finish stair treads, walking decks, walks and platforms shall have a non-slip finish produced by evenly sprinkling not less than 1/4 pound of the specified non-slip aggregate over each square foot of the finish cement, which has been screened level, and finishing as specified.

(6) Tolerance: Cement finished surfaces shall have uniformly true planes with a tolerance of one-eighth (1/8) inch measured along a ten (10) foot straightedge.

(f) Curing:

(1) Liquid: (Except for casting slabs) As soon as concrete has set sufficiently hard to permit application without marring the surface, liquid curing compound as specified shall be applied over the surfaces which will receive floor finishes and all exterior concrete.

(2) Wax: Not more than 24 hours after pouring colored cement finish floors, they shall be given a coat of colored wax and covered immediately with plastic curing membrane.

(g) Stripping Forms and Removal of Shoring: Entirely remove forms for all work, but do not disturb until the concrete has attained necessary strength to support its own weight, and any construction live loads. Minimum time for slabs: 7 days; beams and girders: 15 days; other work 3 days.

(h) Extra Concrete: Should the Owner order extra excavation beyond indicated limits, requiring extra forms, reinforcement and concrete, Contractor shall perform such extra work in accordance with the provisions of the contract.

(i) Defective Cement Work: Cement finish not true to line or planes, not thoroughly troweled as specified; which does not adhere tightly to the underlying concrete; which has any roughed top surface; which is cracked, or does not connect properly to adjoining work, will be deemed to be defective, and shall, upon order of the Architect, be removed and replaced with workmanship and materials conforming to these specifications.

Fig. 7-3. Indented system of typing.

(2) Brown Coat: 1 part of gypsum neat plaster to not more than 3 parts of sand, by weight.

(3) Finish Coats:

(a) Smooth White Finish: 3 parts lime putty to 1 part gauging plaster (calcined plaster), by volume. Prepare lime putty by mixing hydrated lime with water in proportions called for in printed directions of manufacturer. Screen or punch hydrated lime through sieve so as to obtain a smooth, lump-free putty.

(b) Keene's Cement Finish: 3 parts Keene's cement to 1 part lime putty. See above for preparation of lime putty.

10. PLASTER APPLICATION

a. Gypsum plastering work shall be three-coat work when applied over metal and wire lath. Gypsum plastering work may be two-coat work when applied over gypsum lath.

b. Install grounds so as to provide 1/2" minimum thickness for gypsum plaster from face of plaster base to finished plaster surfaces.

c. Gypsum Plaster:

(1) Scratch (First) Coat: Apply with sufficient material and pressure to form a good bond on gypsum lath, and to cover well, and then scratch to rough surface. For two-coat work, double back to bring plaster out to grounds, straighten, and leave rough for finish coat.

(2) Brown (Second) Coat: Apply after scratch coat has set firm and hard, bring out to grounds, and straighten to a true surface with rod and darby; leave rough, ready to receive finish coat.

(3) Finish Coats:

(a) Smooth White Finish: Apply over a base coat which has set and is surface-dry; scratch thoroughly, lay on well, double back, and fill out to a true, even surface. Thickness shall be 1/16" to 1/8". Allow finish to draw a few

DAW/ef
Job 39-5-2

Plaster
9-3

Fig. 7-4. Modified block system of typing.

boned (by placing a sheet of carbon face up behind the first sheet), additional copies may be made by a process of blueprinting, whiteprinting, or photoprinting in the same manner as the drawings are reproduced.

Blueprinting. Some offices prefer to blueprint their specifications. The original is typed on a sheet of thin paper, and the copies are reproduced by one of several methods. These may be classed as wet-process, dryprocess, or photographic reproduction. Those machines using a wet chemical bath are classed as wet-process machines, and those using ammonia fumes are classed as dry-process machines. In order to assure sharp, readable copies, the original sheet is back-carboned (reproducible orange carbon paper works best) in order to deposit a layer of ink on the front and back of the thin paper. Orange carbon paper is used because of its ability to stop light and thereby make sharper prints. There

Fig. 7-5. A "Xerox" machine. (By permission of the Ralph M. Parsons Company.)

are several disadvantages of this type of reproduction. The cost is relatively high, and the copies tend to be difficult to read and fade when exposed to sunlight. A rather recent type of reproduction method has been developed whereby copies may be made from typewritten sheets. The process utilizes infrared light to heat the image and transfers it to copy paper that is sensitive to heat. Machines such as the "Thermo-Fax," manufactured by the Minnesota Mining and Manufacturing Company, and the "Verifax," manufactured by the Eastman Kodak Company, are of this type.

Many offices use these relatively inexpensive machines for reproducing several copies of notes or letters. When specifications have been reproduced by carbon paper, prints may be made by this process. The paper used in this process is rather expensive, and the printing of a large number of copies is much slower than with other systems. It is questionable whether these machines would be used except in an emergency or when very few copies are to be reproduced. The machines can be used by the specifications writer to reproduce material from old specifications or other reference sources. By this method, the old material may be used without the laborious hand-copying that would otherwise be necessary.

Spirit Duplicating. A relatively inexpensive machines for reproducing several copies through the use of a spirit duplicator machine. The master copy is typed on a sheet of paper which is backed up by special paper coated with an aniline dye carbon sheet. As the type is struck on the front sheet, an indelible impression is left on the back. This master is then placed around a rotary cylinder which, when turned by hand or electricity, passes the master through a spirit bath (alcohol plus other volatile substances). As paper is fed through the machine, aniline dye impressions are left on the paper. By this process, several hundred copies of the master may be produced. Near the end of a run of 150 copies, however, the typing tends to become faint. It is rather difficult to obtain sharp, clean copies by this process unless the masters are perfect, the pressure is set correctly, and the master is coated with the exact amount of liquid. Typists, in many instances, object to the use of this process because of the coating of aniline dye that inevitably coats their hands at the end of the day. The typing may be reproduced in black, purple, or other colors. Corrections may be made simply by applying a thin strip of paper tape on the back of the master, covering the error, and retyping. One advantage, in addition to simplicity and economy, of this type of duplication is the ease with which the masters may be proofread. This proofreading can take place from the masters before any copies are run off.

Mimeographing. One of the most common forms of reproduction is mimeographing. This process uses a gelatin stencil into the surface of which the images of the letter are cut. The gelatin stencil is mounted on a revolving cylinder, and the ink is forced through the cuts in the stencil to make an impression on a sheet of paper. The gelatin stencil, or master, will reproduce an unlimited number of copies. Although mimeographing is widely used, the process has some disadvantages. The stencil is extremely delicate and is subject to tearing. It is rather difficult to make changes on the master, and it is very difficult to proofread and make corrections on the master stencil. The running of a single trial copy in order to proofread can be a time-consuming process.

Lithographing. Many offices with a large volume of work are switching to a lithographic process to reproduce their specifications. In lithographic printing, the typing is done on a paper or metal master. This master is placed in a lithographic press, and the copy is reproduced on paper directly as it is automatically fed through the press or is imprinted on a rubber blanket which offsets, or reproduces, the image on paper. The second type described is known as "offset lithography." The big problems in the use of lithography are the high initial cost of the equipment and the necessity of hiring a trained lithographer to operate the equipment. Many large offices have found it advantageous to purchase and use this equipment. In addition to the reproduction of specifications, the equipment can be used for the printing of brochures, art work, renderings, and cover pages. Other offices send the paper masters to lithographers for reproduction rather than purchasing the machinery and paying the operator. Modern trends in lithography have brought the price down to the point where more architects are switching to this excellent type of reproduction.

PAPER
The type of paper to be used for specifications will vary with the reproduction method.

If carbon copies are to be made, the paper that must be used is very thin and easily torn—another disadvantage of this method. Spirit duplicating requires a special duplicating paper, and mimeographing requires a paper which is very absorbent and which tends to be weak and easily damaged. Lithographic printing can use a wide variety of paper. It is very important that the paper used in a set of specifications be of a good quality because it may have to withstand months of hard use in the field on a construction project. Some architects prefer to use colored paper. Each major division of the book of construction documents would then be printed on a different color of paper. In order to cut down on the size of the specifications book, information may be printed on both sides. In order for this to be successful, a heavy opaque paper must be used. This method does cut down the number of sheets of paper to be used but adds to the problems of typing, numbering, reproduction, and gathering the sheets into a set.

BINDING
When the specifications have been reproduced and gathered, they must be bound into a set. The simplest method would probably be to use staples. However, this method can be used on only the smallest sets, and even then it is not always satisfactory. In order to remove a sheet or a section, the set must be

Fig. 7-6. Gathering a set of specifications. (By permission of the Ralph M. Parsons Company.)

torn apart and, if not restapled immediately, soon becomes a jumble of paper. Some architects feel that the set of specifications which is permanently stapled together with heavy staples is difficult for a general contractor to take apart, but this can be considered an advantage. Brass paper fasteners may be inserted into two or three holes punched in the side, or patented fasteners that lock in place may be used. This type of fastener may be removed and replaced with ease. It is wise, when this method is to be used, to buy paper that is prepunched to receive the fasteners. Punched paper costs little more and may save hours of punching sheets after reproduction. All the above methods of binding have a single disadvantage: The set cannot be laid open flat, a feature that would be of great assistance to those working with a large set of specifications.

Plastic Binding. Several companies manufacture inexpensive punching and binding machines to be used for the insertion of plastic ring binders. These rings come in many sizes and are quick and easy to use. Most stationery stores can give information on where this equipment may be purchased. Plastic ring binders have several advantages. The paper is held into the set in many places instead of just two or three, and this helps to eliminate the problem of the missing or torn-out page.

With this type of binding, this book may be laid out flat or folded over on itself. Pages or sections may be removed easily by the specifications writer in the office in order to make corrections, and a new plastic binding may be pressed into place. The contractor in the field is not able to do this easily without special equipment.

QUESTIONS

1. Describe a specifications checklist and its use.
2. What are some of the advantages of streamlined specifications?
3. What is the "cut-and-clip" method, and what are some of the problems involved in the use of this method?
4. Give four factors that influence the location of technical information in the specifications.
5. Describe three numbering systems that may be used in identifying trade sections.
6. Where will the specifications writer obtain the information on a particular project when he is ready to start writing?
7. What factors determine the selection of a particular method of specifications reproduction?

CHAPTER 8 Agreements and Contracts

There is little agreement on the subject of exactly what is meant by the term "specifications." To some, specifications may consist only of the trade sections. To others, they may include the trade sections and the general conditions, supplemental general conditions, and special conditions, which modify or explain the work to be done under the trade sections. Some specifications writers consider all that is bound between the covers of the "book,"—written instructions and documents necessary for the execution of the work—to be specifications.

LEGAL BACKGROUND

The writing of agreements and contracts which are included, by some, in the specifications book requires a legal background. The preparation of agreements and contracts, which are legal documents, for use on a construction project may be considered the work of a lawyer. However, the architect or engineer may assist the owner in the preparation of these documents, or he may suggest the use of standard forms, such as those published by the AIA, contractor groups, or engineering societies. The specifications writer, even though he may not do the actual writing of these agreements and contracts, must be thoroughly familiar with the contents of standard forms, agreements, and contracts. All that he writes in the technical sections and the conduct of all concerned with a project will be based on these documents.

DEFINITION OF TERMS

It is well to begin a discussion of contracts, agreements, and related documents with a definition of terms that are commonly used. The terminology, or nomenclature, used in the various documents differs, to some extent, throughout the country. However, the definitions given here represent the most generally accepted meanings and usage.

Contract. In order for there to be a binding contract, four essential elements must be present:

1. Two or more parties must be present, each of whom has the power to make a contract.
2. A lawful purpose must exist for making a contract.
3. A consideration, or payment, or the exchange of something of value must be agreed upon.
4. There must be a meeting of minds or a mutual understanding.

If any one of these four elements is missing, there is no contract. If all four elements are present, an oral agreement is considered a contract. An oral agreement, such as an agreement for the employment of an architect or engineer, is usually not binding unless the work can be performed within the period of one year.

Agreement. The agreement is that part of the contract documents which presents the legal evidence of a meeting of minds between an owner and a contractor. The agreement is signed by two parties who have a legal right to do so. The signing of the agreement implies that (1) both parties have examined the site and become familiar with the drawings and specifications, (2) the contractor has made a proposal which has been accepted, and (3) the consideration and the terms of the execution of the work have been set.

Owner. The owner may be the person who actually owns a piece of property. A person or company leasing a piece of property may be classed as an owner, and a corporation, municipality, or agency of the Federal government may also be designated an owner. Exactly who is meant by the "owner" is defined in the agreement, and he is then referred to as if he were singular in number and masculine in gender.

Contractor. As in the case of the definition of the word "owner," when the word "contractor" is mentioned in the specifications it will be in reference only to the person or persons mentioned in the agreement. Even though a general or prime contractor has employed or contracted with others who may hold valid contractors' licenses, the contract refers only to those specifically mentioned in the agreement. Thus there is no contract of any nature between an owner and a subcontractor.

Subcontractor. Not only those who have contracts with the general contractor are classed as subcontractors. Anyone who furnishes material worked to a special design as indicated in the drawings or the specifications is also considered a subcontractor. If material is furnished that has not been fabricated to such a design, the person so furnishing the material is not a subcontractor. The following, taken from the general conditions written by an architect for a large Federally financed school, defines the status of the subcontractor:

18. Subcontractors:
   a. The Contractor may utilize the services of Specialty Subcontractors on those parts of the work which, under normal contracting practices, are performed by Specialty Subcontractors.
   b. The Contractor shall not award any work to any Subcontractor without prior written approval of the Owner, which approval will not be given until the Contractor submits to the Owner a written statement concerning the proposed award to the Subcontractor, which statement shall contain such information as the Owner may require.
   c. The Contractor shall be as fully responsible to the Owner for the acts and omissions of his Subcontractors, and of persons either directly or indirectly employed by them, as he is for the acts and omissions of persons directly employed by him.
   d. The Contractor shall cause appropriate provisions to be inserted in all subcontracts relative to the work, to bind Subcontractors to the Contractor by the terms of the General Conditions and other Contract Documents, insofar as applicable to the work of Subcontractors, and to give the Contractor the same power as regards terminating any subcontract that the Owner may exercise over the Contractor under any provisions of the Contract Documents.

   e. Nothing contained in this contract shall create any contractual relation between any Subcontractor and the Owner.

Architect-engineer. Some contracts provide that persons other than the named architect or engineer may act for them. The architect or engineer may be designated in the contract to include associates or employees whose acts will be construed to be acts of the architect or engineer. In case of the architect's or engineer's inability to act, the contract must be altered. Exactly who will be considered the architect or the engineer must be specifically defined in the agreement.

INVITATION TO BID

In order to give notice to contractors who may be interested in submitting bids for a project, it is many times necessary to place advertisements in public and trade papers or magazines. This document is, in fact, called the "advertisement" for this reason. The purpose of advertising is to ensure that the right bidders are attracted to bid on the project. If the project is to be constructed for the Federal government or is a public-works project, the invitation to bid must be advertised for a certain period of time in the public press. This is also true for projects constructed in certain municipalities. The invitation to bid gives an overall picture of the proposed project. It tells prospective bidders when bids will be taken and how and where the documents which will be used on the project may be obtained. It also gives the prospective bidder other information he needs to help him make up his mind whether to undertake the project. The invitation to bid should be mailed out to prospective bidders in addition to being placed as an advertisement. The invitation to bid should be as brief and simple as possible. It is necessary only to inform a prospective bidder of the licenses or qualifications that are necessary to bid on the project and to tell him whether the work is in his line, what bonds or money he will have to post, and the time allowed in which to prepare a bid. Other items of information that are sometimes included are wage scales, rates, form of bids, rejection of bids, and how payments will be made. It is questionable whether these last items should be included. This information is not needed until the contractor begins the preparation of his bid. Certain public agencies require the use of a special form to be used for the advertisement. Figure 8-1 shows an example of a typical invitation to bid.

INSTRUCTIONS TO BIDDERS

It was stated that the invitation to bid should be as brief as possible. This does not hold true in the instructions to bidders. This document, which is often prepared hurriedly, must state fully everything that will be required of the bidder when he is preparing an estimate and upon submission of his bid. The preparation of this document should not be passed over lightly. The instructions to bidders should repeat some of the information given in the invitation to bid and should amplify this information.

Telephone Inquiries. Many time-consuming telephone inquiries may be avoided if the instructions to bidders are complete. If telephone requests for clarification are to be allowed, who should be contacted, and where? If all requests must be in writing, this must be stated. If there is a limit on the time during which requests will be allowed, the date after which no questions will be answered must be indicated. Will requests for clarifications be answered for materials men, for subcontractors, or only for general contractors?

Securing Documents. The instructions must give information on where and how bidders may secure the bidding documents which they will need and must designate who may secure sets of contract documents. Will a contractor be chosen from a selected list, or will the bidding be open to all responsible contractors? Will subcontractors be allowed to pick up sets of the contract documents, or may only general contractors do this?

Deposits. What type of deposit will be required, and how and when will deposits be returned. What bonds or other documents, such as questionnaires, must be submitted with the proposal? The form that must be used for each of these documents will affect the bidders and must be described. Will a certified check be accepted in lieu of a bid bond?

Use of Proposal Forms. The form of proposal to be used and the number of copies that must be submitted are given. It must be stated that a copy of the proposal form is included in the specifications book and that this copy is not to be used for bidding but must be left in the book for future reference. If there are

certain state requirements that the contractor must comply with, these should be carefully spelled out. As an example of this, several states require, on certain projects, that a list of subcontractors who will be used on the project be included with the contractor's proposal. Notice should be given that only the specific information requested should be included in the contractor's proposal. Proposals should not contain a description of the work as seen by the contractor. This can be construed as limiting the contractor's liability to what he has assumed to be the extent of the work. This also applies to alternate proposals or substitutions that are not specifically asked for. If each contractor is allowed to propose alternates or substitutions at this point, it may be next to impossible to determine who is the actual low bidder or to make a valid comparison of bids. The contractor must submit his bid based on the contract documents prepared by the architect. If substitutions or alterations are to be made, this can be done after the successful bidder has been selected. It is important that all bidding be on the same basis.

The bidder should be told how to fill out the proposal form so that it will be acceptable. Instructions such as the following should be noted: "All blank spaces must be filled in and all information typed; the correct, complete legal signatures shall be in longhand, in ink, without interlineation or erasures." Bidders should be required to list all addenda that they have received, and they should be notified that an incorrectly filled in or incomplete proposal may be considered the basis for rejecting a bid.

Subcontractor List. The inclusion of a list of subcontractors in the instructions to bidders, unless required by a specific agency, is of questionable value and can work a hardship on the bidders, who are usually rushed for time. The purpose of the list is to discourage "bid shopping." It is considered better to require only the successful bidder to submit such a list within five or ten days after the bid opening.

Questionnaires. A questionnaire, in which a bidder is asked to describe his experience, work force, and construction plant and the equipment he intends to use, is sometimes required. A financial statement may also be required. This information could be of assistance to the architect and the owner in

INVITATION TO BID

Notice is hereby given that the Board of Trustees of Sierra Madre Union School District, 810 Pine Avenue, Sierra Madre, California, hereinafter called the Owner, will receive up to, but not later than July 4, 1964, sealed proposals for the construction and completion of Pine Avenue Elementary School Addition No. 1, located on the site of the existing Pine Avenue School, on the southwest corner of Pine Avenue and Rodeo Street, in Sierra Madre, Los Angeles County, California.

In general, this project comprises the construction of a classroom addition to Pine Avenue School; all work to be complete in every respect, including appurtenant utilities and other work as shown on the Drawings and as called for in the Specifications.

Bids will be considered on a lump sum basis for the entire work described herein.

Each bid shall be in accordance with the drawings and specifications prepared therefor and the pertinent contract documents now on file in the office of Don A. Watson and Associates, Architects and Engineers, 1624 Hyland Avenue, Arcadia, California.

Drawings and specifications may be examined and sets obtained upon a deposit of $35.00 per set, at the office of the Architects and Engineers; said deposit will be refunded upon return of the sets in good condition within 5 days after the bids are opened.

Each bid shall be made out in the form furnished by Don A. Watson and Associates, and must be accompanied by a certified or cashier's check or bid bond for not less than ten percent (10%) of the amount of the base bid, made payable to the Owner.

The above-mentioned check or bond shall be given as a guarantee that the bidder, if awarded the work or any part thereof, will enter into contract when requested to do so by the Owner; and if he refuses, will be declared forfeited.

Each bid shall be submitted in duplicate and shall be filed with the Superintendent of Schools at Sierra Madre Union School District on or before the hour and date designated above, at which time bids will be opened and read in public at the office of the Superintendent.

The Board of Trustees reserves the right to reject any or all bids and to waive any irregularity in any bid and to determine the lowest responsible bidders.

SIERRA MADRE UNION SCHOOL DISTRICT

By William H. Norwood, Jr., Superintendent

DAW/sk
Job No. 41-2-2

Fig. 8-1. Invitation to bid.

1. **PROPOSALS**

Proposals, to be entitled to consideration, must be made in accordance with the following instructions:

a. Proposals shall be made upon the Bid Form prepared and furnished by the Architect, a copy of which is attached hereto. Proposals shall be completed, including each and every item; bids shall be stated both in writing and in figures. The signatures of all persons shall be in longhand. The complete form shall be without erasures, interlineations, or alterations.

b. Proposals shall not contain any recapitulation of the work to be done, and alternate proposals will not be considered unless called for. No oral, telegraphic, or telephonic proposals or modifications will be considered.

c. Before submitting a proposal, bidders shall carefully examine the drawings, read the specifications and documents, visit the site of the work, fully inform themselves as to all existing conditions and limitations, and shall include in the proposal a sum to cover the cost of all items included in the Contract.

d. Proposals must be accompanied by a certified or cashier's check or a bidder's bond in an amount not less than ten percent (10%) of the amount of the proposal, made payable to the Owner. Said check or bond shall be given as a guarantee that the bidder will enter into contract if awarded the work and, in case of refusal or failure to enter into said Contract, the check or bond will be declared forfeited to the Owner.

e. Pursuant to the provisions of Sections 4100 to 4108, inclusive, of the Government Code of the State of California, each bidder shall set forth, on a form provided by the Architect and attached hereto, the name and address of each subcontractor who will perform work or labor or render services to the bidder in or about the work in an amount in excess of one-half (1/2) of one percent (1%) of the bidder's total bid. If the bidder fails to specify a subcontractor for any portion of the work to be performed under the Contract, he shall be deemed to have agreed to perform that portion of the work himself. The successful bidder shall not, without the consent of the Owner:

    (1) Substitute any person as a subcontractor in place of the subcontractor designated in the original bid.

    (2) Permit any subcontract to be assigned or transferred, or permit it to be performed by anyone other than the original subcontractor designated.

    (3) Sublet or subcontract any portion of the work in excess of one-half (1/2) of one percent (1%) of the total bid for which his original bid did not designate a subcontractor.

Fig. 8-2. Instructions to bidders (three pages).

f.   Proposals shall be delivered to the Owner's Representative on or before the day and hour set for the opening of bids in the advertised "Notice to Contractors", exclosed in an opaque sealed envelope and bearing the title of the work and the name of the bidder.

2.   BIDDERS INTERESTED IN MORE THAN ONE BID

No person, firm, or corporation shall be allowed to make or file or be interested in more than one bid for the same work unless alternative bids are called for. A person, firm, or corporation that has submitted a sub-proposal to a bidder is not hereby disqualified from submitting a sub-proposal or quoting prices to other bidders.

3.   WITHDRAWAL OF PROPOSALS

Proposals may be withdrawn by bidders prior to, but not later than, the time fixed for the opening of bids.

4.   INTERPRETATION OF DRAWINGS AND DOCUMENTS

Should a bidder find discrepancies in, or omissions from, the drawings or specifications, or should he be in doubt as to their meaning, he shall at once notify the Architect.   If it should be found necessary, a written Addendum will be sent to each bidder; neither the Owner nor the Architect will be responsible for any oral instructions.

5.   ADDENDA

All addenda issued by the Architect during the time of bidding shall become a part of the drawings and specifications loaned to the bidder for the preparation of his proposal, shall be covered in the proposal, and will be made a part of the contract.

6.   FORM OF CONTRACT

The Agreement and the form of Bonds which the successful bidder, as Contractor, will be required to execute are attached hereto and are made a part hereof.

7.   TIME FOR COMPLETION

The time limit established for completion of said work shall be as set forth in the Bid Form.

8.   OPENING OF BIDS

Proposals will be opened and read at the time and place set forth in the advertised "Notice to Contractors".   Bidders, or their representatives, and other interested persons may be present at the opening of bids.

Fig. 8-2 (Continued.)

9. AWARD OR REJECTION OF BIDS

The contract will be awarded to the lowest responsible bidder complying with these Instructions and with the advertised "Notice to Contractors" inviting bids, provided his proposal is reasonable and it is to the interest of the Owner to accept it. The Owner reserves the right to reject any or all bids, or to waive any informality in any one or all bids received. The competency and responsibility of bidders and of their proposed subcontractors will be considered in making the awards.

10. BONDS

The successful bidder, simultaneously with the execution of the contract, will be required to furnish a Labor and Material Bond in an amount equal to fifty percent (50%) of the contract price, and a Faithful Performance Bond in an equal amount to one hundred percent (100%) of the contract price. Said bonds shall be secured from a surety company or surety companies satisfactory to the Owner.

11. COST BREAKDOWN

The successful bidder will be required to submit, upon request of the Architect, a breakdown of construction costs as itemized on the prepared form, a copy of which is attached hereto. These costs will be used for accounting purposes only, and are not to be confused with alternate bids or unit prices.

Fig. 8-2 (Continued.)

LIST OF SUBCONTRACTORS

Listed below is the name of each subcontractor, the price of whose work constitutes one-half of 1% of the total bid or more, who it is proposed to employ, and the segregated portion of the work each will perform if the contract is awarded to the undersigned.   Where a normally segregated portion of the work equals or exceeds one-half of 1% of the bid and no subcontractor is listed, the undersigned represents that he is competent, experienced and equipped to do that segregated portion of the work and that it will not be subcontracted.

Segregated Part of Work	Subcontractor
1.	
2.	
3.	
4.	
5.	
6.	
7.	
8.	
9.	
10.	
11.	
12.	
13.	
14.	
15.	
16.	
17.	
18.	
19.	
20.	
21.	

MUSIC BUILDING - UNIVERSITY OF RENO   FORM OF PROPOSAL
NEVADA NORTHERN REGIONAL BRANCH   Page 2 of 3

Fig. 8-3. A subcontractor list.

assessing the competency or responsibility of the various bidders. The questionnaire may be considered a part of the proposal and be placed immediately after the proposal form. If such a questionnaire is to be required upon the presentation of the proposal, this fact must be noted. A questionnaire is used only when it is felt that the information given will be of assistance to the owner in selecting a contractor.

Bid Opening. The bidders should be informed of the procedure to be followed at the bid opening. Certain public agencies require that the bids be opened publicly at a given place and time. All who wish may attend this opening. The sealed bids are opened at that time and read aloud to those present. On private work the decision of who may be present is left up to the owner and the architect. Some architects prefer to open the bids with only the owner present. This private opening of bids, while it may have certain advantages, leaves the architect open to possible criticism for favoritism. Each bidder has gone to considerable expense preparing an estimate and should have the right to see that his bid is considered.

Items Not Included in Instructions to Bidders. There are some items of information that need not be included in the instructions to bidders. Information that is in the specifications or in other contract forms, such as location of the site, insurance, taxes, and patents, should not be repeated here. Only items of information that are of interest to all bidders during the bidding period are included. Note that the instructions are addressed to bidders, not contractors.

Checklist for Instructions to Bidders. A summation and checklist of items that will be found in the instructions to bidders follows (not all these items would be needed in some instances, and additional items may be added for particular projects):

1. Manner and place of securing documents
2. Number of copies available to each bidder
3. Who may secure sets
4. Who may bid
5. Deposits for, and cost of, additional sets
6. Return of documents and deposits
7. Bid bonds required
8. Return of bid bonds
9. Certified check in lieu of bond
10. Financial statement required
11. Questionnaire required
12. Oath or collusion affidavit
13. Other forms required
14. Visit to site
15. Examination of, and familiarity with, the contract documents
16. Forms to use for proposals
17. Filling out proposal forms
18. All blanks filled
19. Erasures, interlineations, or alterations
20. Signing of proposal forms
21. Notarizing of proposal
22. Submission of proposal
23. Date of submission and number of copies to be submitted
24. Telegraphic bids
25. Opening of proposals
26. Withdrawing proposals
27. Rejecting proposals
28. Questions regarding contract documents
29. Award of contract
30. Execution of contract
31. Failure of bidder to execute contract
32. Failure of owner to execute contract
33. Time of completion
34. Liquidated damages
35. Substitutions
36. Addenda
37. Alternates
38. Unit prices
39. Cost breakdowns
40. Subcontractor lists

PROPOSAL

This document is a written offer given by the contractor to the owner stating the cost of performing certain items of work as designated in the contract documents. It also presents other pertinent information. By comparing the various proposals submitted by those who are bidding on a project, the owner can make a selection of the particular contractor with whom he wishes to enter into an agreement. By inspecting the proposals, the owner should be able to determine whether there is actually a meeting of minds. The term "bid" or "the bid" is sometimes used in place of "proposal." In order to be sure all bidders are bidding on the same basis, most architects insist that the proposals be made on a specific form such as shown in Fig. 8-4.

By using a prescribed form, the owner can be assured that each bidder is submitting a proposal that can be compared on an equal basis with those of other bidders. It is good practice to furnish the contractor with as many copies of the proposal form as he will need

PROPOSAL FORM

To: The Board of Trustees
Sierra Madre Union School District
Sierra Madre, California

GENTLEMEN:

The undersigned, having examined the Documents, Specifications, and Drawings entitled

PINE AVENUE ELEMENTARY SCHOOL ADDITION NO. 1

which compose the Contract Documents, and having visited the site and examined all conditions affecting the work, hereby proposes and agrees to furnish all labor, materials, equipment, and appliances, and to perform all operations necessary to complete the entire work as required by said Documents, for the stipulated sum of

_____
_____Dollars ($_____).

The undersigned agrees, if awarded the Contract, to execute and complete the work within 170 calendar days from and after receipt of notice to proceed with the work.

Should the work not be completed within the time hereinbefore stated, it is understood and agreed that there will be deducted from the final payment the sum of Thirty-five Dollars ($35.00) per day as liquidated damages, but not as a penalty, for each day's delay after the expiration of such period and until the final completion of the work and its acceptance by the Owner.

If awarded the Contract, the undersigned hereby agrees to sign a Contract and furnish the necessary bonds within five (5) days from the date of notification from the Owner, and to begin work within ten (10) days after receipt of notice from the Owner to proceed with the work.

The undersigned has checked carefully all the above figures and understands that the Owner will not be responsible for any errors or omissions on the part of the undersigned in making up this bid.

The undersigned hereby certifies that this bid is genuine and not sham or collusive, or made in the interests or in behalf of any person not herein named, and that the undersigned has not directly or indirectly induced or solicited any other bidder to put in a sham bid, or any other person, firm, or corporation to refrain from bidding, and that the undersigned has not in any manner sought by collusion to secure for himself an advantage over any other bidder.

The undersigned acknowledges receipt of the following Addenda, and the cost, if any, of such revisions has been included in the bid sum:

Addendum No. _____, dated _____
Addendum No. _____, dated _____
Addendum No. _____, dated _____
Addendum No. _____, dated _____

Enclosed find Bidder's Bond, Certified Check, or Cashier's Check No. _____
in the amount of ten percent (10%) of the Base Bid.

CONTRACTOR:

_____

License No.:   _____

_____   By _____

Type: Address _____

_____   _____

Dated this _____ day of _____, 1962.

Fig. 8-4. A proposal form.

for his submission and with extra copies for his files.

Proposal Forms. A form such as shown in Fig. 8-4 can be used only on a relatively simple project where a contract is to be let on a lump-sum basis. The language of the proposal must conform with the applicable laws, codes of the particular area, and policies of the agency or owner for which the work will be done. Most governmental agencies require the use of a prescribed form. Many of the larger industrial firms have developed their own forms of proposals. Many contractors prefer to use a proposal form developed by the Associated General Contractors of America, Inc. (AGC). This form is directed toward the protection of the contractor rather than the owner. Several protective clauses are included in the AGC proposal form which, in most instances, are well covered in the general conditions of the contract documents. These clauses, covering items such as depths of excavations, pay for extras, defense of the contractor in legal actions, adequacy of the architect's or engineer's drawings, and others, tend to lengthen the proposal form and duplicate information included in other documents. Any duplication such as this is undesirable.

Unit Prices. If unit prices are included in the proposal, a section must be added. These unit prices must be broken down into units that can be estimated, and the cost of each must be analyzed. The following was inserted in a proposal where it was impossible to determine all subsurface soil conditions before work started:

Unit Prices
1. The following unit prices may be used for establishing the cost of added or omitted work of this project in accordance with General Conditions, Special Conditions, and applicable Trade Sections of the Specifications and conforming to applicable Drawings. Unit prices shall include both labor and material and all related costs required to produce the unit, unless specifically noted otherwise.
2. Unit prices for establishing the cost of added work of this project shall be as set forth in the following schedule for omitted work with ten percent (10%) added to cover any costs which may not be accounted for in the deductible unit price.

	Unit	Basis of Unit Cost
1. Caissons (including drilling, casing, reinforcing steel, concrete, testing, and inspections complete).	Lin ft	(Add)_____
2. Cabled tool well:	Lin ft	
a. Price per lin ft to be DEDUCTED for well drilled and cased less than 500'.		(Deduct)_____
b. Price per lin ft to be ADDED for well drilled and cased in excess of 500', with a maximum depth of 750'.		(Add)_____
3. Mass concrete in place against earth below elevations as shown on the Drawings.	Cu yd	(Add)_____

Alternates. If alternates are to be included in the proposal, a section such as that which follows must be added:

1. In compliance with the Invitation to Bid, Instructions to Bidders, and General Conditions of the Contract Documents, the undersigned, being familiar with the local conditions affecting the cost of the work and having carefully examined the Drawings, Specifications, Addendum, and other Contract Documents for the construction of a science building for the University of Denver, Denver, Colorado, proposed to provide and furnish all required labor, materials, tools, equip-

ment, utilities, and transportation services to perform and complete the work as follows:

Base Bid

Construction of the concrete and masonry science building for the University of Denver as per Drawings and Specifications, for the sum of _____

_____ dollars ($ _____).

Alternate "A"

For the use of white cement matrix in lieu of gray cement for precast wall panels as per information on Alternates, Drawings, and Trade Sections, add to the BASE BID the sum of _____

_____ dollars ($ _____).

Alternate "B"

For the use of rubber tile in lieu of asphalt tile as per information on Alternates, Drawings, and Trade Sections, add to the BASE BID the sum of _____

_____ dollars ($_____).

Alternate "C"

For the installation of a glass mosaic mural as per information on Alternates, Drawings, and Trade Sections, add to the BASE BID the sum of _____

_____ dollars ($ _____).

Subcontractor Lists. It may be difficult for a general contractor, because of the short time he has in which to secure bids from subcontractors during the bidding period, to know exactly which subcontractors he will use on a project. However, some public agencies require, and some architects prefer, that a list of the subcontractors be submitted as a part of the proposal. The following form must then be inserted and made part of the proposal:

List of Subcontractors

Listed below is the name of each Subcontractor, the price of whose work constitutes one-half of 1 percent of the total bid or more, whom it is proposed to employ and the segregated portion of the work each will perform if the contract is awarded to the undersigned. Where a normally segregated portion of the work equals or exceeds one-half of 1 percent of the bid and no subcontractor is listed, the undersigned represents that he has the necessary experience and is able and equipped to do that segregated portion of the work and that it will not be subcontracted.

Segregated Part of Work	Subcontractor
1. _____	_____
2. _____	_____
3. _____	_____
4. _____	_____
5. _____	_____
6. _____	_____
7. _____	_____
8. _____	_____
9. _____	_____
10. _____	_____

Substitutions. If the architect has included trade names of specific products but still wishes to allow the contractor to offer substitutes for these products before a contract is let, a substitution sheet such as is shown below is made a part of the proposal:

A. Substitutions: The undersigned desires to use the materials, apparatus, or equipment described below as a substitute for the materials, apparatus, or equipment specified. The amounts set forth in the last columns are those to be deducted from, or added to, the lump-sum prices bid if substitution is used.

If the Architect finds any or all of the substitute materials, apparatus, or equipment so described to be the equal of that which is specified and shall require the use of such substitutes, a change order shall be issued, and the undersigned agrees to furnish the substitute materials, apparatus, or equipment, together with all labor required, necessary to perform and complete the work.

No substitutes will be allowed unless included in the list below and approved by the Architect.

Proposed substitute	Manufacturer and catalog number	$Add	$Deduct

Contractor's Option. A similar list without the cost columns may be required when the specifications have been written on a performance basis or the contractor has been given the choice of several products. The inclusion of this list would be required of the bidder only to the extent necessary to determine whether his bid conforms with the specifications.

Cost Breakdown. Some architects and engineers require the successful bidder to furnish a "cost breakdown" for a project. This form would not be a part of the proposal because not all bidders are required to fill it in. Only the successful bidder is asked to submit this when an agreement is signed. The cost breakdown is used as a check on the progress of the project. Below is a portion of a cost breakdown as used on a large project:

Cost Breakdown
  NOTE: This form is to be completed by the successful bidder only.
Project _____
Contractor _____

For accounting purposes, the successful bidder, upon request by the Architect, shall submit a breakdown of construction costs as outlined below. The cost of each item shall be complete in place and include all fees, taxes, and other expenses. The costs are not to be confused with alternate bids or unit prices and shall not be deemed a qualification of the bid. The Contractor shall cross out any items not applicable to the work and insert any additional items, if necessary.

Construction Cost
I. Site development
  A. Utility service
    1. Water system
      a. Off-site main
         extension $_____
      b. Lines connected
         to public system   _____
      c. Well, pump,
         lines, controls   _____
    2. Sewage system
      a. Off-site main   _____
         extension
      b. Lines connected
         to public system   _____
      c. Septic tanks,
         cesspools,
         lines   _____

    3. Fuel system $_____
    4. Electric power
       system   _____
    5. Telephone service   _____
    6. _____   _____
  Total $_____

ADDENDA
  The preparation and issuance of addenda during the bidding period present a problem because of the limited time available for this important aspect of the work. Addenda tend to be rambling and not tied down to the work of the specific trades or materials. Addenda are permanent legal documents and become part of the contract documents. Therefore, as much care must be given to the writing of the addenda as was given to the writing of the original trade sections. A properly written addendum, like the specifications, should be clear, concise, and correct. An addendum issued during the bidding period should not be the cause of numerous telephone calls to the architect requesting clarification. It must enumerate exactly what is to be added to, and deleted from, the contract documents and must state who will be involved in the change.

  Addenda Format. The arrangement of data to be presented in an addendum should follow a definite format. Each office should set up a guide to be used by all specifications writers. One person in an office should be charged with the responsibility of preparing addenda. The use of a guide, by one person, tends to eliminate omissions that could be dangerous. The following arrangement of data has been used successfully in an architect-engineer office for several years:
  1. Name and address of architect or engineer
  2. Addendum number
  3. Date of issuance
  4. Project name
  5. Project address
  6. Project number
  7. Notice to bidders
    a. Date of original specifications
    b. Date of previous addenda
    c. Statement that this addendum will become part of the contract documents
    d. Statement that cost will be included in the contract price
  8. Changes in prior addenda
  9. Changes in invitations to bid
  10. Changes in instructions to bidders
  11. Changes in alternates

12. Changes in general conditions
13. Changes in supplemental general conditions
14. Changes in special conditions
15. Changes in drawings
16. Changes in specifications

A portion of an addendum as prepared for a school building using this guide is presented below:

Don A. Watson	Architect
1624 Hyland Avenue	Arcadia, California
	February 16, 1964

Addendum No. 2
to the
Drawings and Specifications
for
Pine Avenue Elementary School
Addition No. 2
located at
1242 Pine Avenue
Sierra Madre, California
Project No. 364

Notice to Bidders: It is intended that all work affected by the following provisions shall conform to the original Specifications dated January 7, 1964, and Drawings accompanying Specifications listed in paragraph 1-18 of Section 1, Supplementary General Conditions, and Addendum No. 1, dated February 3, 1964. This Addendum shall be recognized by all concerned as an incorporated part or parts of the Contract Documents. Before executing the Contract, the Contractor shall assure himself that all changes and interpretations covered by the contents herein are thoroughly understood and that all Addenda have been correctly listed in the Form of Proposal and the Contract and fully accounted for in the contract price.

1. Invitation to Bid—Page 1 of 2
   Refer to paragraph 1, line 8, reference to closing date: Change "May 15" to read "May 16."
2. Instructions to Bidders—Page 1 of 6
   Refer to bid closing date at top of page: Change "May 15" to read "May 16."
3. Information on Alternates—Page 3 of 3
   a. Alternate No. 10, line 3: Change the word "joist" to read "roof rafters."
   b. Add the following alternate to page 3 of 3: "Alternate No. 13 (pendant-type Sprinkler Heads)—An amount

shall be stated by the Contractor in the bid form to install pendant-type sprinkler heads with chrome-plated escutcheons in all interior plastered ceilings of offices and conferences in lieu of flush-type heads as specified. Consideration shall be given to fewer heads and less piping required for pendant-type head.

4. General Conditions—Temporary Toilet Facilities
   Refer to Section 43, paragraph 5 of the General Conditions. Item (b) shall be amended and expanded to read as follows: "This space shall be sufficiently large to permit the installation of three toilets, two 4'-2" trough urinals, and four lavatories, which shall be furnished and installed by the Plumbing and Heating Contractors." The remainder of the paragraph shall remain as written.
5. Drawings
   a. Sheet No. A8—Window & Door Frames and Roof Plan
      Refer to door frame, jamb, and mullion details: Change number for aluminum extrusion from "#31205" to "#31204."
   b. Sheet M1—Mechanical Plot Plan, Details, and Schedules: Details 1/M1. Sheet M2—Mechanical Floor Plan & Details: Detail 2/M2: Extend cold-water line from existing 2-1/2" cold water in existing building to the fire-alarm valve assembly. Change to 2-1/2" in lieu of 2" as indicated.
6. Specifications—Section J: Aluminum Windows
   Refer to pages J-1 & J-2: Delete subparagraph 5a in its entirety and insert the following in lieu thereof:
   a. Projected aluminum windows: Shall be Series 3000 as manufactured by Druwhit Metal Products Co. or as manufactured by Metal Frame Co., Soule Steel Co., or Michel and Pfeffer Co.

Precautions in Writing Addenda. Changes made by addenda during the bidding period must be analyzed carefully. Is the change of such a nature that it can be described in words, or will it be necessary to issue addendum drawings or sketches? Must an addendum be written and distributed to all bidders, or can this change wait until a contractor has been selected and the costs involved be negotiated with him in awarding the contract? Each item must be described in a manner that gives a general idea of what will be affected. A statement such as the following conveys no meaning in itself: "Delete the third sentence in subparagraph 5b of Section J. Add the following to the last sentence of paragraph 6d of Section J: 'Type 1'." Every bidder and subbidder must go through the entire specifications to see whether paragraph 5b or 6d refers to items that would affect his work. In most instances, the addendum need not repeat the entire section, paragraph, or sentence, but enough should be included to give the reader a clue as to what is involved. A typographical error or transposed numbers in this case could completely change the meaning of a correction or even make it meaningless.

TYPES OF CONSTRUCTION CONTRACTS

Construction contracts, which are formalized by the agreement, may be divided into three basic types. In the first type, a stipulated sum, or lump sum, forms the basis of payment to the contractor; in the second type, unit prices based on estimated quantities of well-defined units of work form the basis of payment; and in the third type, the cost of labor and materials, plus a fixed fee, is due the contractor. This third type would also include contracts in which the contractor's fee is based on a percentage of the direct costs, a sliding-scale percentage of the cost, a percentage of the cost with a guaranteed maximum, a fixed fee with a bonus payable for reduced time or costs, or a fixed fee with a profit-sharing agreement.

AGREEMENT FORMS

Many forms of agreements have been developed to be used with each type of contract. Large corporations have developed forms that must be used when construction contracts are prepared. Governmental agencies have prepared forms that must be used in their contracts; for example, the General Services Administration requires the use of Standard Forms 23 and 23A. Building-contractors' associations have developed forms of agreements, and engineers' societies have forms that they recommend. Some architects-engineers firms have developed forms for their use. The AIA publishes forms for use on building construction. Each of these forms, although most of them cover the same information, varies to some extent. Those developed by contractors' associations tend to emphasize protection of the contractor. Governmental forms are developed to permit all responsible suppliers an equal chance to bid on government supply needs and to protect the public from fraud and collusion. It would be impossible to cover in detail all the contract forms that have been developed and are now in use on construction projects. Only those published AIA documents, which are reproduced at the end of the chapter, will be covered.

AIA DOCUMENTS

The AIA has developed documents for use in connection with construction projects. They are being revised and refined constantly, and the use of these standard printed documents has many advantages. The form and content of the various documents are familiar to most persons in the construction industry. They have been developed and perfected through practical experience over a period of many years. If the AIA forms are to be used, it is best to use the printed copyrighted forms as published by the AIA; these will be recognized as standard forms. If the form is typed, the value of standardization, which is obvious in the printed form, is lost. A catalog which lists the publications and documents distributed by the AIA is available, without charge, from the American Institute of Architects, 1735 New York Avenue, Washington 6, D. C.

AIA Short Form for Small-Construction Contracts. This form, Document No. A107, reproduced in Fig. 8-5, was developed by the AIA as the result of numerous requests for an agreement that could be used for simple construction projects. The use of this form should be confined to uncomplicated, though not necessarily inexpensive, projects. A small project may need the added instructions given when the Standard Form of Agreement is used in conjunction with the Standard General Conditions. The short form includes an abbreviated set of general conditions and can be used only in contracts where a stipulated sum forms the basis of the agreement.

The Standard Form of Agreement Between Contractor and Owner for Construction of Building. Figure 8-6 is a reproduction of this document, AIA Document No. A-101. This form is for use with contracts where a

AIA DOC. A107   SEPT. 1963 ED.

THE STANDARD FORM OF AGREEMENT BETWEEN OWNER AND CONTRACTOR

THE AIA SHORT FORM CONTRACT FOR

SMALL CONSTRUCTION CONTRACTS

WHERE THE BASIS OF PAYMENT IS A

STIPULATED SUM

FOR OTHER CONTRACTS THE AIA ISSUES THE STANDARD FORMS OF OWNER-CONTRACTOR AGREEMENTS AND THE STANDARD GENERAL CONDITIONS FOR THE CONSTRUCTION OF BUILDINGS FOR USE IN CONNECTION THEREWITH

THIS AGREEMENT

made the   day of   in the year Nineteen Hundred and

BY AND BETWEEN

hereinafter called the Owner, and

hereinafter called the Contractor.

WITNESSETH,

That the Owner and the Contractor, for the considerations hereinafter named agree as follows:

ARTICLE 1. SCOPE OF THE WORK—
The Contractor shall furnish all of the material and perform all of the work for

as shown on the Drawings and described in the Specifications entitled

prepared by   Architect
all in accordance with the terms of the Contract Documents.

ARTICLE 2. TIME OF COMPLETION—The work shall be commenced and completed as follows:

ARTICLE 3. CONTRACT SUM—The Owner shall pay the Contractor for the performance of the Contract subject to the additions and deductions provided therein in current funds, the sum of

dollars. ($)

© 1963 The American Institute of Architects
1735 New York Ave NW., Washington, D. C.

PAGE 1

AIA DOC. A107   SEPT. 1963 ED.

Fig. 8-5. AIA Short Form of Agreement between Contractor and Owner for Construction of Buildings, AIA Document No. A107, 1963 edition (four pages). (By permission of the American Institute of Architects.)

ARTICLE 4. PROGRESS PAYMENTS—The Owner shall make payments on account of the contract, upon requisition by the Contractor, as follows:

ARTICLE 5. ACCEPTANCE AND FINAL PAYMENT—Final payment shall be due   days after completion of the work, provided the contract be then fully performed, subject to the provisions of Article 16 of the General Conditions.

ARTICLE 6. CONTRACT DOCUMENTS—Contract Documents are as noted in Article 1 of the General Conditions. The following is an enumeration of the drawings and specifications:

Fig. 8-5 (Continued.)

ARTICLE 1. CONTRACT DOCUMENTS

The contract includes the AGREEMENT and its GENERAL CONDITIONS, the DRAWINGS, and the SPECIFICATIONS. Two or more copies of each, as required, shall be signed by both parties and one signed copy of each retained by each party.

The intent of these documents is to include all labor, materials, appliances and services of every kind necessary for the proper execution of the work, and the terms and conditions of payment therefor.

The documents are to be considered as one, and whatever is called for by any one of the documents shall be as binding as if called for by all.

ARTICLE 2. SAMPLES

The Contractor shall furnish for approval all samples as directed. The work shall be in accordance with approved samples.

ARTICLE 3. MATERIALS, APPLIANCES, EMPLOYEES

Except as otherwise noted, the Contractor shall provide and pay for all materials, labor, tools, water, power and other items necessary to complete the work.

Unless otherwise specified, all materials shall be new, and both workmanship and materials shall be of good quality.

All workmen and sub-contractors shall be skilled in their trades.

ARTICLE 4. ROYALTIES AND PATENTS

The Contractor shall pay all royalties and license fees. He shall defend all suits or claims for infringement of any patent rights and shall save the Owner harmless from loss on account thereof.

ARTICLE 5. SURVEYS, PERMITS, AND REGULATIONS

The Owner shall furnish all surveys unless otherwise specified. Permits and licenses necessary for the prosecution of the work shall be secured and paid for by the Contractor. Easements for permanent structures or permanent changes in existing facilities shall be secured and paid for by the Owner, unless otherwise specified. The Contractor shall comply with all laws and regulations bearing on the conduct of the work and shall notify the Owner if the drawings and specifications are at variance therewith.

ARTICLE 6. PROTECTION OF WORK, PROPERTY, AND PERSONS

The Contractor shall adequately protect the work, adjacent property and the public and shall be responsible for any damage or injury due to his act or neglect.

ARTICLE 7. ACCESS TO WORK

The Contractor shall permit and facilitate observation of the work by the Owner and his agents and public authorities at all times.

ARTICLE 8. CHANGES IN THE WORK

The Owner may order changes in the work, the Contract Sum being adjusted accordingly. All such orders and adjustments shall be in writing. Claims by the Contractor for extra cost must be made in writing before executing the work involved.

ARTICLE 9. CORRECTION OF WORK

The Contractor shall re-execute any work that fails to conform to the requirements of the contract and that appears during the progress of the work, and shall remedy any defects due to faulty materials or workmanship which appear within a period of one year from the date of completion of the contract. The provisions of this article apply to work done by subcontractors as well as to work done by direct employees of the Contractor.

ARTICLE 10. OWNER'S RIGHT TO TERMINATE THE CONTRACT

Should the Contractor neglect to prosecute the work properly, or fail to perform any provision of the contract, the Owner, after seven days' written notice to the Contractor, and his surety if any may, without prejudice to any other remedy he may have, make good the deficiencies and may deduct the cost thereof from the payment then or thereafter due the contractor or, at his option, may terminate the contract and take possession of all materials, tools, and appliances and finish the work by such means as he sees fit, and if the unpaid balance of the contract price exceeds the expense of finishing the work, such excess shall be paid to the Contractor, but if such expense exceeds such unpaid balance, the Contractor shall pay the difference to the Owner.

ARTICLE 11. CONTRACTOR'S RIGHT TO TERMINATE CONTRACT

Should the work be stopped by any public authority for a period of thirty days or more, through no fault of the Contractor, or should the work be stopped through act or neglect of the Owner for a period of seven days, or should the Owner fail to pay the Contractor any payment within seven days after it is due, then the Contractor upon seven days' written notice to the Owner, may stop work or terminate the contract and recover from the Owner payment for all work executed and any loss sustained and reasonable profit and damages.

ARTICLE 12. PAYMENTS

Payments shall be made as provided in the Agreement. The making and acceptance of the final payment shall constitute a waiver of all claims by the Owner, other than those arising from unsettled liens or from faulty work appearing thereafter, as provided for in Article 9, and of all claims by the Contractor except any previously made and still unsettled. Payments otherwise due may be withheld on account of defective work not remedied, liens filed, damage by the Contractor to others not adjusted, or failure to make payments properly to subcontractors or for material or labor.

ARTICLE 13. CONTRACTOR'S LIABILITY INSURANCE

The Contractor shall maintain such insurance as will protect him from claims under workmen's compensation acts and other employee benefits acts, from claims for damages because of bodily injury, including death, and from claims for damages to property which may arise both out of and during operations under this contract, whether such operations be by himself or by any subcontractor or anyone directly or indirectly employed by either of them. This insurance shall be written for not less than any limits of liability specified as part of this contract. Certificates of such insurance shall be filed with the Owner and architect.

ARTICLE 14. OWNER'S LIABILITY INSURANCE

The Owner shall be responsible for and at his option may maintain such insurance as will protect him from his contingent liability to others for damages because of bodily injury, including death, which may arise from operations under this contract, and any other liability for damages which the Contractor is required to insure under any provision of this contract.

ARTICLE 15. FIRE-INSURANCE WITH EXTENDED COVERAGE

The Owner shall effect and maintain fire insurance with extended coverage upon the entire structure on which the work of this contract is to be done to one hundred per cent of the insurable value thereof, including items of labor and materials connected therewith whether in or adjacent to the structure insured, materials in place or to be used as part of the permanent construction including surplus materials, shanties, protective fences, bridges, temporary structures, miscellaneous materials and supplies incident to the work, and such scaffoldings, stagings, towers, forms, and equip-

Fig. 8-5 (Continued.)

ment as are not owned or rented by the contractor, the cost of which is included in the cost of the work. EXCLUSIONS: The insurance does not cover any tools owned by mechanics, any tools, equipment, scaffolding, staging, towers, and forms owned or rented by the Contractor, the capital value of which is not included in the cost of the work, or any cook shanties, bunk houses or other structures erected for housing the workmen. The loss, if any, is to be made adjustable with and payable to the Owner as Trustee for the insureds and contractors and subcontractors as their interests may appear, except in such cases as may require payment of all or a proportion of said insurance to be made to a mortgagee as his interests may appear.

Certificates of such insurance shall be filed with the Contractor if he so requires. If the Owner fails to effect or maintain insurance as above and so notifies the Contractor, the Contractor may insure his own interests and that of the subcontractors and charge the cost thereof to the Owner. If the Contractor is damaged by failure of the Owner to maintain such insurance or to so notify the Contractor, he may recover as stipulated in the contract for recovery of damages. If other special insurance not herein provided for is required by the Contractor, the Owner shall effect such insurance at the Contractor's expense by appropriate riders to his fire insurance policy. The Owner, Contractor, and all subcontractors waive all rights, each against the others, for damages caused by fire or other perils covered by insurance provided for under the terms of this article except such rights as they may have to the proceeds of insurance held by the Owner as Trustee.

The Owner shall be responsible for and at his option may insure against loss of use of his existing property, due to fire or otherwise, however caused.

If required in writing by any party in interest, the Owner as Trustee shall, upon the occurrence of loss, give bond for the proper performance of his duties. He shall deposit any money received from insurance in an account separate from all his other funds and he shall distribute it in accordance with such agreement as the parties in interest may reach or under an award of arbitrators appointed, one by the Owner, another by joint action of the other parties in interest, all other procedure being as provided elsewhere in the contract for arbitration. If after loss no special agreement is made, replacement of injured work shall be ordered and executed as provided for changes in the work.

The Trustee shall have power to adjust and settle any loss with the insurers unless one of the Contractors interested shall object in writing within three working days of the occurrence of loss, and thereupon arbitrators shall be chosen as above. The Trustee shall in that case make settlement with the insurers in accordance with the directions of such arbitrators, who shall also, if distribution by arbitration is required, direct such distribution.

ARTICLE 16. LIENS

The final payment shall not be due until the Contractor has delivered to the Owner a complete release of all liens arising out of this contract, or receipts in full covering all labor and materials for which a lien could be filed, or a bond satisfactory to the Owner indemnifying him against any lien.

ARTICLE 17. SEPARATE CONTRACTS

The Owner has the right to let other contracts in connection with the work and the Contractor shall properly cooperate with any such other contractors.

ARTICLE 18. THE ARCHITECT'S STATUS

The Architect shall be the Owner's representative during the construction period. He has authority to stop the work if necessary to insure its proper execution. He shall certify to the Owner when payments under the contract are due and the amounts to be paid. He shall make decisions on all claims of the Owner or Contractor. All his decisions are subject to arbitration.

ARTICLE 19. ARBITRATION

Any disagreement arising out of this contract or from the breach thereof shall be submitted to arbitration, and judgment upon the award rendered may be entered in the court of the forum, state or federal, having jurisdiction. It is mutually agreed that the decision of the arbitrators shall be a condition precedent to any right of legal action that either party may have against the other. The arbitration shall be held under the Standard Form of Arbitration Procedure of The American Institute of Architects or under the Rules of the American Arbitration Association.

ARTICLE 20. CLEANING UP

The Contractor shall keep the premises free from accumulation of waste material and rubbish and at the completion of the work he shall remove from the premises all rubbish, implements and surplus materials and leave the building broom-clean.

IN WITNESS WHEREOF the parties hereto executed this Agreement, the day and year first above written.

Owner _____   Contractor _____

Fig. 8-5 (Continued.)

THE STANDARD FORM OF AGREEMENT BETWEEN CONTRACTOR AND OWNER FOR CONSTRUCTION OF BUILDINGS

Issued by The American Institute of Architects
for use when a Stipulated Sum Forms the Basis of Payment

Approved by THE ASSOCIATED GENERAL CONTRACTORS OF AMERICA; THE CONTRACTING PLASTERERS' AND LATHERS' INTERNATIONAL ASSOCIATION; COUNCIL OF MECHANICAL SPECIALTY CONTRACTING INDUSTRIES, INC.; THE NATIONAL BUILDING GRANITE QUARRIES ASSOCIATION, INC.; THE NATIONAL ELECTRICAL CONTRACTORS ASSOCIATION; THE PAINTING AND DECORATING CONTRACTORS OF AMERICA, AND THE PRODUCERS' COUNCIL, INC.*

Copyright 1915-1918-1925-1937 © 1958 by The American Institute of Architects, the Octagon, Washington, D. C. Reproduction of the material herein or substantial quotation of its provisions without permission of The American Institute of Architects violates the copyright laws of the United States and will be subject to legal prosecution.

This form is to be used only with the standard general conditions of the contract for construction of buildings.

THIS AGREEMENT made the ....

day of .... in the year Nineteen Hundred and ....

by and between ....

.... hereinafter called the Contractor, and ....

.... hereinafter called the Owner,

WITNESSETH, that the Contractor and the Owner for the considerations hereinafter named agree as follows:

ARTICLE 1. SCOPE OF THE WORK

The Contractor shall furnish all of the materials and perform all of the work shown on the Drawings and described in the Specifications entitled ....

....

(Here insert the caption descriptive of the work as used on the Drawings and in the other Contract Documents)

prepared by ....
acting as and in these Contract Documents entitled the Architect; and shall do everything required by this Agreement, the General Conditions of the Contract, the Specifications and the Drawings.

* Formal approval, which has been given previous editions, has not yet been received from all of these organizations.

AGREEMENT BETWEEN CONTRACTOR AND OWNER.
Sixth Edition / Five pages / Page 1.

Fig. 8-6. The Standard Form of Agreement between Contractor and Owner for Construction of Buildings, AIA Document No. A101, 1958 edition (five pages). (By permission of the American Institute of Architects.)

ARTICLE 2. TIME OF COMPLETION

The work to be performed under this Contract shall be commenced ....

and shall be substantially completed ....
(Here insert stipulation as to liquidated damages, if any.)

ARTICLE 3. THE CONTRACT SUM

The Owner shall pay the Contractor for the performance of the Contract, subject to additions and deduc-

tions provided therein, in current funds as follows: ....
(State here the lump sum amount, unit prices, or both, as desired in individual cases.)

....

Where the quantities originally contemplated are so changed that application of the agreed unit price to the quantity of work performed is shown to create a hardship to the Owner or the Contractor, there shall be an equitable adjustment of the Contract to prevent such hardship.

AGREEMENT BETWEEN CONTRACTOR AND OWNER.
Sixth Edition / Five pages / Page 2.

Fig. 8-6 (Continued.)

ARTICLE 4. PROGRESS PAYMENTS

The Owner shall make payments on account of the Contract as provided therein, as follows:

On or about the .... day of each month .... per cent of the

value, based on the Contract prices of labor and materials incorporated in the work and of materials suit-

ably stored at the site thereof up to the .... day of that month, as estimated by the

Architect, less the aggregate of previous payments; and upon substantial completion of the entire work,

a sum sufficient to increase the total payments to .... per cent of the Contract price ....

(Insert here any provision made for limiting or reducing the amount retained after the work reaches a certain stage of completion.)

ARTICLE 5. ACCEPTANCE AND FINAL PAYMENT

Final payment shall be due .... days after substantial completion of the work provided the
work be then fully completed and the contract fully performed.

Upon receipt of written notice that the work is ready for final inspection and acceptance, the Architect
shall promptly make such inspection, and when he finds the work acceptable under the Contract and the
Contract fully performed he shall promptly issue a final certificate, over his own signature, stating that the
work provided for in this Contract has been completed and is accepted by him under the terms and conditions thereof, and that the entire balance found to be due the Contractor, and noted in said final certificate,
is due and payable.

Before issuance of final certificate the Contractor shall submit evidence satisfactory to the Architect that all
payrolls, material bills, and other indebtedness connected with the work have been paid.

If after the work has been substantially completed, full completion thereof is materially delayed through
no fault of the Contractor, and the Architect so certifies, the Owner shall, upon certificate of the Architect,
and without terminating the Contract, make payment of the balance due for that portion of the work fully
completed and accepted. Such payment shall be made under the terms and conditions governing final
payment, except that it shall not constitute a waiver of claims.

AGREEMENT BETWEEN CONTRACTOR AND OWNER.
Sixth Edition / Five pages / Page 3.

Fig. 8-6 (Continued.)

The General Conditions of the Contract, the Specifications and the Drawings, together with this Agreement, form the Contract, and they are as fully a part of the Contract as if hereto attached or herein repeated. The following is an enumeration of the Specifications and Drawings:

AGREEMENT BETWEEN CONTRACTOR AND OWNER.

Sixth Edition / Five pages / Page 4.

Fig. 8-6 (Continued.)

IN WITNESS WHEREOF the parties hereto have executed this Agreement, the day and year first above written.

AGREEMENT BETWEEN CONTRACTOR AND OWNER.
Sixth Edition / Five pages / Page 5.

Fig. 8-6 (Continued.)

lump sum or unit prices form the basis of the contract. It consists of brief instructions that can be used on most projects of this type, adequate blank spaces to be filled in for additional special provisions, and space for the signatures of the parties to the contract. Article 1 delineates the scope of the work and identifies the architect. Article 2 states the dates of starting and the number of calendar days to substantial completion. If liquidated damages are to be included in the contract, they are stipulated here. Liquidated damages are defined as damages to be paid to the owner for loss of revenue or hardship incurred in the event that the contractor fails to complete the project within the time specified in the contract. A note should be included, if liquidated damages are to be assessed, such as the following:

It is hereby understood and agreed that as it is, and will be, difficult and impossible to ascertain and determine the actual damage which the Owner will sustain should the Contractor fail to complete the work of this contract within the time as stated above, the owner may deduct fifty ($50) dollars for each and every calendar day's delay beyond the time for completing the work, as liquidated damages and not as a penalty, from any money that is due or that may become due the Contractor under the contract.

Article 4 states the contract sum. If alternates or unit prices are to be included in the bid, they should be enumerated here. Those alternates which are accepted are noted and made a part of the contract. Unit prices are listed here, or a notation is made that a list of unit prices is attached and made a part of the contract.

Articles 4 and 5 describe the method to be followed in the making of payments by the owner to the contractor as the project progresses. The withholding of a percentage of the money due the contractor is here defined.

Article 6 identifies the contract documents. Under this article are enumerated the page numbers of the general conditions, supplementary general conditions, special conditions, specifications, drawings, and addenda.

The final article includes the signatures of all persons who are a part of the contract. Care must be taken that all the signatures are correct and legally binding. This is especially important if partnerships or corporations are involved.

A Form of Agreement between Contractor and Owner. AIA Document No. A-111, shown in Fig. 8-7, is used when agreement to be the cost of work plus a fee forms the basis of payment. This "cost-plus-fee" system is in use on many projects and has been employed successfully on those consisting of simple alterations to complicated buildings. The cost-plus-fee system has several advantages over the lump-sum system for both the owner and the contractor, but there are also disadvantages to the owner who wishes his work to be executed for a certain fixed sum of money. As is the case with most documents published by the AIA, a circular of information, Document A-112, should be carefully studied when using this form of agreement. This form, with modifying clauses, may be used when the contractor's fee is based on a percentage of the cost of the work. Other modifications of this system are also possible. Some of the disadvantages to the owner of the cost-plus-fee type of contract may be eliminated by the addition of a guaranteed-maximum-cost clause in this agreement. If the actual cost of the work exceeds this maximum, the contractor assumes the additional cost. A bonus clause may be inserted for savings made by the contractor. A variation of the guaranteed-maximum agreement is a sliding-scale agreement, in which there is a provision for adding to the contractor's fee if costs are below the estimated cost and for decreasing the fee if the costs are above the estimate. A maximum fee is usually set which would be due the contractor regardless of the final cost.

Standard Form of Subcontract. This form, AIA Document No. A401, illustrated in Fig. 8-8, is intended for use with the standard form of agreement and the general conditions in the contract with the owner. The owner and the architect have only an indirect interest in the relationship and contract between the contractor and the subcontractor. However, if a dispute arises, a subcontractor will, in all probability, be involved. If a subcontract agreement such as this has been used, the architect can be assured that the contractor and the subcontractor have each been informed of their responsibilities.

Standard Form of Acceptance of Subcontractor's Proposal. AIA Document No. A411, shown in Fig. 8-9, is a short form of subcon-

A.I.A. DOCUMENT NO. A-111

1961 Edition

A FORM OF AGREEMENT
BETWEEN CONTRACTOR AND OWNER

Issued by The American Institute of Architects for use when
the cost of the work plus a fee forms the basis of payment

Copyright 1920-1925-1951-1958 © 1961 by The American Institute of Architects, 1735 New York Ave., N.W.,
Washington 6, D. C.

This form is to be used only with The Institute's standard general conditions of the Contract, 1961 edition, and it should
not be used without careful study of its accompanying "Circular of Information."

THIS AGREEMENT made the _____ day of _____

in the year Nineteen Hundred and _____ by and between _____

_____

_____ hereinafter called the Contractor, and

_____

_____ hereinafter called the Owner,

WITNESSETH, that whereas the Owner intends to erect _____

_____

_____

NOW, THEREFORE, the Contractor and the Owner, for the considerations hereinafter named, agree
as follows:

ARTICLE 1. THE WORK TO BE DONE AND THE DOCUMENTS FORMING THE CONTRACT.
The Contractor agrees to provide all the labor and materials and to do all things necessary for the proper

construction and completion of the work shown and described on Drawings bearing the title _____

_____

and numbered _____

and in Specifications bearing the same title, the pages of which are numbered _____

_____

A.I.A. DOCUMENT NO. A-111

1961 Edition

Fig. 8-7. A Form of Agreement between Contractor and Owner, AIA Document No. A111, 1961
edition (five pages). (By permission of the American Institute of Architects.)

The said Drawings and Specifications and the General Conditions of the Contract consisting of Articles

numbered one to ....
together with this Agreement, constitute the Contract; the Drawings, Specifications and General Conditions being as fully a part thereof and hereof as if hereto attached or herein repeated. If anything in the said General Conditions is inconsistent with this Agreement, the Agreement shall govern.

    The said documents have been prepared by ....

....
therein and hereinafter called the Architect.

ARTICLE 2. TIME OF COMPLETION.
The work to be performed under this Contract shall be commenced ....

and shall be substantially completed ....

ARTICLE 3. CHANGES IN THE WORK.
The Owner, through the Architect, may from time to time, by written instructions or drawings issued to the Contractor, make changes in the above-named Drawings and Specifications, issue additional instructions, require additional work or direct the omission of work previously ordered, and the provisions of this contract shall apply to all such changes, modifications and additions with the same effect as if they were embodied in the original Drawings and Specifications. Since the cost of all such changes is to merge in the final cost of the work, Articles 15 and 16 of the General Conditions of the Contract are annulled, unless elsewhere especially made applicable.

ARTICLE 4. THE CONTRACTOR'S DUTIES AND STATUS.
The Contractor recognizes the relations of trust and confidence established between him and the Owner by this Agreement. He covenants with the Owner to furnish his best skill and judgment and to cooperate with the Architect in forwarding the interests of the Owner. He agrees to furnish efficient business administration and superintendence and to use every effort to keep upon the work at all times an adequate supply of workmen and materials, and to secure its execution in the best and soundest way and in the most expeditious and economical manner consistent with the interests of the Owner.

ARTICLE 5. FEE FOR SERVICES.
In consideration of the performance of the contract, the Owner agrees to pay the Contractor, in current

funds as compensation for his services hereunder .... ($........................)

which shall be paid as follows: ....

....

ARTICLE 6. COSTS TO BE REIMBURSED.
The Owner agrees to reimburse the Contractor in current funds all costs necessarily incurred for the proper execution of the work and paid directly by the Contractor, such costs to include the following items, and to be at rates not higher than the standard paid in the locality of the work except with prior consent of the Owner;
    (a) All labor directly on the Contractor's pay roll, including social security and old age benefit taxes and other taxes related thereto.

Agreement between Contractor and Owner
Cost Plus Fee Basis / Five pages / Page 2

Fig. 8-7 (Continued.)

(*b*) Salaries of Contractor's Employees stationed at the field office, in whatever capacity employed. Employees engaged, at shops or on the road, in expediting the production or transportation of material, shall be considered as stationed at the field office and their salaries paid for such part of their time as is employed on this work.

(*c*) The proportion of transportation, traveling and hotel expenses of the Contractor or of his officers or employees incurred in discharge of duties connected with this work.

(*d*) All expenses incurred for transportation to and from the work of the force required for its prosecution.

(*e*) Permit fees, royalties, damages for infringement of patents, and costs of defending suits therefor and for deposits lost for causes other than the Contractor's negligence.

(*f*) Losses and expenses, not compensated by insurance or otherwise, sustained by the Contractor in connection with the work, provided they have resulted from causes other than the fault or neglect of the Contractor. Such losses shall include settlements made with the written consent and approval of the Owner. No such losses and expenses shall be included in the cost of the work for the purpose of determining the Contractor's fee, but if, after a loss from fire, flood or similar cause not due to the fault or neglect of the Contractor, he be put in charge of reconstructon, he shall be paid for his services a fee proportionate to that named in Article 5 hereof.

(*g*) Minor expenses, such as telegrams, telephone service, expressage, and similar petty cash items.

(*h*) Cost of hand tools, not owned by the workmen, canvas and tarpaulins, consumed in the prosecution of the work, and depreciation on such tools, canvas and tarpaulins used but not consumed and which shall remain the property of the Contractor.

(*i*) Materials, supplies, equipment and transportation required for the proper execution of the work, which shall include all temporary structures and their maintenance, including sales and other taxes related thereto.

(*j*) The amounts of all sub-contracts.

(*k*) Premiums on all bonds and insurance policies called for under the Contract.

(*l*) Rentals of all construction plant or parts thereof, whether rented from the Contractor or others, in accordance with rental agreements approved by the Architect. Transportation of said construction plant, costs of loading and unloading, cost of installation, dismantling and removal thereof and minor repairs and replacements during its use on the work—all in accordance with the terms of the said rental agreements.

ARTICLE 7. COSTS NOT TO BE REIMBURSED.

Reimbursement of expenses to the Contractor shall not include any of the following:

(*a*) Salary of the Contractor, if an individual, or salary of any member of the Contractor, if a firm, or salary of any officer of the Contractor, if a corporation.

(*b*) Salary of any person employed, during the execution of the work, in the main office or in any regularly established branch office of the Contractor.

(*c*) Overhead or general expenses of any kind, except as these may be expressly included in Article 6.

(*d*) Interest on capital employed either in plant or in expenditures on the work, except as may be expressly included in Article 6.

ARTICLE 8. DISCOUNTS, REBATES, REFUNDS.

All cash discounts shall accrue to the Contractor unless the Owner deposits funds with the Contractor with which to make payments, in which case the cash discounts shall accrue to the Owner. All trade discounts,

Agreement between Contractor and Owner
Cost Plus Fee Basis / Five pages / Page 3

Fig. 8-7 (Continued.)

rebates and refunds, and all returns from sale of surplus materials and equipment shall accrue to the Owner, and the Contractor shall make provisions so that they can be secured.

ARTICLE 9. CONTRACTOR'S FINANCIAL RESPONSIBILITY.

Any cost due to the negligence of the Contractor or anyone directly employed by him, either for the making good of defective work, disposal of material wrongly supplied, making good of damage to property, or excess costs for material or labor, or otherwise, shall be borne by the Contractor, and the Owner may withhold money due the Contractor to cover any such cost already paid by him as part of the cost of the work.

This article supersedes the provisions of Articles 13, 19 and 20 of the General Conditions of the Contract so far as they are inconsistent herewith.

ARTICLE 10. SUB-CONTRACTS.

All portions of the work that the Contractor's organization has not been accustomed to perform or that the Owner may direct, shall be executed under sub-contracts unless otherwise directed by the Owner. The Contractor shall ask for bids from sub-contractors approved by the Architect and shall deliver such bids to him, or the Architect shall procure such bids himself, and in either case the Architect shall determine, with the advice of the Contractor and subject to the approval of the Owner, the award and amount of the accepted bid. Such work shall be contracted for with such approved bidders in accordance with the terms of this agreement and the General Conditions of the Contract which conditions shall, for the purposes of such contracts, stand as printed or written and not be subject to the modifications set forth herein.

The Contractor, being fully responsible for the general management of the building operation, shall have full directing authority over the execution of the sub-contracts.

If the Owner lets any portions of the work under separate contracts the separate Contractors shall not only cooperate with each other and with the Contractor as provided in Article 35 of the General Conditions of the Contract, but they shall conform to all directions of the Contractor in regard to the progress of the work.

ARTICLE 11. TITLE TO THE WORK.

The title of all work completed and in course of construction and of all materials on account of which any payment has been made, shall be in the Owner.

ARTICLE 12. ACCOUNTING, INSPECTION, AUDIT.

The Contractor shall check all materials and labor entering into the work and shall keep such full and detailed accounts as may be necessary to proper financial management under this Agreement and the system shall be such as is satisfactory to the Architect or to an auditor appointed by the Owner. The Architect, the auditor and their timekeepers and clerks shall be afforded access to the work and to all the Contractor's books, records, correspondence, instructions, drawings, receipts, vouchers, memoranda, etc., relating to this contract, and the Contractor shall preserve all such records for a period of two years after the final payment hereunder.

ARTICLE 13. APPLICATIONS FOR PAYMENT.

The Contractor shall, between the first and seventh of each month, deliver to the Architect a statement, sworn to if required, showing in detail and as completely as possible all moneys paid out by him on account of the cost of the work during the previous month for which he is to be reimbursed under Article 6 hereof, with original pay rolls for labor, checked and approved by a person satisfactory to the Architect, and all receipted bills.

The provisions of this Article supersede those of Article 24 of the General Conditions of the Contract.

Agreement between Contractor and Owner
Cost Plus Fee Basis / Five pages / Page 4

Fig. 8-7 (Continued.)

ARTICLE 14. CERTIFICATE FOR PAYMENT.

The Architect shall check the Contractor's statements of moneys due, called for in Article 13, and shall promptly issue certificates to the Owner for all such as he approves, which certificates shall be payable on issuance.

The provisions of this Article supersede the first paragraph of Article 25 of the General Conditions of the Contract.

ARTICLE 15. DISBURSEMENTS.

Should the Contractor neglect or refuse to pay, within five days after it falls due, any bill legitimately incurred by him hereunder (and for which he is to be reimbursed under Article 6) the Owner, after giving the Contractor twenty-four hours' written notice of his intention so to do, shall have the right to pay such bill directly, in which event such payment shall not, for the purpose either of reimbursement or of calculating the Contractor's fee, be included in the cost of the work.

ARTICLE 16. TERMINATION OF CONTRACT.

(The provisions of this Article supersede all of Article 22 of the General Conditions of the Contract except the first sentence.)

If the Owner should terminate the contract under the first sentence of Article 22 of the General Conditions of the Contract, he shall reimburse the Contractor for the balance of all payments made by him under Article 6, plus a fee computed upon the cost of the work to date at the rate of percentage named in Article 5 hereof, or if the Contractor's fee be stated as a fixed sum, the Owner shall pay the Contractor such an amount as will increase the payments on account of his fee to a sum which bears the same ratio to the said fixed sum as the cost of the work at the time of termination bears to a reasonable estimated cost of the work completed, and the Owner shall also pay to the Contractor fair compensation, either by purchase or rental, at the election of the Owner, for any equipment retained. In case of such termination of the contract the Owner shall further assume and become liable for obligations, commitments and unliquidated claims that the Contractor may have theretofore, in good faith, undertaken or incurred in connection with said work and the Contractor shall, as a condition of receiving the payments mentioned in this Article, execute and deliver all such papers and take all such steps, including the legal assignment of his contractual rights, as the Owner may require for the purpose of fully vesting in him the rights and benefits of the Contractor under such obligations or commitments.

The Contractor and the Owner for themselves, their successors, executors, administrators and assigns hereby agree to the full performance of the covenants herein contained.

IN WITNESS WHEREOF they have executed this agreement the day and year first above written.

Agreement between Contractor and Owner
Cost Plus Fee Basis / Five pages / Page 5

Fig. 8-7 (Continued.)

STANDARD FORM OF SUBCONTRACT

THIS FORM TO BE USED IN CONNECTION WITH THE LATEST
EDITION OF AIA DOCUMENT A201, GENERAL CONDITIONS OF THE CONTRACT

THIS AGREEMENT

made this   day of   in the year Nineteen Hundred and

BY AND BETWEEN

hereinafter called the Contractor, and

hereinafter called the Subcontractor.

WITNESSETH,

That the Contractor and Subcontractor for the consideration hereinafter named agree as follows:

ARTICLE 1. The Subcontractor agrees to furnish all material and perform all work as described in Article
2 hereof for (Here name the kind of building)

for   (Here insert name of Owner)

hereinafter called the Owner, at (Here insert location of work)

in accordance with the General Conditions of the Contract between the Owner and the Contractor and in
accordance with Supplementary General Conditions, the Drawings and the Specifications prepared by

hereinafter called the Architect, all of which General Conditions, Drawings and Specifications, signed by
the parties thereto or identified by the Architect, form a part of a Contract between the Contractor and the
Owner dated,   19   , and hereby become a part of this contract.

STANDARD FORM OF SUBCONTRACT
AIA DOC. A401   SEPT. 1963 ED.   THREE PAGES

© 1963 The American Institute of Architects   PAGE 1
1735 New York Ave NW., Washington, D. C.

Fig. 8-8. Standard Form of Subcontract, AIA Document No. A401, 1963 edition (three pages).
(By permission of the American Institute of Architects.)

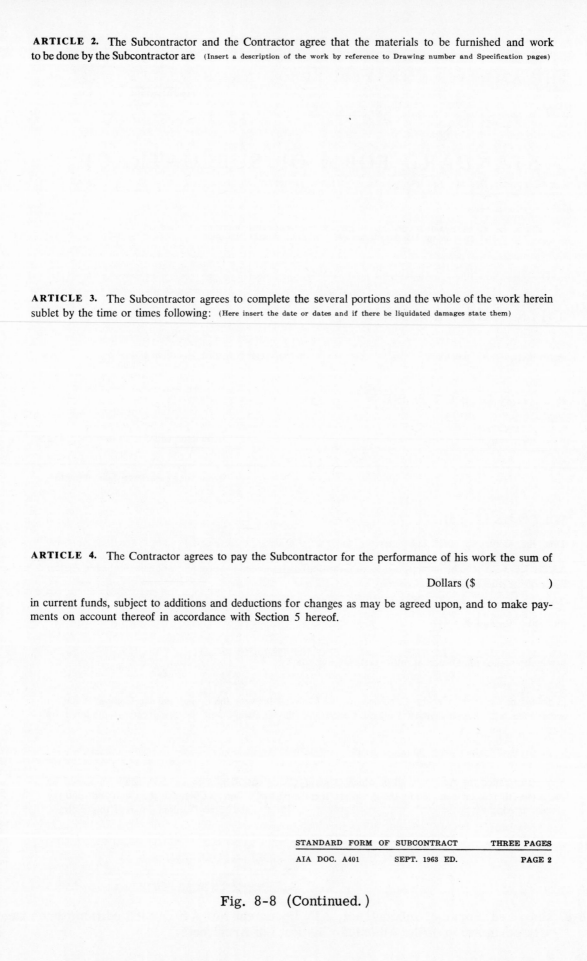

ARTICLE 2. The Subcontractor and the Contractor agree that the materials to be furnished and work to be done by the Subcontractor are (Insert a description of the work by reference to Drawing number and Specification pages)

ARTICLE 3. The Subcontractor agrees to complete the several portions and the whole of the work herein sublet by the time or times following: (Here insert the date or dates and if there be liquidated damages state them)

ARTICLE 4. The Contractor agrees to pay the Subcontractor for the performance of his work the sum of

Dollars ($)

in current funds, subject to additions and deductions for changes as may be agreed upon, and to make payments on account thereof in accordance with Section 5 hereof.

STANDARD FORM OF SUBCONTRACT   THREE PAGES

AIA DOC. A401   SEPT. 1963 ED.   PAGE 2

Fig. 8-8 (Continued.)

ARTICLE 5. The Contractor and Subcontractor agree to be bound by the terms of the Agreement, the General Conditions, Supplementary General Conditions, Drawings and Specifications as far as applicable to this subcontract, and also by the following provisions:

The Subcontractor agrees—

a) To be bound to the Contractor by the terms of the Agreement, General Conditions of the Contract, the Supplementary General Conditions, the Drawings and Specifications, and to assume toward him all the obligations and responsibilities that he, by those documents, assumes toward the Owner.

b) To submit to the Contractor applications for payment in such reasonable time as to enable the Contractor to apply for payment under Article 24 of the General Conditions.

c) To make all claims for extras, for extensions of time and for damage for delays or otherwise, to the Contractor in the manner provided in the General Conditions of the Contract and Supplementary General Conditions for like claims by the Contractor upon the Owner, except that the time for making claims for extra cost is one week.

The Contractor agrees—

d) To be bound to the Subcontractor by all the obligations that the Owner assumes to the Contractor under the Agreement, General Conditions of the Contract, the Supplementary General Conditions, the Drawings and Specifications, and by all the provisions thereof affording remedies and redress to the Contractor from the Owner.

e) To pay the Subcontractor, upon the payment of certificates, if issued under the schedule of values described in Article 24 of the General Conditions, the amount allowed to the Contractor on account of the Subcontractor's work to the extent of the Subcontractor's interest therein.

f) To pay the Subcontractor, upon the payment of certificates, if issued otherwise than as in (e), so that at all times his total payments shall be as large in proportion to the value of the work done by him as the total amount certified to the Contractor is to the value of the work done by him.

g) To pay the Subcontractor to such extent as may be provided by the Contract Documents or the subcontract, if either of these provide for earlier or larger payments than the above.

h) To pay the Subcontractor on demand for his work or materials as far as executed and fixed in place, less the retained percentage, at the time the certificate should issue, even though the Architect fails to issue it for any cause not the fault of the Subcontractor.

j) To pay the Subcontractor a just share of any fire insurance money received by him, the Contractor, under Article 29 of the General Conditions.

k) To make no demand for liquidated damages or penalty for delay in any sum in excess of such amount as may be specifically named in the subconract.

l) That no claim for services rendered or materials furnished by the Contractor to the Subcontractor shall be valid unless written notice thereof is given by the Contractor to the Subcontractor during the first ten days of the calendar month following that in which the claim originated.

m) To give the Subcontractor an opportunity to be present and to submit evidence in any arbitration involving his rights.

n) To name as arbitrator under arbitration proceeding as provided in the General Conditions the person nominated by the Subcontractor, if the sole cause of dispute is the work, materials, rights or responsibilities of the Subcontractor; or if, of the Subcontractor and any other subcontractor jointly, to name as such arbitrator the person upon whom they agree.

The Contractor and the Subcontractor agree that—

o) In the matter of arbitration, their rights and obligations and all procedure shall be analogous to those set forth in this contract; provided, however, that a decision by the Architect shall not be a condition precedent to arbitration.

Nothing in this article shall create any obligation on the part of the Owner to pay or to see the payment of any sums to any Subcontractor.

IN WITNESS WHEREOF
the parties hereto have executed this Agreement, the day and year first above written.

Contractor _____   Subcontractor _____

Fig. 8-8 (Continued.)

AIA DOC. A411   SEPT. 1963 ED.

STANDARD FORM OF ACCEPTANCE
OF SUBCONTRACTOR'S PROPOSAL

THIS FORM TO BE USED IN CONNECTION WITH THE LATEST
EDITION OF AIA DOCUMENT A201, GENERAL CONDITIONS OF THE CONTRACT

NAME OF
SUBCONTRACTOR:

ADDRESS OF
SUBCONTRACTOR:

DEAR SIR: Having entered into a contract with (Here insert name, address or corporate title of Owner.)

for the erection of (Here insert the kind of work and the place at which it is to be erected.)

in accordance with Drawings and Specifications prepared by (Here insert the name and address of the Architect.)

and in accordance with the General Conditions of the Contract prefixed to the Specifications, the undersigned hereby accepts your proposal of .... 19...... to provide all the materials and do all the work of
(Here insert the work to be done, describing by number, page, etc., the drawings and specifications governing such work.)

The Undersigned agrees to pay you in current funds for the faithful performance of the subcontract established by this acceptance of your proposal the sum of

Dollars ($).

Our relations in respect of this subcontract are to be governed by the Drawings and Specifications named above, by the Agreement, and the General Conditions of the Contract as far as applicable to the work thus sublet, and especially by Article 37 of those conditions printed hereinafter.

Very truly yours,

AIA DOC. A411   SEPT. 1963 ED.

Fig. 8-9. Standard Form of Acceptance of Subcontractor's Proposal, AIA Document No. A411, 1958 edition (two pages). (By permission of the American Institute of Architects.)

Relations of Contractor and Subcontractor

The Contractor agrees to bind every Subcontractor and every Subcontractor agrees to be bound by the terms of the Agreement, the General Conditions of the Contract, the Supplementary General Conditions, the Drawings and Specifications as far as applicable to his work, including the following provisions of this article, unless specifically noted to the contrary in a subcontract approved in writing as adequate by the Owner or Architect.

This does not apply to minor contracts.

The Subcontractor agrees—

a) To be bound to the Contractor by the terms of the Agreement, General Conditions, Supplementary General Conditions, Drawings and Specifications, and to assume toward him all the obligations and responsibilities that he, by those documents, assumes toward the Owner.

b) To submit to the Contractor applications for payment in such reasonable time as to enable the Contractor to apply for payment under Article 24 of the General Conditions.

c) To make all claims for extras, for extensions of time, and for damages for delays or otherwise to the Contractor in the manner provided in the General Conditions of the Contract and Supplementary General Conditions for like claims by the Contractor upon the Owner, except that the time for making claims for extra cost is one week.

The Contractor agrees—

d) To be bound to the Subcontractor by all the obligations that the Owner assumes to the Contractor under the Agreement, General Conditions of the Contract, the Supplementary General Conditions, Drawings and Specifications, and by all the provisions thereof affording remedies and redress to the Contractor from the Owner.

e) To pay the Subcontractor, upon the payment of certificates, if issued under the schedule of values described in Article 24 of the General Conditions, the amount allowed to the Contractor on account of the Subcontractor's work to the extent of the Subcontractor's interest therein.

f) To pay the Subcontractor, upon the payment of certificates, if issued otherwise than as in (e), so that at all times his total payments shall be as large in proportion to the value of the work done by him as the total amount certified to the Contractor is to the value of the work done by him.

g) To pay the Subcontractor to such extent as may be provided by the Contract Documents or the subcontract, if either of these provides for earlier or larger payments than the above.

h) To pay the Subcontractor on demand for his work or materials as far as executed and fixed in place, less the retained percentage, at the time the certificate should issue, even though the Architect fails to issue it for any cause not the fault of the Subcontractor.

j) To pay the Subcontractor a just share of any fire insurance money received by him, the Contractor, under Article 29 of the General Conditions.

k) To make no demand for liquidated damages or penalty for delay in any sum in excess of such amount as may be specifically named in the subcontract.

l) That no claim for services rendered or materials furnished by the Contractor to the Subcontractor shall be valid unless written notice thereof is given by the Contractor to the Subcontractor during the first ten days of the calendar month following that in which the claim originated.

m) To give the Subcontractor an opportunity to be present and to submit evidence in any arbitration involving his rights.

n) To name as arbitrator under arbitration proceedings as provided in the General Conditions the person nominated by the Subcontractor, if the sole cause of dispute is the work, materials, rights or responsibilities of the Subcontractor; or, if of the Subcontractor and any other subcontractor jointly, to name as such arbitrator the person upon whom they agree.

The Contractor and the Subcontractor agree that—

o) In the matter of arbitration, their rights and obligations and all procedure shall be analogous to those set forth in this Contract; provided, however, that a decision by the Architect shall not be a condition precedent to arbitration.

Nothing in this article shall create any obligation on the part of the Owner to pay or to see to the payment of any sums to any subcontractor.

The Subcontractor entering into this Agreement should be sure that not merely the above Article 37, but the full text of the General Conditions of the Contract as signed by the Owner and Contractor is known to him, since such full text, though not herein repeated, is binding on him.

ACCEPTANCE OF SUBCONTRACTOR'S PROPOSAL   TWO PAGES

AIA DOCUMENT A411   SEPT. 1963 ED.   PAGE 2

Fig. 8-9 (Continued.)

tract usually used for material or work of a minor nature. It includes most of the essential features of the standard subcontract agreement. This form does not include the signature of the subcontractor but, along with the subcontractor's proposal, is a valid agreement. If the subcontractor delivers material or starts work on the project, it will be considered that a valid contract exists between the contractor and the subcontractor.

QUESTIONS

1. Why is a knowledge of business law essential for a specifications writer, architect, or engineer?
2. Describe five types of contracts that may be used between owner and contractor for construction and give the advantages of each.
3. Define an agreement.
4. Outline the important information that should be included in the instructions to bidders.
5. What is included in a proposal?
6. What is a questionnaire, and under what conditions would it be required of a bidder?
7. Define liquidated damages.

9 The General Conditions and Related Documents

There are many conditions of a general nature that affect or are related to a large portion of the work on most projects. These general conditions must be thoroughly familiar to those who are preparing estimates for bidding purposes. The general conditions establish the legal rights, responsibilities, and relationships of all parties to the contract and are gathered together into one document called the "general conditions of the contract." Clauses that would apply to all trade sections are grouped into one section of the specifications instead of being repeated in a description of the work performed by each trade.

The topics covered by the general conditions and the title given to each will vary with the project and with the architect or the engineer who writes them. However, each set of these conditions will cover the same general information. The Consulting Engineers Council, which publishes a standard form of general conditions, shown in Fig. 9-1, breaks them down into the following general categories:
1. Definitions
2. Drawings, specifications, and related data
3. Engineer-owner-contractor relations
4. Materials and workmanship
5. Insurance, legal responsibilities, and public safety
6. Progress and completion of work
7. Measurement and payment
8. Modification of the general conditions

The state of California divides the content of its general conditions as follows:
1. General definitions
2. Bidding requirements and conditions
3. Award and execution of contract
4. Legal relations and responsibilities
5. Performance, prosecution, and progress of work
6. Change in work
7. Acceptance and payment
8. Standard form of guaranty

The AIA breaks this information into forty-four separate articles. No attempt is made in the AIA general conditions to classify the information according to broad categories.

HISTORY

All conditions that would be needed to govern a contract were originally spelled out in the agreement. This formed a lengthy, involved document, and, as few architects or engineers were equipped by education or experience to prepare such a legal document, a lawyer, retained by the owner, would prepare the agreement. Since the lawyer was retained by the owner, the agreement would be so written that every possible protection would be assured the owner. Any rights the contractor might have were of a secondary nature, and his activities were severely restricted. The AIA, in an attempt to develop forms of agreement that would be fair to all, including the contractor, has been working with contractors' associations and lawyers since 1911 to develop a document that could be used for all projects on a nationwide basis. At that time, the AIA published a set of contract documents for use on building construction. The first general conditions of the contract developed by the AIA had many of the faults of the lawyer-prepared documents. Some architects and most contractors objected to many of the provisions. Since that time, general conditions have been under constant study by the AIA, in cooperation with all segments of the construction industry, the purpose being to develop a nationally accepted standard form of agreement and general conditions that would be fair to the contractor as well as the owner. This process of study and revision is continuing, and, as conditions and usage point up a need for change, new editions will be published.

RELATION OF GENERAL CONDITIONS TO AGREEMENT

When the general conditions are gathered together as one document that may be used on most projects, the agreement may be quite brief. Items such as contract sums, payments, time of completion, and others which will vary with each job can be inserted in blank spaces in a standard form of agreement. The general conditions set forth the manner in which the agreement will be carried out in the course of a project in accordance with accepted construction practices. The general conditions do not attempt to describe or regulate the specific work of any party of the agreement except where the activities of one party will affect the rights of others on the project. The general conditions are identified as a part of the contract in the agreement between the owner and the contractor. AIA Document No. A-101, the Standard Form of Agreement between Contractor and Owner for the Construction of Buildings, defines this relationship as follows: "Article 6. THE CONTRACT DOCUMENTS. The General Conditions of the Contract, the Specifications and the Drawings, together with this Agreement, form the Contract, and are fully a part of the Contract as if hereto attached or herein repeated. The following is an enumeration of the Specifications and Drawings. . . ."

RELATION OF GENERAL CONDITIONS TO TRADE SECTIONS

The general conditions apply to each trade section of the specifications, and each subcontractor is required to follow the provisions set forth in the general conditions. It is the general contractor's responsibility to see that the provisions are followed because no contract exists between the owner and any subcontractor. Many architects and engineers prefer to include a statement in each trade section that will notify subcontractors and materials dealers of the relationship that exists between the general conditions and the trade section.

ARCHITECT-ENGINEER-DEVELOPED GENERAL CONDITIONS

Some architects-engineers firms have developed agreements and general conditions which they use on all projects designed in their offices. Only large offices with legal departments or lawyers retained on a continuing basis can usually afford to produce general conditions for each project. It is better for the smaller office to use one of the published accepted forms than to take a chance on errors and oversights that can occur in legal documents. A meaning of a word inserted in a contract may seem clear to the architect or engineer, but if trouble develops it is the court that will determine what was meant, not the architect or engineer who wrote it. It is better, for the most part, to use a standard form in which clauses have been interpreted and which have stood the test of time.

CORPORATION AND MUNICIPAL GENERAL CONDITIONS

Many large corporations and municipalities have developed sets of general conditions, the use of which is required on all projects designed for them. Their architectural and legal staffs have developed these documents, which may be a part of the agreement or considered a separate section of the general conditions of the contract. These general conditions cover local requirements such as state regulations, codes, or laws and also cover the more general requirements that would apply to all contracts on a nationwide basis. They are tailored to fit the operational organization and the fiscal policies of the particular corporation or municipality that developed them. Specifications writers must be thoroughly familiar with this type of general conditions if they are to write specifications to accompany them. Certain items could materially affect the writing of the trade sections and change the conditions under which the work will proceed.

FEDERAL GENERAL CONDITIONS

Most Federal agencies require the use of standardized general conditions that have been developed for their own use. The General Services Administration, which controls much Federal work, uses a form designated as Form No. 23A, General Contract Provisions. These general contract provisions generally take the place of what would be called the general conditions in private work. They cover such items as variations in quality, inspection requirements, payments of claims, taxes, liabilities upon default, settlement of disputes, infringement of patents, contingent fees, the Buy America Act, the Walsh-Healy Public Contracts Acts, and the Eight Hour Law of 1912. Certain other provisions are included on the reverse side of Standard Forms 22 and 33 and GSA Form 1424. It is well for the specifications writer to have these forms at hand when preparing specifications for a Federal agency. Many items of information presented in these documents differ from standard clauses and requirements generally used on private projects. For further information on Federal requirements, see Chap. 13.

STANDARDIZED GENERAL CONDITIONS

Several associations in the construction industry have developed standard sets of general conditions. While each set is written to fit a particular set of circumstances and requirements, each covers the same basic information. Specialized construction requires special instructions. Special groups have interest that will be emphasized in their standards. Attempts have been made to coordinate the work and standardize the method to be used by these various associations. The CSI, through its T-1 and T-2 national committees, is working toward this end. The AIA, through joint committees composed of architects, engineers, and contractors, is working constantly to develop standard documents that would be fair to everyone in the construction industry.

ASSOCIATION STANDARD GENERAL CONDITIONS

Various associations have published standardized sets of general conditions. Copies of published, copyrighted association general conditions can be purchased from the following:

Consulting Engineers Council
World Center Building
16th and K Streets N.W.
Washington 6, D.C.

American Association of State Highway
  Officials
917 National Press Building
Washington 4, D.C.

American Society of Civil Engineers
33 West 39th Street
New York, N.Y.

Associated General Contractors
1918 E Street
Washington 6, D.C.

American Public Works Association
1313 East 60th Street
Chicago 37, Ill.

American Institute of Architects
1735 New York Avenue N.W.
Washington 6, D.C.

NEW EDITIONS OF STANDARD DOCUMENTS

No standard documents should ever be looked upon as permanent. However, constant revision of standardized forms can cancel many of the advantages of standardization. A standard form becomes recognized by those in the industry. The architect and engineer become familiar, over a period of time, with the contents and need only add additional instructions to make the standard conform to their methods of operations. The courts, through repeated interpretations of the standard document, define its meaning. A new edition of the standard document does not have this definition as given by the courts. The AIA has established a policy of continued use of a proved document until it is shown to be inadequate for its purpose.

USE OF PORTIONS OF PUBLISHED GENERAL CONDITIONS

Some architects and engineers copy portions of standard general conditions and include these in the general conditions which are prepared in their offices. Not only does this practice defeat the advantages gained through the use of standardized documents, but it definitely violates the copyright laws. These are copyrighted documents, and the unauthorized use of any portion of them is forbidden. The documents, as published or printed by the association, may be bound with the specifications, but they may not be copied or reproduced. They are complete documents, and the interrelationship of the clauses and provisions is the result of many years of study. The use of isolated clauses, out of context, is dangerous.

AIA SHORT FORM GENERAL CONDITIONS

The AIA Short Form of Agreement between Contractor and Owner for Construction of Buildings, AIA Document No. A107, illustrated in Fig. 8-5, includes a condensed version of the AIA general conditions. The information is grouped under twenty articles. Unless a project is extremely simple, extensive supplemental general conditions must be included in the specifications when this form is used. For the more complex projects, the use of standard general conditions is recommended.

AIA GENERAL CONDITIONS

AIA Document No. A201, the General Conditions of the Contract for the Construction of Buildings, illustrated in Fig. 9-1, is a document widely used by both architects and engineers. It has found wide acceptance in the building industry. This document is the result of many years of study and experience and

THE AMERICAN INSTITUTE OF ARCHITECTS

THE GENERAL CONDITIONS OF THE CONTRACT FOR THE CONSTRUCTION OF BUILDINGS

The Standard Form of General Conditions, 1961 Edition, has received the approval of THE ASSOCIATED GENERAL CONTRACTORS OF AMERICA; THE CONTRACTING PLASTERERS' AND LATHERS' INTERNATIONAL ASSOCIATION; COUNCIL OF MECHANICAL SPECIALTY CONTRACTING INDUSTRIES, INC.; THE NATIONAL ASSOCIATION OF ARCHITECTURAL METAL MANUFACTURERS; THE NATIONAL BUILDING GRANITE QUARRIES ASSOCIATION, INC.; THE NATIONAL ELECTRICAL CONTRACTORS ASSOCIATION; THE PAINTING AND DECORATING CONTRACTORS OF AMERICA; AND THE PRODUCERS' COUNCIL, INC.

Copyright 1911, 1915, 1918, 1925, 1937, 1951, 1958, © 1961, by The American Institute of Architects, 1735 New York Avenue, N.W., Washington 6, D. C. Reproduction of the material herein or substantial quotation of its provisions without permission of The American Institute of Architects violates the copyright laws of the United States and will be subject to legal prosecution.

INDEX TO THE ARTICLES

GENERAL CONDITIONS. 1961 EDITION.
Ten pages / Page 1

Fig. 9-1.   The General Conditions of the Contract for the Construction of Buildings, AIA Document No. A201, 1961 edition (ten pages). (By permission of the American Institute of Architects.)

ARTICLE 1

DEFINITIONS

a) The Contract Documents consist of the Agreement, the General Conditions of the Contract, the Supplementary General Conditions, the Drawings and Specifications, including all modifications thereof incorporated in the documents before their execution. These form the Contract.

b) The Owner, the Contractor and the Architect are those mentioned as such in the Agreement. They are treated throughout the Contract Documents as if each were of the singular number and masculine gender.

c) The term Subcontractor, as employed herein, includes only those having a direct contract with the Contractor and it includes one who furnishes material worked to a special design according to the plans or specifications of this work, but does not include one who merely furnishes material not so worked.

d) Written notice shall be deemed to have been duly served if delivered in person to the individual or to a member of the firm or to an officer of the corporation for whom it is intended, or if delivered at or sent by registered mail to the last business address known to him who gives the notice.

e) The term "work" of the Contractor or Subcontractor includes labor or materials or both.

f) All time limits stated in the Contract Documents are of the essence of the Contract.

g) The law of the place of building shall govern the construction of this Contract.

ARTICLE 2

EXECUTION, CORRELATION AND INTENT OF DOCUMENTS

The Contract Documents shall be signed in duplicate by the Owner and the Contractor. In case either the Owner or Contractor or both fail to sign the General Conditions, Drawings or Specifications, the Architect shall identify them.

The Contract Documents are complementary, and what is called for by any one shall be as binding as if called for by all. The intention of the documents is to include all labor and materials, equipment and transportation necessary for the proper execution of the work. Materials or work described in words which so applied have a well-known technical or trade meaning shall be held to refer to such recognized standards.

It is not intended, that work not covered under any heading, section, branch, class or trade of the specifications, shall be supplied unless it is shown on drawings or is reasonably inferable therefrom as being necessary to produce the intended results.

ARTICLE 3

DETAIL DRAWINGS AND INSTRUCTIONS

The Architect shall furnish with reasonable promptness, additional instructions by means of drawings or other-

GENERAL CONDITIONS. 1961 EDITION.
Ten pages / Page 2

wise, necessary for the proper execution of the work. All such drawings and instructions shall be consistent with the Contract Documents, true developments thereof, and reasonably inferable therefrom.

The work shall be executed in conformity therewith and the Contractor shall do no work without proper drawings and instructions.

Immediately after being awarded the contract the Contractor shall prepare an estimated Progress Schedule and submit same for Architect's approval. It shall indicate the dates for the starting and completion of the various stages of construction.

ARTICLE 4

COPIES FURNISHED

Unless otherwise provided in the Contract Documents the Contractor will be furnished, free of charge, all copies of drawings and specifications reasonably necessary for the execution of the work.

ARTICLE 5

SHOP DRAWINGS

The Contractor shall check and verify all field measurements and shall submit with such promptness as to cause no delay in his own work or in that of any other Contractor, three copies, checked and approved by him, of all shop or setting drawings and schedules required for the work of the various trades. The Architect shall check and approve, with reasonable promptness, such schedules and drawings only for conformance with the design concept of the Project and compliance with the information given in the Contract Documents. The Contractor shall make any corrections required by the Architect, file with him two corrected copies and furnish such other copies as may be needed. The Architect's approval of such drawings or schedules shall not relieve the Contractor from responsibility for deviations from drawings or specifications, unless he has in writing called the Architect's attention to such deviations at the time of submission, and secured his written approval, nor shall it relieve him from responsibility for errors in shop drawings or schedules.

ARTICLE 6

DRAWINGS AND SPECIFICATIONS ON THE WORK

The Contractor shall keep one copy of all drawings and specifications on the work, in good order, available to the Architect and to his representative.

ARTICLE 7

OWNERSHIP OF DRAWINGS

All drawings, specifications and copies thereof furnished by the Architect are his property. They are not to be used on other work, and, with the exception of the signed Contract set, are to be returned to him on request, at the completion of the work.

Fig. 9-1 (Continued.)

ARTICLE 8

SAMPLES

The Contractor shall furnish for approval, with reasonable promptness, all samples as directed by the Architect. The Architect shall check and approve such samples, with reasonable promptness, only for conformance with the design concept of the Project and for compliance with the information given in the Contract Documents. The work shall be in accordance with approved samples.

ARTICLE 9

MATERIALS, APPLIANCES, EMPLOYEES

Unless otherwise stipulated, the Contractor shall provide and pay for all materials, labor, water, tools, equipment, light, power, transportation and other facilities necessary for the execution and completion of the work.

Unless otherwise specified all materials shall be new and both workmanship and materials shall be of good quality. The Contractor shall, if required, furnish satisfactory evidence as to the kind and quality of materials.

The Contractor shall at all times enforce strict discipline and good order among his employees, and shall not employ on the work any unfit person or anyone not skilled in the work assigned to him.

ARTICLE 10

ROYALTIES AND PATENTS

The Contractor shall pay all royalties and license fees. He shall defend all suits or claims for infringement of any patent rights and shall save the Owner harmless from loss on account thereof, except that the Owner shall be responsible for all such loss when a particular process or the product of a particular manufacturer or manufacturers is specified, but if the Contractor has information that the process or article specified is an infringement of a patent, he shall be responsible for such loss unless he promptly gives such information to the Architect or Owner.

ARTICLE 11

SURVEYS, PERMITS, LAWS, TAXES AND REGULATIONS

The Owner shall furnish all surveys unless otherwise specified.

Permits and licenses necessary for the prosecution of the work shall be secured and paid for by the Contractor. Easements for permanent structures or permanent changes in existing facilities shall be secured and paid for by the Owner, unless otherwise specified.

The Contractor shall give all notices and comply with all laws, ordinances, rules and regulations bearing on the conduct of the work as drawn and specified. If the Contractor observes that the drawings and specifications are at variance therewith, he shall promptly notify the Architect in writing and any necessary changes shall be adjusted as provided in the Contract for changes in the

GENERAL CONDITIONS. 1961 EDITION.
Ten pages / Page 3

work. If the Contractor performs any work knowing it to be contrary to such laws, ordinances, rules and regulations, and without such notice to the Architect, he shall bear all costs arising therefrom.

Wherever the law of the place of building requires a sales, consumer, use, or other similar tax, the Contractor shall pay such tax.

ARTICLE 12

PROTECTION OF WORK AND PROPERTY

The Contractor shall continuously maintain adequate protection of all his work from damage and shall protect the Owner's property from injury or loss arising in connection with this Contract. He shall make good any such damage, injury or loss, except such as may be directly due to errors in the Contract Documents or caused by agents or employees of the Owner, or due to causes beyond the Contractor's control and not to his fault or negligence. He shall adequately protect adjacent property as provided by law and the Contract Documents.

The Contractor shall take all necessary precautions for the safety of employees on the work, and shall comply with all applicable provisions of Federal, State, and Municipal safety laws and building codes to prevent accidents or injury to persons on, about or adjacent to the premises where the work is being performed. He shall erect and properly maintain at all times, as required by the conditions and progress of the work, all necessary safeguards for the protection of workmen and the public and shall post danger signs warning against the hazards created by such features of construction as protruding nails, hoists, well holes, elevator hatchways, scaffolding, window openings, stairways and falling materials; and he shall designate a responsible member of his organization on the work, whose duty shall be the prevention of accidents. The name and position of any person so designated shall be reported to the Architect by the Contractor.

In an emergency affecting the safety of life or of the work or of adjoining property, the Contractor, without special instruction or authorization from the Architect or Owner, is hereby permitted to act, at his discretion, to prevent such threatened loss or injury, and he shall so act, without appeal, if so authorized or instructed. Any compensation, claimed by the Contractor on account of emergency work, shall be determined by agreement or Arbitration.

ARTICLE 13

ACCESS TO WORK

The Architect and his representatives shall at all times have access to the work wherever it is in preparation or progress and the Contractor shall provide proper facilities for such access and so that the Architect may perform his functions under the Contract Documents.

If the specifications, the Architect's instructions, laws, ordinances or any public authority require any work to be specially tested or approved, the Contractor shall give the Architect timely notice of its readiness for observation by the Architect or inspection by another authority,

Fig. 9-1 (Continued.)

and if the inspection is by another authority than the Architect, of the date fixed for such inspection, required certificates of inspection being secured by the Contractor. Observations by the Architect shall be promptly made, and where practicable at the source of supply. If any work should be covered up without approval or consent of the Architect, it must, if required by thet Architect, be uncovered for examination at the Contractor's expense.

Re-examination of questioned work may be ordered by the Architest and if so ordered the work must be uncovered by the Contractor. If such work be found in accordance with the Contract Documents the Owner shall pay the cost of re-examination and replacement. If such work be found not in accordance with the Contract Documents the Contractor shall pay such cost, unless it be found that the defect in the work was caused by a Contractor employed as provided in Article 35, and in that event the Owner shall pay such cost.

ARTICLE 14

SUPERINTENDENCE: SUPERVISION

The Contractor shall keep on his work, during its progress, a competent superintendent and any necessary assistants, all satisfactory to the Architect. The superintendent shall not be changed except with the consent of the Architect, unless the superintendent proves to be unsatisfactory to the Contractor and ceases to be in his employ. The superintendent shall represent the Contractor in his absence and all directions given to him shall be as binding as if given to the Contractor. Important directions shall be confirmed in writing to the Contractor. Other directions shall be so confirmed on written request in each case. The Architect shall not be responsible for the acts or omissions of the superintendent or his assistants.

The Contractor shall give efficient supervision to the work, using his best skill and attention. He shall carefully study and compare all drawings, specifications and other instructions and shall at once report to the Architect any error, inconsistency or omission which he may discover, but he shall not be liable to the Owner for any damage resulting from any errors or deficiencies in the contract documents or other instructions by the architect.

ARTICLE 15

CHANGES IN THE WORK

The Owner, without invalidating the Contract, may order extra work or make changes by altering, adding to or deducting from the work, the Contract Sum being adjusted accordingly. All such work shall be executed under the conditions of the original contract except that any claim for extension of time caused thereby shall be adjusted at the time of ordering such change.

In giving instructions, the Architect shall have authority to make minor changes in the work, not involving extra cost, and not inconsistent with the purposes of the building, but otherwise, except in an emergency endangering life or property, no extra work or change shall be made unless in pursuance of a written order

from the Owner signed or countersigned by the Architect, or a written order from the Architect stating that the Owner has authorized the extra work or change, and no claim for an addiion to the contract sum shall be valid unless so ordered.

The value of any such extra work or change shall be determined in one or more of the following ways:
a) By estimate and acceptance in a lump sum.
b) By unit prices named in the contract or subsequently agreed upon.
c) By cost and percentage or by cost and a fixed fee.

If none of the above methods is agreed upon, the Contractor, provided he receives an order as above, shall proceed with the work. In such case and also under case (c), he shall keep and present in such form as the Architect may direct, a correct account of the cost, together with vouchers. In any case, the Architect shall certify to the amount, including reasonable allowance for overhead and profit, due to the Contractor. Pending final determination of value, payments on account of changes shall be made on the Architect's certificate.

Should conditions encountered below the surface of the ground be at variance with the conditions indicated by the drawings and specifications the contract sum shall be equitably adjusted upon claim by either party made within a reasonable time after the first observance of the conditions.

ARTICLE 16

CLAIMS FOR EXTRA COST

If the Contractor claims that any instructions by drawings or otherwise involve extra cost under this Contract, he shall give the Architect written notice thereof within a reasonable time after the receipt of such instructions, and in any event before proceeding to execute the work, except in emergency endangering life or property, and the procedure shall then be as provided for changes in the work. No such claim shall be valid unless so made.

ARTICLE 17

DEDUCTIONS FOR UNCORRECTED WORK

If the Architect and Owner deem it inexpedient to correct work injured or done not in accordance with the Contract, an equitable deduction from the contract price shall be made therefor.

ARTICLE 18

DELAYS AND EXTENSION OF TIME

If the Contractor be delayed at any time in the progress of the work by any act or neglect of the Owner or the Architect, or of any employee of either, or by any separate Contractor employed by the Owner, or by changes ordered in the work, or by strikes, lockouts, fire, unusual delay in transportation, unavoidable casualties or any causes beyond the Contractor's control, or by delay authorized by the Architect pending arbitration, or by any cause which the Architect shall decide

GENERAL CONDITIONS. 1961 EDITION.
Ten pages / Page 4

Fig. 9-1 (Continued.)

to justify the delay, then the time of completion shall be extended for such reasonable time as the Architect may decide.

No such extension shall be made for delay occurring more than seven days before claim therefor is made in writing to the Architect. In the case of a continuing cause of delay, only one claim is necessary.

If no schedule or agreement stating the dates upon which drawings shall be furnished is made, then no claim for delay shall be allowed on account of failure to furnish drawings until two weeks after demand for such drawings and not then unless such claim be reasonable.

This article does not exclude the recovery of damages for delay by either party under other provisions in the Contract Documents.

ARTICLE 19

CORRECTION OF WORK BEFORE FINAL PAYMENT

The Contractor shall promptly remove from the premises all work condemned by the Architect as failing to conform to the Contract, whether incorporated or not, and the Contractor shall promptly replace and re-execute his own work in accordance with the Contract and without expense to the Owner and shall bear the expense of making good all work of other contractors destroyed or damaged by such removal or replacement.

If the Contractor does not remove such condemned work within a reasonable time, fixed by written notice, the Owner may remove it and may store the material at the expense of the Contractor. If the Contractor does not pay the expenses of such removal within ten days' time thereafter, the Owner may, upon ten days' written notice, sell such materials at auction or at private sale and shall account for the net proceeds thereof, after deducting all the costs and expenses that should have been borne by the Contractor.

ARTICLE 20

CORRECTION OF WORK AFTER FINAL PAYMENT

The Contractor shall remedy any defects due to faulty materials or workmanship and pay for any damage to other work resulting therefrom, which shall appear within a period of one year from the date of final payment, or from the date of the Owner's substantial usage or occupancy of the Project, whichever is earlier, and in accordance with the terms of any special guarantees provided in the Contract. The Owner shall give notice of observed defects with reasonable promptness. All questions arising under this Article shall be decided by the Architect subject to arbitration, notwithstanding final payment.

ARTICLE 21

THE OWNER'S RIGHT TO DO WORK

If the Contractor should neglect to prosecute the work properly or fail to perform any provision of this con-

tract, the Owner, after three days' written notice to the Contractor may, without prejudice to any other remedy he may have, make good such deficiencies and may deduct the cost thereof from the payment then or thereafter due the Contractor, provided, however, that the Architect shall approve both such action and the amount charged to the Contractor.

ARTICLE 22

OWNER'S RIGHT TO TERMINATE CONTRACT

If the Contractor should be adjudged a bankrupt, or if he should make a general assignment for the benefit of his creditors, or if a receiver should be appointed on account of his insolvency, or if he should persistently or repeatedly refuse or should fail, except in cases for which extension of time is provided, to supply enough properly skilled workmen or proper materials, or if he should fail to make prompt payment to subcontractors or for material or labor, or persistently disregard laws, ordinances or the instructions of the Architect, or otherwise be guilty of a substantial violation of any provision of the Contract, then the Owner, upon the certificate of the Architect that sufficient cause exists to justify such action, may, without prejudice to any other right or remedy and after giving the Contractor, and his surety if any, seven days' written notice, terminate the employment of the Contractor and take possession of the premises and of all materials, tools and appliances thereon and finish the work by whatever method he may deem expedient. In such case the Contractor shall not be entitled to receive any further payment until the work is finished. If the unpaid balance of the contract price shall exceed the expense of finishing the work including compensation for additional architectural, managerial and administrative services, such excess shall be paid to the Contractor. If such expense shall exceed such unpaid balance, the Contractor shall pay the difference to the Owner. The expense incurred by the Owner as herein provided, and the damage incurred through the Contractor's default, shall be certified by the Architect.

ARTICLE 23

THE CONTRACTOR'S RIGHT TO STOP WORK OR TERMINATE CONTRACT

If the work should be stopped under an order of any court, or other public authority, for a period of thirty days, through no act or fault of the Contractor or of anyone employed by him, then the Contractor may, upon seven days' written notice to the Owner and the Architect, terminate this Contract and recover from the Owner payment for all work executed and any proven loss sustained upon any plant or materials and reasonable profit and damages.

Should the Architect fail to issue any Certificate for Payment, through no fault of the Contractor, within seven days after the Contractor's formal request for payment or if the Owner should fail to pay to the Contractor within seven days of its maturity and presentation, any sum certified by the Architect or awarded by arbitrators, then the Contractor may, upon seven

GENERAL CONDITIONS. 1961 EDITION.
Ten pages / Page 5

Fig. 9-1 (Continued.)

day's written notice to the Owner and the Architect, stop the work or terminate this Contract as set out in the preceding paragraph.

ARTICLE 24

APPLICATIONS FOR PAYMENTS

At least ten days before each payment falls due, the Contractor shall submit to the Architect an itemized application for payment, supported to the extent required by the Architect by receipts or other vouchers, showing payments for materials and labor, payments to subcontractors and such other evidence of the Contractor's right to payment as the Architect may direct.

If payments are made on valuation of work done, the Contractor shall, before the first application, submit to the Architect a schedule of values of the various parts of the work, including quantities, aggregating the total sum of the Contract, divided so as to facilitate payments to subcontractors in accordance with Article 37(e), made out in such form as the Architect and the Contractor may agree upon, and, if required, supported by such evidence as to its correctness as the Architect may direct. This schedule, when approved by the Architect, shall be used as a basis for Certificates for Payment, unless it be found to be in error. In applying for payments, the Contractor shall submit a statement based upon this schedule.

If payments are made on account of materials not incorporated in the work but delivered and suitably stored at the site, or at some other location agreed upon in writing, such payments shall be conditioned upon submission by the Contractor of bills of sale or such other procedure as will establish the Owner's title to such material or otherwise adequately protect the Owner's interest including applicable insurance.

ARTICLE 25

CERTIFICATES FOR PAYMENTS

If the Contractor has made application for payment as above, the Architect shall, not later than the date when each payment falls due, issue a Certificate for Payment to the Contractor for such amount as he decides to be properly due, or state in writing his reasons for withholding a certificate.

No certificate issued nor payment made to the Contractor, nor partial or entire use or occupancy of the work by the Owner, shall be an acceptance of any work or materials not in accordance with this contract. The making and acceptance of the final payment shall constitute a waiver of all claims by the Owner, other than those arising from unsettled liens, from faulty work appearing after final payment or from failure to comply with drawings and specifications and the terms of any special guarantees specified in the Contract and of all claims by the Contractor, except those previously made and still unsettled.

Should the Owner fail to pay the sum named in any Certificate for Payment issued by the Architect or in any award by arbitration, upon demand when due, the Contractor shall receive, in addition to the sum named in the certificate, interest thereon at the legal rate in force at the place of building.

ARTICLE 26

PAYMENTS WITHHELD

The Architect may withhold or, on account of subsequently discovered evidence, nullify the whole or a part of any certificate to such extent as may be necessary in his reasonable opinion to protect the Owner from loss on account of:
a) Defective work not remedied.
b) Claims filed or reasonable evidence indicating probable filing of claims.
c) Failure of the Contractor to make payments properly to subcontractors or for material or labor.
d) A reasonable doubt that the contract can be completed for the balance then unpaid.
(e) Damage to another Contractor.

When the above grounds are removed payment shall be made for amounts withheld because of them.

ARTICLE 27

CONTRACTOR'S LIABILITY INSURANCE

The Contractor shall maintain such insurance as will protect him from claims under workmen's compensation acts and other employee benefits acts; from claims for damages because of bodily injury, including death, to his employees and all others; and from claims for damages to property—any or all of which may arise out of or result from the Contractor's operations under this Contract, whether such operations be by himself or by any subcontractor or anyone directly or indirectly employed by either of them. This insurance shall be written for not less than any limits of liability specified as part of this Contract. Certificates of such insurance shall be filed with the Owner and Architect.

ARTICLE 28

OWNER'S LIABILITY INSURANCE

The Owner shall be responsible for and at his option may maintain such insurance as will protect him from his contingent liability to others for damages because of bodily injury, including death, which may arise from operations under this contract, and any other liability for damages which the Contractor is required to insure under any provision of this contract.

ARTICLE 29

FIRE INSURANCE WITH EXTENDED COVERAGE

Unless otherwise provided, the Owner shall effect and maintain fire insurance with extended coverage upon the entire structure on which the work of this contract is to be done to one hundred per cent of the insurable value thereof, including items of labor and materials

Fig. 9-1 (Continued.)

connected therewith whether in or adjacent to the structure insured, materials in place or to be used as part of the permanent construction including surplus materials, shanties, protective fences, bridges, temporary structures, miscellaneous materials and supplies incident to the work, and such scaffoldings, stagings, towers, forms, and equipment as are not owned or rented by the Contractor, the cost of which is included in the cost of the work. EXCLUSIONS: This insurance does not cover any tools owned by mechanics, any tools, equipment, scaffolding, staging, towers, and forms owned or rented by the Contractor, the capital value of which is not included in the cost of the work, or any cook shanties, bunk houses or other structures erected for housing the workmen. The loss, if any, is to be made adjustable with and payable to the Owner as Trustee for the insureds and Contractors and subcontractors as their interests may appear, except in such cases as may require payment of all or a proportion of said insurance to be made to a mortgagee as his interests may appear.

Certificates of such insurance shall be filed with the Contractor if he so requires. If the Owner fails to effect or maintain insurance as above and so notifies the Contractor, the Contractor may insure his own interests and that of the subcontractors and charge the cost thereof to the Owner. If the Contractor is damaged by failure of he Owner to maintain such insurance or to so notify the Contractor, he may recover as stipulated in the Contract for recovery of damages. If other special insurance not herein provided for is required by the Contractor, the Owner shall effect such insurance at the Contractor's expense by appropriate riders to his fire insurance policy. The Owner, Contractor, and all subcontractors waive all rights, each against the others, for damages caused by fire or other perils covered by insurance provided for under the terms of this article, except such rights as they may have to the proceeds of insurance held by the Owner as Trustee.

The Owner shall be responsible for and at his option may insure against loss of use of his existing property, due to fire or otherwise, however caused. If required in writing by any party in interest, the Owner as Trustee shall, upon the occurrence of loss, give bond for the proper performance of his duties. He shall deposit any money received from insurance in an account separate from all his other funds and he shall distribute it in accordance with such agreement as the parties in interest may reach, or under an award of arbitrators appointed, one by the Owner, another by joint action of the other parties in interest, all other procedure being as provided elsewhere in the Contract for arbitration. If after loss no special agreement is made, replacement of injured work shall be ordered and executed as provided for changes in the work.

The Trustee shall have power to adjust and settle any loss with the insurers unless one of the Contractors interested shall object in writing within three working days of the occurrence of loss, and thereupon arbitrators shall be chosen as above. The Trustee shall in that case make settlement with the insurers in accordance with the directions of such arbitrators, who shall also, if distribution by arbitration is required, direct such distribution.

GENERAL CONDITIONS. 1961 EDITION.
Ten pages / Page 7

ARTICLE 30

GUARANTY BONDS

The Owner shall have the right, prior to the signing of the Contract, to require the Contractor to furnish bond covering the faithful performance of the Contract and the payment of all obligations arising thereunder, in such form as the Owner may prescribe and with such sureties as he may approve. If such bond is required by instructions given previous to the submission of bids, the premium shall be paid by the Contractor; if subsequent thereto, it shall be paid by the Owner.

ARTICLE 31

DAMAGES

Should either party to this Contract suffer damages because of any wrongful act or neglect of the other party or of anyone employed by him, claim shall be made in writing to the party liable within a reasonable time of the first observance of such damage and not later than the final payment, except as expressly stipulated otherwise in the case of faulty work or materials, and shall be adjusted by agreement or arbitration.

ARTICLE 32

LIENS

Neither the final payment nor any part of the retained percentage shall become due until the Contractor, if required, shall deliver to the Owner a complete release of all liens arising out of this Contract, or receipts in full in lieu thereof and, if required in either case, an affidavit that so far as he has knowledge or information the releases and receipts include all the labor and material for which a lien could be filed; but the Contractor may, if any subcontractor refuses to furnish a release or receipt in full, furnish a bond satisfactory to the Owner, to indemnify him against any lien. If any lien remains unsatisfied after all payments are made, the Contractor shall refund to the Owner all moneys that the latter may be compelled to pay in discharging such a lien, including all costs and a reasonable attorney's fee.

ARTICLE 33

ASSIGNMENT

Neither party to the Contract shall assign the Contract or sublet it as a whole without the written consent of the other, nor shall the Contractor assign any moneys due or to become due to him hereunder, without the previous written consent of the Owner.

ARTICLE 34

MUTUAL RESPONSIBILITY OF CONTRACTORS

Should the Contractor cause damage to any separate contractor on the work the Contractor agrees, upon due notice, to settle with such contractor by agreement or arbitration, if he will so settle. If such separate con-

Fig. 9-1 (Continued.)

tractor sues the Owner on account of any damage alleged to have been so sustained, the Owner shall notify the Contractor, who shall defend such proceedings at the Owner's expense and, if any judgment against the Owner arise therefrom, the Contractor shall pay or satisfy it and pay all costs incurred by the Owner.

ARTICLE 35

SEPARATE CONTRACTS

The Owner reserves the right to let other contracts in connection with this work under similar General Conditions. The Contractor shall afford other contractors reasonable opportunity for the introduction and storage of their materials and the execution of their work, and shall properly connect and coordinate his work with theirs.

If any part of the Contractor's work depends for proper execution or results upon the work of any other contractor, the Contractor shall inspect and promptly report to the Architect any defects in such work that render it unsuitable for such proper execution and results. His failure so to inspect and report shall constitute an acceptance of the other contractor's work as fit and proper for the reception of his work, except as to defects which may develop in the other contractor's work after the execution of his work.

To insure the proper execution of his subsequent work the Contractor shall measure work already in place and shall at once report to the Architect any discrepancy between the executed work and the drawings.

ARTICLE 36

SUBCONTRACTS

As soon as practicable and before awarding any subcontracts, the Contractor shall notify the Architect in writing of the names of the subcontractors proposed for the principal parts of the work, and for such other parts as the Architect may direct, and shall not employ any to whom the Architect may have a reasonable objection.

If before or after the execution of the Contract, the Contractor has submitted a list of subcontractors which has been approved by the Architect, and the change of any subcontractor on such list is required by the Owner after such approval, the contract price shall be increased or decreased by the difference in cost occasioned by such change.

The Contractor shall not be required to employ any subcontractor against whom he has a reasonable objection.

The Architect shall, on request, furnish to any subcontractor, wherever practicable, evidence of the amounts certified on his account.

The Contractor agrees that he is as fully responsible to the Owner for the acts and omissions of his subcontractors and of persons either directly or indirectly employed by them, as he is for the acts and omissions of persons directly employed by him.

Nothing contained in the Contract Documents shall create any contractual relation between any subcontractor and the Owner.

ARTICLE 37

RELATIONS OF CONTRACTOR AND SUBCONTRACTOR

The Contractor agrees to bind every Subcontractor and every Subcontractor agrees to be bound by the terms of the Agreement, the General Conditions of the Contract, the Supplementary General Conditions, the Drawings and Specifications as far as applicable to his work, including the following provisions of this article, unless specifically noted to the contrary in a subcontract approved in writing as adequate by the Owner or Architect.

The Subcontractor agrees—

a) To be bound to the Contractor by the terms of the Agreement, General Conditions of the Contract, the Supplementary General Conditions, the Drawings and Specifications, and to assume toward him all the obligations and responsibilities that he, by those documents, assumes toward the Owner.

b) To submit to the Contractor applications for payment in such reasonable time as to enable the Contractor to apply for payment under Article 24 of the General Conditions.

c) To make all claims for extras, for extensions of time and for damages for delays or otherwise, to the Contractor in the manner provided in the General Conditions of the Contract and the Supplementary General Conditions for like claims by the Contractor upon the Owner, except that the time for making claims for extra cost is one week.

The Contractor agrees—

d) To be bound to the Subcontractor by all the obligations that the Owner assumes to the Contractor under the Agreement, General Conditions of the Contract, the Supplementary General Conditions, the Drawings and Specifications, and by all the provisions thereof affording remedies and redress to the Contractor from the Owner.

e) To pay the Subcontractor, upon the payment of certificates, if issued under the schedule of values described in Article 24 of the General Conditions, the amount allowed to the Contractor on account of the Subcontractor's work to the extent of the Subcontractor's interest therein.

f) To pay the Subcontractor, upon the payment of certificates, if issued otherwise than as in (e), so that at all times his total payments shall be as large in proportion to the value of the work done by him as the total amount certified to the Contractor is to the value of the work done by him.

g) To pay the Subcontractor to such extent as may be provided by the Contract Documents or the subcontract, if either of these provides for earlier or larger payments than the above.

h) To pay the Subcontractor on demand for his work or materials as far as executed and fixed in place, less the retained percentage, at the time the certificate should issue, even though the Architect fails to issue it for any cause not the fault of the Subcontractor.

j) To pay the Subcontractor a just share of any fire insurance money received by him, the Contractor, under Article 29 of the General Conditions.

Fig. 9-1 (Continued.)

k) To make no demand for liquidated damages or penalty for delay in any sum in excess of such amount as may be specifically named in the subcontract.

l) That no claim for services rendered or materials furnished by the Contractor to the Subcontractor shall be valid unless written notice thereof is given by the Contractor to the Subcontractor during the first ten days of the calendar month following that in which the claim originated.

m) To give the Subcontractor an opportunity to be present and to submit evidence in any arbitration involving his rights.

n) To name as arbitrator under arbitration proceedings as provided in the General Conditions the person nominated by the Subcontractor, if the sole cause of dispute is the work, materials, rights or responsibilities of the Subcontractor; or, if of the Subcontractor and any other subcontractor jointly, to name as such arbitrator the person upon whom they agree.

The Contractor and the Subcontractor agree that—

o) In the matter of arbitration, their rights and obligations and all procedure shall be analogous to those set forth in this Contract; provided, however, that a decision by the Architect shall not be a condition precedent to arbitration.

Nothing in this article shall create any obligation on the part of the Owner to pay or to see to the payment of any sums to any subcontractor.

ARTICLE 38

ARCHITECT'S STATUS

The Architect shall be the Owner's representative during the construction period and he shall observe the work in process on behalf of the Owner. He shall have authority to act on behalf of the Owner only to the extent expressly provided in the Contract Documents or otherwise in writing, which shall be shown to the Contractor. He shall have authority to stop the work whenever such stoppage may be necessary in his reasonable opinion to insure the proper execution of the Contract.

The Architect shall be, in the first instance, the interpreter of the conditions of the Contract and the judge of its performance. He shall side neither with the Owner nor with the Contractor, but shall use his powers under the Contract to enforce its faithful performance by both.

In case of the termination of the employment of the Architect, the Owner shall appoint a capable and reputable Architect against whom the Contractor makes no reasonable objection, whose status under the contract shall be that of the former Architect; and dispute in connection with such appointment shall be subject to arbitration.

ARTICLE 39

ARCHITECT'S DECISIONS

The Architect shall, within a reasonable time, make decisions on all claims of the Owner or Contractor and on all other matters relating to the execution and progress of the work or the interpretation of the Contract Documents.

GENERAL CONDITIONS. 1961 EDITION.
Ten pages / Page 9

The Architect's decision, in matters relating to artistic effect, shall be final, if within the terms of the Contract Documents.

Except as above or as otherwise expressly provided in the Contract Documents, all the Architect's decisions are subject to arbitration.

If, however, the Architect fails to render a decision within ten days after the parties have presented their evidence, either party may then demand arbitration. If the Architect renders a decision after arbitration proceedings have been initiated, such decision may be entered as evidence but shall not disturb or interrupt such proceedings except where such decision is acceptable to the parties concerned.

ARTICLE 40

ARBITRATION

All disputes, claims or questions subject to arbitration under this contract shall be submitted to arbitration in accordance with the provisions, then obtaining, of the Standard Form of Arbitration Procedure of The American Institute of Architects, and this agreement shall be specifically enforceable under the prevailing arbitration law, and judgment upon the award rendered may be entered in the court of the forum, state or federal, having jurisdiction. It is mutually agreed that the decision of the arbitrators shall be a condition precedent to any right of legal action that either party may have against the other.

The Contractor shall not cause a delay of the work during any arbitration proceedings, except by agreement with the Owner.

Notice of the demand for arbitration of a dispute shall be filed in writing with the other party to the contract, and a copy filed with the Architect. The demand for arbitration shall be made within a reasonable time after the dispute has arisen; in no case, however, shall the demand be made later than the time of final payment, except as otherwise expressly stipulated in the contract.

The arbitrators, if they deem that the case requires it, are authorized to award to the party whose contention is sustained, such sums as they or a majority of them shall deem proper to compensate him for the time and expense incident to the proceeding and, if the arbitration was demanded without reasonable cause, they may also award damages for delay. The arbitrators shall fix their own compensation, unless otherwise provided by agreement, and shall assess the costs and charges of the proceedings upon either or both parties.

ARTICLE 41

CASH ALLOWANCES

The Contractor shall include in the contract sum all allowances named in the Contract Documents and shall cause the work so covered to be done by such contractors and for such sums as the Architect may direct, the contract sum being adjusted in conformity therewith. The Contractor declares that the contract sum includes such sums for expenses and profit on account of cash

Fig. 9-1 (Continued.)

allowances as he deems proper. No demand for expenses or profit other than those included in the contract sum shall be allowed. The Contractor shall not be required to employ for any such work persons against whom he has a reasonable objection.

ARTICLE 42

USE OF PREMISES

The Contractor shall confine his apparatus, the storage of materials and the operations of his workmen to limits indicated by law, ordinances, permits or directions of the Architect and shall not unreasonably encumber the premises with his materials.

The Contractor shall not load or permit any part of the structure to be loaded with a weight that will endanger its safety.

ARTICLE 43

CUTTING, PATCHING

The Contractor shall do all cutting, fitting or patching of his work that may be required to make its several parts come together properly and fit it to receive or be received by work of other contractors shown upon, or reasonably implied by, the Drawings and Specifications for the completed structure, and he shall make good after them as the Architect may direct.

Any cost caused by defective or ill-timed work shall be borne by the party responsible therefor.

The Contractor shall not endanger any work by cutting, excavating or otherwise altering the work and shall not cut or alter the work of any other contractor save with the consent of the Architect.

ARTICLE 44

CLEANING UP

The Contractor shall at all times keep the premises free from accumulation of waste materials or rubbish caused by his employees or work, and at the completion of the work he shall remove all his rubbish from and about the building and all his tools, scaffolding and surplus materials and shall leave his work "broom-clean" or its equivalent, unless more exactly specified. In case of dispute the Owner may remove the rubbish and charge the cost to the several contractors as the Architect shall determine to be just.

GENERAL CONDITIONS. 1961 EDITION.
Ten pages / Page 10

Fig. 9-1 (Continued.)

will be used here as a guide in the discussion of the information included in most standardized general conditions. The AIA general conditions contain subject matter that is applicable to most construction contracts, grouped under forty-four articles. Parker and Adams have written an excellent book on the AIA contract documents.[1]

No attempt will be made to cover all the conditions and the legal interpretations that have been placed on the various articles and subjects included. This document is in a constant state of revision, as it should be, to keep up with the latest thinking on this matter.

The specifications writer must keep abreast of the latest developments and study new editions of the AIA standard documents as they are published. Circulars of information are published by the AIA as each new edition is issued, such as the one published in 1961.[2]

SUMMARY OF AIA GENERAL CONDITIONS

This summary is based on the 1961 edition of Document No. A201.

Article 1: Definitions. These definitions are rather brief and general in nature. They repeat some of the information given in the agreement. Although they are brief, they can be important in identifying terms, such as who will be considered a subcontractor. The definitions are of a general nature that will apply to most projects. The exact names of the parties who will be named as part of the contract and any modifications of this article must be given in the supplemental general conditions.

Article 2: Execution, Correlation, and Intent of Documents. This article contains two important provisions concerning (1) the signing and identification of the documents and (2) the intent of the document. Irregularities in the signing of documents when an agreement is made can cause controversy at a later date. The architect will then be called upon to identify the documents. If critical items are inadvertently left out of the drawings or specifications, the courts, in case of a controversy, will look for intent.

[1] W. S. Parker and F. Adams, "The AIA Standard Contract Forms and the Law," Little, Brown and Company, Boston, 1954.

[2] J. R. Clarke, "Concerning Some Legal Responsibilities in the Practice of Architecture and Engineering and Some Recent Changes in the Contract Document," American Institute of Architects, Washington, D.C.

If necessary items of work are not covered in the specifications or noted on the drawings, the question then becomes, "Can the inclusion of this work be reasonably inferred from the drawings or specifications?" Again it is a question of intent.

Article 3: Detail Drawings and Instructions. Additional drawings or instructions that are issued by the architect during the progress of the work are described with particular emphasis on promptness and content. The time schedule for the addition of instructions or drawings will be based on the time schedule of work submitted by the contractor as required by this article.

Article 4: Copies Furnished. This article is stated in such broad terms that it should always be amplified in the supplemental general conditions. Each project may require a different number of sets of drawings or specifications. The phrase "all copies reasonably necessary for the execution of the work" could be interpreted in a different manner by every contractor, architect, and engineer.

Article 5: Shop Drawings. The limit of the responsibility of the architect or engineer for detecting errors or deviations from what is shown in the contract drawings is spelled out in Article 5. The architect or engineer checks for conformity with the design concept and conformity with the contract documents, not for accuracy. The contractor is made responsible for verifying all field measurements and for the accuracy of shop drawings. It should be noted that the contractor referred to is the general contractor, not a subcontractor. There have been many controversies over the architect's function in the checking of shop drawings submitted by contractors. For a more complete discussion of shop drawings and their functions, see Chap. 4.

Article 6: Drawings and Specifications on the Work. If special care of the documents is desired, such as provision of a rack to hold drawings or a plan table, this must be noted in the supplemental general conditions.

Article 7: Ownership of Drawings. This article repeats information in the AIA agreement form. The drawings are instruments of service, prepared by the architect in the design of a particular project, and, as such, are the property of the architect. The authorized use by the contractor of the contract documents is controlled here. In previous editions, Article 7 included ownership of models. This has been eliminated in this edition, and the ownership of models must be defined in supplemental general conditions.

Article 8: Samples. Samples are to be furnished as directed by the architect. What samples are to be required, and how, is covered in the supplemental general conditions and specifically in each trade section. As with the shop drawings, the architect does not check samples for other than the design concept or compliance with the contract documents.

Article 9: Materials, Appliances, and Employees. The first provision of this article concerns the furnishing of, and paying for, all materials, labor, equipment, power, light, water, and other facilities necessary to finish the project. The important point covered is the paying for these items. Other articles give the owner the right to withhold payment if the contractor does not pay for material or labor. These articles are based on the requirements of Article 9. The architect's authority to make decisions on the quality of materials and workmanship and the competence of the contractor's superintendent is also based on this article.

Article 10: Royalties and Patents. The contractor is required to pay all royalties or license fees necessary for the use of patented materials. The architect must so note in the drawings or specifications when a product or process is patented. If the product or process is not so noted, the contractor will not be held liable.

Article 11: Surveys, Permits, Laws, Taxes, and Regulations. The material as presented is of a somewhat controversial nature. There is no question as to the owner's responsibility in the furnishing of surveys of the property; however, the question of who will pay for the building permit is still uncertain in the minds of many architects. Previous editions of the general conditions stated that the owner was to secure and pay for building permits for permanent changes to structures or for the construction of new structures. The contractor was to secure and pay for permits or licenses for work of a temporary nature, such as those for installing temporary lights and utilities and breaking of the curb to install drives, barricades, and entering sewers and similar permits required in the prosecution of the work. Later editions shifted the responsibility of securing and paying for all building permits from the owner to the contractor. The owner, or the architect acting as his representative, must sign the permit and make any changes in the contract documents required by the building department. Why, then, should the contractor be required to apply for this permit? This article, as now written, usually needs further clarification or modification in supplemental general conditions. The owner is required to pay for easements for permanent structures. The exact meaning of the word "easements" must be defined. Taxes that are assessed in the normal conduct of business, such as sales and consumer taxes, are to be paid by the contractor.

Article 12: Protection of Work and Property. The contractor is required to protect his work, the work of others, and adjacent property. He must make good for any damage done unless the cause of the damage is beyond his control or due to errors in the contract documents. Danger or safety regulations that are peculiar to a particular job should be enumerated and emphasized in the supplemental general conditions. Article 12 covers barricades, signs, and safety devices in a general way. These instructions must be supplemented with specific safety precautions. The contractor is authorized to act in emergencies.

Article 13: Access to Work. In addition to access to the work, this article covers inspection or observation and interpretation of test reports by the architect.

Special note should be taken that the architect is not acting as an inspector but as a specially qualified observer. If the architect, or an employee of the architect or owner, is to act as an inspector, this article must be modified and clarified in the supplemental general conditions. Notices of tests and promptness of the architect in observing these tests are covered. An important point covered by Article 13 is the correction of faulty work and reexamination of questioned work. When work is uncovered for reexamination, the cost of uncovering and replacing this work, when it is found to be faulty, must be paid by the contractor. If the work is found to be in accordance with the contract documents, the owner must pay for the reexamination and replacement.

Article 14: Superintendence and Supervision. The contractor is required to keep on the job a superintendent who is satisfactory to the architect. The architect may use his judgment as to who will be satisfactory. Orders given to the contractor's superintendent will have the same force as though given to the contractor. The architect is cautioned to confirm all important decisions in writing to the contractor. The contractor is further instructed to check the contract documents and report to the architect any errors, inconsistencies, or omissions he may find. He is not held responsible for any error he does not find. The architect will not be held for errors or omissions of the contractor's superintendent or his assistant.

Article 15: Changes in the Work. This article gives the owner the right to make changes in the work. The important provision here is the one which limits the contractor's ability to collect additional money for extras unless he has received a written change order from the owner, countersigned by the architect. The method of determining the value of the work is to be established by agreement between the contractor and the owner. Conditions encountered under the surface have caused many disputes. Some architects put on the contractor the onus of finding what subsurface conditions exist through visits to the site or, in some instances, making soil tests before he submits his bid. The contractor must then either raise his bid to take care of any possible contingencies or gamble that he will encounter no difficulty. Article 15 provides for the adjustment of the contract sum if the conditions vary from what is shown or indicated in the drawings or specifications. This variance from what is indicated may result in a saving or in additional costs for the owner.

Article 16: Claims for Extra Costs. The contractor must present a claim for extras before performing any extra work. This is to forestall the practice followed by some contractors of presenting a claim for many extras at the end of a project. Article 15 gives the architect or owner the authority to order changes of a minor nature not involving additional costs. If the contractor claims that these instructions do involve extra costs, he must make a claim for extra costs before proceeding with the work.

Article 17: Deductions for Uncorrected Work. The architect may not accept defective work and make a deduction from the contract price. Only the owner may do so because this would constitute a change in the contract. The owner, on the advice of the architect or engineer, may accept defective work that does not affect the stability of a building.

Article 18: Delays and Extension of Time. Requests by the contractor for extension of time for completion of the project due to specific occurrences or other occurrences which, in the opinion of the architect, are justified must be made not later than seven days after the cause of the delay has occurred. The architect, in the absence of a schedule, has two weeks to furnish additional drawings or instructions before the contractor can present a claim for delay. This article does not provide for damages caused by delay. However, it does not preclude damages being recovered under other articles.

Article 19: Correction of Work before Final Payment. The contractor is required to remove and replace any work that does not conform to the contract documents. Defective work may cause extensive damage to other parts of the work or to the work of other contractors. A leaky roof may cause extensive damage to interior finish, coverings, or furnishings. The contractor must pay for this damage in addition to repairing his work.

Article 20: Correction of Work after Final Payment. The contractor is specifically directed to repair or pay for damage occurring for a period of one year after final payment has been received for the work. The date of substantial completion is established by the next-to-final payment.

The owner may occupy the work upon substantial completion. The one-year guaranty period would then start from the date of the owner's substantial occupancy or usage. This period is usually covered by the performance bond. It is stated that the one-year provision does not relieve the contractor from responsibility for faults discovered at a later date. Specific guaranties in the trade sections such as ten-year roofing guaranties and other such requirements will overrule the one-year provision. Only the statutes of limitations in force in each state will entirely relieve the contractor from all responsibilities.

Article 21: Owner's Right to Do Work. If the contractor fails to prosecute the work or fails to live up to the conditions of the contract, the owner may make good any deficiencies. Two items are spelled out here: The owner must give three days' written notice, and the action of the owner must be approved by the architect. These actions should be taken only after careful consideration by the owner and on the advice of the architect.

Article 22: Owner's Right to Terminate Contract. If the contractor should fail to prosecute the work or comply with the contract documents within a reasonable time, the owner may take over and complete the work seven days after written notice has been given. The architect must issue a certificate of cause before the owner may take this action. Unless the architect has issued such a certificate, the owner may not act. If a surety bond has been required by the agreement, the surety may complete the project or pay the owner the money necessary to complete the project. If the cost of completion exceeds the amount due the contractor for completion, the contractor must pay the owner the additional amount. If a surplus remains after completion, the owner must return this to the contractor. The architect should understand that the additional work he must undertake in supervising the remaining portion of the work is a rightful charge against the contractor or surety.

Article 23: Contractor's Right to Stop Work or Terminate Contract. The contractor has the right to stop work for three basic reasons: (1) if the Architect fails to issue a certificate after seven days; (2) if the owner fails to pay after seven days; and (3) if an action by a court or public authority halts the work for a period of thirty days. The contractor can then recover for work performed regardless of the contract price.

Article 24: Applications for Payments. The contractor's applications for payments, submitted ten days before they are due, will be based on a schedule of values proportionate to the value of the total work. If payments are to be made on materials delivered and stored on the site, it may be necessary to require bills of sale in case the materials dealers have not been paid and should attempt to repossess the materials.

Article 25: Certificates for Payments. The architect must issue a certificate of payment or a statement which gives his reasons for withholding a certificate. The issuance of the certificate of payment does not constitute a waiver to claims for work that is not in accordance with the contract documents or for faulty work that may be discovered at a later date. There is no time limit stated in this clause. Regardless of the one-year time limit,

as described in Article 20, the contractor is not relieved of responsibility for faults discovered later. The statutes of limitations in force in the particular state are made a part of the contract in the first article of the general conditions with the following statement: "The law of the place of building shall govern the construction of this contract."

Article 26: Payments Withheld. The reasons an architect may have for withholding a certificate are enumerated. The purpose of withholding these certificates is to protect the owner. The work may be stopped if such action is necessary in the "reasonable opinion" of the architect.

Article 27: Contractor's Liability Insurance. This article covers insurance against claims for bodily injury and damage to property. The contractor is required to carry insurance to protect himself from claims due to his own, his employees', or any of his subcontractors' negligence. There are several types of contractor's liability insurance. The limited form protects the contractor if his employees are negligent. A second form protects the contractor if he and another party are jointly negligent. A "hold harmless" clause may be required which will protect the architect, engineer, or owner. Workmen's compensation acts and other employee provisions vary greatly in different states. The provisions in Article 27 are very broad, and the supplemental general conditions must spell out exactly what is required.

Article 28: Owner's Liability Insurance. The owner has a contingent liability for injuries that may arise out of a contract. Owner's liability insurance will be necessary unless the contractor is required to carry a type of insurance which will protect the owner from this contingent liability.

Article 29: Fire Insurance with Extended Coverage. The owner is required to maintain fire insurance with extended coverage. This coverage will include labor, materials, and temporary structures. Mechanics' tools, rented equipment, and equipment owned by the contractor are not covered. The extended coverage will cover other hazards normally present; however, hazards such as earthquakes, hurricanes, and special conditions that may be present on a particular job site must be covered in the supplemental general conditions.

The contractor may demand a certificate of

such insurance carried by the owner. If the owner fails to maintain this insurance, the contractor may insure his own interests and charge the cost of such insurance to the owner. The contractor may require the owner to maintain special insurance other than that provided for here. The owner then has these special insurance provisions attached to his fire insurance policy and charges the contractor for the additional premium. The owner, contractors, and subcontractors waive all rights, each against the other, for damage covered by this insurance.

The owner may desire "loss of use" insurance. This is generally the case when alterations or additions to existing structures are under way. Modification of fire insurance policies in force on existing buildings may be necessary because of the additional hazard caused by the alterations or additions.

The owner is made a trustee to handle and pay claims occasioned by loss under these policies. For further information on insurance, see AIA Document No. A301, Circular of Information on Insurance Requirements.

Article 30: Guaranty Bonds. The owner has the right to require the contractor to furnish bonds covering the faithful performance of the contract and payment for labor and materials. The forms to be used and surety selected must be approved by the architect. The designation of a particular surety company is not recommended. A contractor's regular surety company, if it is financially sound, will usually be satisfactory. However, most architects do require that standard forms, as published by the AIA, be used. (See Fig. 9-2.)

Article 31: Damages. This article sets forth the procedure to be followed in the event of damage to one party of the contract due to the negligence of another party. The claim must be set forth in writing within a reasonable time. The claim will then be settled by agreement or arbitration.

Article 32: Liens. The owner may withhold final payment and any retained percentages until he is entirely satisfied that the contractor has paid all bills and that no lien will be filed on the property. The architect must study the records of the project and the laws of the place of building to make sure that all persons who have performed work or furnished materials that may be subject to a lien have been covered by releases before he certifies a final payment. For further information on liens, see Chap. 4.

Article 33: Assignment. Neither party may assign the rights or moneys due under this contract without the written consent of the other.

Article 34: Mutual Responsibility of Contractors. If several contractors are working on a job as prime contractors, each will be governed by the general conditions and will have the same responsibilities to the owner as set forth in the general conditions. In a dispute between two prime contractors, they must settle any differences by agreement or arbitration. If, regardless of this provision, a separate contractor sues the owner for recovery for damages caused by a second contractor, the second contractor agrees to defend the owner, at the owner's expense. If the second contractor is found to be at fault, he must reimburse the owner. If he is found to be free from fault, the owner, through his contingent liability insurance, will be liable.

Article 35: Separate Contracts. The architect is given the right to let portions of the work under separate contracts. These separate contracts will be governed by the same general conditions and tied to Article 34, which governs the mutual responsibilities of separate contractors. The coordination of the work and the responsibilities of each contractor, where his work abuts or adjoins the work of another, are covered. If special coordination as to time, storage of materials, or similar conditions will be necessary, this should be carefully described in supplemental general conditions.

Article 36: Subcontracts. The contractor must submit a list of subcontractors for the architect's approval. The architect may object to any subcontractor, but, after approval of the list, any change required by the architect will be a reason for a change in the contract. The architect may not require the contractor to employ a subcontractor unsuitable to the contractor. If an architect chooses a subcontractor and requires the contractor to employ him, this could, in effect, create a contractual relationship between the owner and the subcontractor, even though this article specifically states that no contractual relationship exists between the owner and any subcontractor. Problems of this nature usually concern the employing of a subcontractor who employs nonunion labor.

Article 37: Relations of Contractor and Subcontractor. The major relationships that

PERFORMANCE BOND

KNOW ALL MEN BY THESE PRESENTS: that (Here insert name and address or legal title of Contractor)

as Principal, hereinafter called Contractor, and, (Here insert the legal title and address of Surety)

as Surety, hereinafter called Surety, are held and firmly bound unto (Name and address or legal title of Owner)

as Obligee, hereinafter called Owner, in the amount of

Dollars ($),

for the payment whereof Contractor and Surety bind themselves, their heirs, executors, administrators, successors and assigns, jointly and severally, firmly by these presents.

WHEREAS,

Contractor has by written agreement dated   19   , entered into a contract with Owner for

in accordance with drawings and specifications prepared by (Here insert full name, title and address)

which contract is by reference made a part hereof, and is hereinafter referred to as the Contract.

PERFORMANCE/LABOR-MATERIAL BOND
AIA DOC. A311   SEPT. 1963 ED.   FOUR PAGES

© 1963 The American Institute of Architects
1735 New York Ave N.W., Washington, D. C.

PAGE 1

AIA DOC. A311   SEPT. 1963 ED.

AIA DOC. A311   SEPT. 1963 ED.

Fig. 9-2. Performance Bond—Labor and Material Payment Bond, AIA Document No. A311, 1963 edition (four pages). (By permission of the American Institute of Architects.)

151

NOW, THEREFORE, THE CONDITION OF THIS OBLIGATION is such that, if Contractor shall promptly and faithfully perform said Contract, then this obligation shall be null and void; otherwise it shall remain in full force and effect.

The Surety hereby waives notice of any alteration or extension of time made by the Owner.

Whenever Contractor shall be, and declared by Owner to be in default under the Contract, the Owner having performed Owner's obligations thereunder, the Surety may promptly remedy the default, or shall promptly

1) Complete the Contract in accordance with its terms and conditions, or

2) Obtain a bid or bids for submission to Owner for completing the Contract in accordance with its terms and conditions, and upon determination by Owner and Surety of the lowest responsible bidder, arrange for a contract between such bidder and Owner, and make available as work progresses (even though there should be a default or a succession of defaults under the contract or contracts of completion arranged under this paragraph) sufficient funds to pay the cost of completion less the balance of the contract price; but not exceeding, including other costs and damages for which the Surety may be liable hereunder, the amount set forth in the first paragraph hereof. The term "balance of the contract price," as used in this paragraph, shall mean the total amount payable by Owner to Contractor under the Contract and any amendments thereto, less the amount properly paid by Owner to Contractor.

Any suit under this bond must be instituted before the expiration of two (2) years from the date on which final payment under the contract falls due.

No right of action shall accrue on this bond to or for the use of any person or corporation other than the Owner named herein or the heirs, executors, administrators or successors of Owner.

Signed and sealed this   day of   A.D. 19

IN THE PRESENCE OF:

_____   _____
                                          (Principal)   (Seal)

                                          _____
                                          (Title)

_____   _____
                                          (Surety)   (Seal)

                                          _____
                                          (Title)

PERFORMANCE/LABOR-MATERIAL BOND   FOUR PAGES

AIA DOC. A311   SEPT. 1963 ED.   PAGE 2

Fig. 9-2 (Continued.)

LABOR AND MATERIAL PAYMENT BOND

THIS BOND IS ISSUED SIMULTANEOUSLY WITH PERFORMANCE BOND IN FAVOR OF THE
OWNER CONDITIONED ON THE FULL AND FAITHFUL PERFORMANCE OF THE CONTRACT

KNOW ALL MEN BY THESE PRESENTS: that (Here insert name and address or legal title of Contractor)

as Principal, hereinafter called Principal, and, (Here insert the legal title and address of Surety)

as Surety, hereinafter called Surety, are held and firmly bound unto (Name and address or legal title of Owner)

as Obligee, hereinafter called Owner, for the use and benefit of claimants as hereinbelow defined, in the

amount of   Dollars ($),
         (Here insert a sum equal to at least one-half of the contract price)

for the payment whereof Principal and Surety bind themselves, their heirs, executors, administrators, successors and assigns, jointly and severally, firmly by these presents.

WHEREAS,

Principal has by written agreement dated   19   , entered into a contract with Owner for

in accordance with drawings and specifications prepared by (Here insert full name, title and address)

which contract is by reference made a part hereof, and is hereinafter referred to as the Contract.

PERFORMANCE/LABOR-MATERIAL BOND   FOUR PAGES

AIA DOC. A311   SEPT. 1963 ED.   PAGE 3

Fig. 9-2 (Continued.)

NOW, THEREFORE, THE CONDITION OF THIS OBLIGATION is such that, if Principal shall promptly make payment to all claimants as hereinafter defined, for all labor and material used or reasonably required for use in the performance of the Contract, then this obligation shall be void; otherwise it shall remain in full force and effect, subject, however, to the following conditions:

1. A claimant is defined as one having a direct contract with the Principal or with a subcontractor of the Principal for labor, material, or both, used or reasonably required for use in the performance of the contract, labor and material being construed to include that part of water, gas, power, light, heat, oil, gasoline, telephone service or rental of equipment directly applicable to the Contract.

2. The above named Principal and Surety hereby jointly and severally agree with the Owner that every claimant as herein defined, who has not been paid in full before the expiration of a period of ninety (90) days after the date on which the last of such claimant's work or labor was done or performed, or materials were furnished by such claimant, may sue on this bond for the use of such claimant, prosecute the suit to final judgment for such sum or sums as may be justly due claimant, and have execution thereon. The Owner shall not be liable for the payment of any costs or expenses of any such suit.

3. No suit or action shall be commenced hereunder by any claimant:

a) Unless claimant, other than one having a direct contract with the Principal, shall have given written notice to any two of the following: The Principal, the Owner, or the Surety above named, within ninety (90) days after such claimant did or performed the last of the work or labor, or furnished the last of the materials for which said claim is made, stating with substantial accuracy the amount claimed and the name of the party to whom the materials were furnished, or for whom the work or labor was done or performed. Such notice shall be served by mailing the same by registered mail or certified mail, postage prepaid, in an envelope addressed to the Principal, Owner or Surety, at any place where an office is regularly maintained for the transaction of business, or served in any manner in which legal process may be served in the state in which the aforesaid project is located, save that such service need not be made by a public officer.

b) After the expiration of one (1) year following the date on which Principal ceased work on said Contract, it being understood, however, that if any limitation embodied in this bond is prohibited by any law controlling the construction hereof such limitation shall be deemed to be amended so as to be equal to the minimum period of limitation permitted by such law.

c) Other than in a state court of competent jurisdiction in and for the county or other political subdivision of the state in which the project, or any part thereof, is situated, or in the United States District Court for the district in which the project, or any part thereof, is situated, and not elsewhere.

4. The amount of this bond shall be reduced by and to the extent of any payment or payments made in good faith hereunder, inclusive of the payment by Surety of mechanics' liens which may be filed of record against said improvement, whether or not claim for the amount of such lien be presented under and against this bond.

Signed and sealed this   day of   A.D. 19

IN THE PRESENCE OF:

_____

(Principal)   (Seal)

_____

(Title)

(Surety)   (Seal)

_____

(Title)

PERFORMANCE/LABOR-MATERIAL BOND   FOUR PAGES

AIA DOC. A311   SEPT. 1963 ED.   PAGE 4

Fig. 9-2 (Continued.)

exist between the contractor and a subcontractor are covered in this article. No contract exists between the owner and a subcontractor, so the provisions included here cannot bind a third party, the subcontractor, to these conditions. The general contractor, however, is bound to these conditions and can be required to bind the subcontractor to them in a separate contract. This will usually take the form of AIA Document No. A401, Standard Form of Subcontract, illustrated in Fig. 8-8. The conditions of this article and the use of this form establish the same relationships, responsibilities, and rights between the contractor and the subcontractor as exist between the owner and the contractor, except that any arbitration proceedings need not be based on the architect's decision. The owner is relieved of any responsibility to force the contractor to pay a subcontractor.

Article 38: Architect's Status. The exact status of the architect has been the basis of many disputes. Older editions of the general conditions have held the architect to be the agent of the owner, and the owner has been held liable for all acts of the architect. Article 38 defines the architect as a representative of the owner during the construction process and only to the extent provided for in the contract documents. This limits the "agency" relationship of the architect to those responsibilities specifically granted in the contract documents or in writing. The architect is held to be the interpreter of the documents and the judge of their meanings. As such, he must side with neither the owner nor the contractor but enforce the faithful performance of both. If the employment of the architect is terminated, the owner may appoint, with the approval of the contractor, a capable and reputable architect who will then assume the duties and authority granted the originally named architect.

Article 39: Architect's Decisions. Decisions by the architect must be made within a reasonable length of time after a dispute has arisen. If a decision is not rendered within ten days, either party may resort to arbitration. The architect is empowered to make decisions on all matters related to the execution and progress of the work. His decisions on matters related to artistic effect are final, but all other decisions are subject to arbitration.

Article 40: Arbitration. All disputes and claims under the contract documents are subject to arbitration except those specifically excluded in Article 39. The architect must be thoroughly familiar with the laws of the state in which he is operating. Many states do not have laws requiring arbitration, and some of those that do have such laws require special or separate forms of agreement before a dispute can be submitted to arbitration. The use of Standard Form of Arbitration Procedure, published by the AIA, is recommended. If the architect is operating in a state that has no arbitration laws, or if the project is being constructed in such a state, it is advisable to retain legal help to investigate the situation thoroughly. If modifications must be made to this article, the supplemental general conditions must define the architect's authority to make and enforce his decisions.

Article 41: Cash Allowance. The contractor is instructed to include work furnished or installed under an allowance. He agrees to have the work done for a particular sum which has been established as an allowance. A detailed description of exactly what will be covered in an allowance is necessary. Does the work include materials furnished, delivered, stored, and installed, or will the general contractor have to include some of these items in his bid? If all information is not included in the allowance which may be included in the instructions to bidders, the agreement, the supplemental general conditions, or the trade sections, the contractor may have the basis for a claim for extras.

Article 42: Uses of Premises. The restrictions and regulations relating to the use of the premises, as given in this article, are the minimum requirements and are stated in broad terms. Directions of the architect to fit a particular project in a given area must be defined in the supplemental general conditions.

Article 43: Cutting and Patching. The prime contractor is responsible for all cutting, fitting, or patching of the work, whether done by persons directly employed by him or under a subcontract. If the exact responsibility for cutting and patching is not defined in the individual trade sections or the supplemental general conditions, this responsibility must be assigned by the prime contractor. If more than one prime contractor is performing work on a project, the responsibility may be assigned by the architect. Each prime contractor is responsible for defective or ill-timed work performed by him. Each contractor is directed not to endanger or alter the work of others without the written consent of the architect.

Article 44: Cleaning up. The terms of this article cover the responsibilities of the contractor for keeping the premises free from an accumulation of rubbish and debris and provide for the final cleanup of the project. Supplemental instructions are usually needed for specific projects.

SUPPLEMENTAL GENERAL CONDITIONS

If a standardized form of general conditions is used, individual projects will usually require additional instructions. This will be true whether general conditions used are the printed forms published by an association or those developed by architects-engineers offices. These additional conditions, which will apply to a major portion of the work, may be called "supplemental general conditions" or "special conditions." The terms "special conditions," "supplemental general conditions," and "supplementary general conditions" are used, to some extent, interchangeably. Supplemental general conditions, as the name implies, cover revisions or supplements to specific articles of the general conditions. Special conditions cover provisions of a general nature, pertaining to a specific project, which are not closely related to any of the articles of the general conditions. As supplemental or additional information to modify the general conditions, they will follow the general conditions in the book of specifications.

Relation to Other Contract Documents. The supplemental general conditions or special conditions must start with a statement defining their relationship to the other contract documents, for example:

1. General: The provisions of the General Conditions are supplemental and are modified by the Special Conditions and are hereby made a part of the Trade Sections of the Specifications with the same force and effect as though fully repeated in each section. Provisions in the Special Conditions supersede any conflicting provisions in the General Conditions or Trade Sections.

or

1. General: The Supplemental General Conditions modify the General Conditions and shall form a part of the contract and all subcontracts.

Some architects and engineers, when they use standard general conditions, do not bind them in each book of specifications. This is a questionable procedure and could be construed as a violation of the rights of the copyright owner of the published general conditions. However, if this procedure is followed, a statement such as that which follows must be inserted in the supplemental general conditions:

Section I—Supplemental General Conditions
1-10. Attention General Contractor and All Subcontractors: General Conditions of the Contract, Standard Form A201, current edition of the American Institute of Architects, pages 1 to 10 inclusive, is hereby made a part of this contract to the same extent as if bound herein. The General Conditions, including these Supplemental General Conditions, shall become a part of the contract and shall apply to the Contractor and all Subcontractors. Copies of the General Conditions may be examined or obtained at the Architect's office.

It might be possible, when this paragraph is used, for a contractor who is constructing a building in Arizona which was designed by a New York architect to claim that the information was not available to him and that he cannot be held to the terms set forth in the general conditions. New bidders are constantly entering the construction field. It is hardly reasonable to ask them and their employees to have memorized all the general conditions that will affect their work.

The use of the words "current edition" in the above quotation is questionable. Does "current edition" mean current during the planning stage of a project, during the construction phase, or during a court procedure after the project is completed? This entire process may cover several years, and a new edition of the documents, published after the job was bid, may have extended the document or given it new meanings. The question is, then, "Exactly what is meant by the word 'current'?" If reference is made to a standardized document, it must be to a specific edition.

Location of the Supplemental General Conditions. The supplemental general conditions may follow the general conditions and be numbered consecutively starting after the last article in the published form. If the AIA general conditions form, which has forty-four articles, is used, the supplemental general conditions will continue with Article 45. This tends to eliminate confusion that could be caused by duplication of article numbers.

Information in Supplemental General Conditions. The supplemental general conditions are written for a specific project and set forth any revisions of the general conditions, for example:

3. Drawings Furnished, Article 4 of the General Conditions, shall be changed to read as follows: "The Architect shall furnish the Contractor free of charge fifteen sets of Drawings and Specifications. The Contractor shall pay the costs of reproduction of additional copies of the Drawings or Specifications."
10. Cleanup, Article 44 of the General Conditions shall be modified as follows: "In addition to the removal of rubbish and leaving the building broom clean, the Contractor shall clean all glass; replace any broken glass; remove stains, spots, marks, and dirt from decorated work; clean hardware; remove paint, spots, and smears from all surfaces; clean fixtures; and wash all concrete and tile floors."

The AIA general conditions have been prepared for use on a contract where a lump sum is used as the basis of bids. If a contract such as a cost-plus or unit-price contract is desired, the supplemental general conditions must modify the general conditions. It would be difficult to enumerate all items that would be needed for all projects. The following checklist was developed by a large firm of architects-engineers and contains supplementary headings to be considered:

Checklist of Supplemental General Conditions. (Not all the following items will be needed on all projects. Additional supplemental or special conditions may be necessary on some projects.)

Extent of project
Legal description of property
Examination of site
Survey, soil reports, certificates
Alterations to existing structures
Future extensions and additions
Time of completion
Progress schedule
Liquidated damages
Definitions
  Owner
  Architect-engineer
  Architect-engineer's representative
Execution, correlation, and intent of documents
List of documents
  Titles
  Pages
Priority of precedence of documents
Modification of documents for cost-plus contracts
Errors or omissions in documents
Dimensions and scaling of drawings
Copies of documents
  Free copies of documents
  Extra copies of documents
  Who may obtain documents, and where
Return of documents
Changes in documents
Changes in work
Extras
Shop drawings
Samples
Substitutions
Options
Alternates
Progress photographs
Signs
Laws
  Permits
  Vault permits
  Local building codes
  National building codes
  State and Federal labor laws
  Agency regulations
  Wage rates
  Prison labor
  Foreign labor
  Foreign materials
Insurance
  Owner's liability
  Contractor's liability
  Subcontractor's liability
  Windstorm
  Lightning

Flood
Earthquake
Vandalism
Loss of use
Extended coverage
Liens
Taxes
  Sales tax
  Excise tax exemption
Job office
  Telephone
  Power
  Light
  Heat
  Drinking water
  Furniture
  Storage of drawings
  Storage of samples
Sanitary facilities
Public utilities
Temporary utilities
  Power
  Light
  Water
  Heat
Use of existing facilities and utilities
Dustproof facilities
Barricades
  Fences
  Overhead protection
  Gates
  Locks
  Painting
  Maintenance
  Warning lights, lanterns
Watchmen
Security checks
Temporary construction
  Stairs
  Ramps
  Ladders
  Lifts
  Guardrails
  Openings
  Scaffolding
  Enclosures
Protection of adjacent property
  Structures
  Sidewalks
  Streets
  Trees
  Shrubs
  Public Property
Protection of adjacent work
Cutting and patching

Bracing, shoring, and underpinning
Storage and delivery of materials
  Access roads
  Sheds
  Protection from weather
  Protection from theft
  Protection from vandalism
  Assignment of storage areas
Layout of work
  Benchmarks
  Levels
  Lines
Stoppage of work
  Rain
  Snow
  Freezing weather
Overtime work
  Night work
  Lights
  Power
  Heat
Safety precautions
  Industrial Accident Commission
  Signs
  Lights
  Smoking regulations
  Protective clothing
Noise and smoke abatement
Test
  Inspections
  Inspectors
  Laboratories
  Reports
  Notices
Architect-engineer's authority and responsibility
Architect-engineer's representative
Owner's authority
Certificates of payment
Payment
Access to property
Owner's use before completion
As-built drawings
Guaranty-warranty
  Time limits
  Forms
  Bonds
  Maintenance
Manufacturer's directions and operating instructions
Cutting and patching
Broken glass
Salvage
Rubbish removal
Special cleaning

The numbering of paragraphs and sections in PART 1, LEGAL & PROCEDURAL DOCUMENTS AND BONDS, PART 2, GENERAL CONDITIONS OF THE CONTRACT, and PART 3, SPECIAL CONDITIONS requires a project organization approximately as indicated by the following index:

CONTRACT DOCUMENTS

For

(TITLE AND LOCATION OF PROJECT)

For

(NAME AND ADDRESS OF OWNER)

When binding the standard Contract Documents of Consulting Engineers Council with other contract documents, this index sheet should be removed.

CONSULTING ENGINEERS COUNCIL
Index To Contract Documents
Copyright 1961 — 1st Printing   1.0

Fig. 9-3. CED Contractor Documents Index and General Conditions of the Contract, 1958 edition (fourteen pages). (By permission of the Consulting Engineers Council.)

GENERAL CONDITIONS OF THE CONTRACT
Copyright 1958
CONSULTING ENGINEERS COUNCIL

SECTION 2.1 DEFINITIONS

2.1.01 CONTRACT DOCUMENTS: The Contract comprises the following documents, including all additions, deletions and modifications incorporated therein before the execution of the Contract:

a. Legal and Procedural Documents
  1. Advertisement
  2. Information for Bidders
  3. Proposal
  4. Proposal Guaranty
  5. Contract
  6. Performance Bond

b. General Conditions of the Contract

c. Detailed Specification Requirements

d. Drawings

2.1.02 ENGINEER is the Engineer named in the Contract Documents or his representative duly authorized in writing to act for the Engineer.

2.1.03 OWNER is the Owner named in the Contract Documents.

2.1.04 CONTRACTOR is the Contractor named in the Contract Documents.

2.1.05 SUB-CONTRACTOR is any person, firm or corporation with a direct contract with the Contractor who acts for or in behalf of the Contractor in executing any part of the Contract, but does not include one who merely furnishes material.

2.1.06 PROPOSAL: The offer of a Bidder to perform the work described by the Contract Documents when made out and submitted on the prescribed Proposal Form, properly signed and guaranteed.

2.1.07 PROPOSAL GUARANTY: The cashier's check or Bidder's bond accompanying the Proposal submitted by the Bidder, as a guaranty that the Bidder will enter into a Contract with the Owner for the construction of the work, if the Contract is awarded to him.

2.1.08 CONTRACT is the agreement covering the performance of the work described in the Contract Documents including all supplemental agreements thereto and all general and special provisions pertaining to the work or materials therefor.

2.1.09 PERFORMANCE BOND is the approved form of security furnished by the Contractor and his Surety as a guaranty of good faith on the part of the Contractor to execute the work in accordance with the terms of the Contract.

2.1.10 SURETY is the person, firm or corporation who executes the Contractor's Performance Bond.

2.1.11 SPECIFICATIONS shall mean the Legal and Procedural Documents, General Conditions of the Contract, together with the modifications thereof, and the Detailed Specification Requirements, with all addenda thereto.

2.1.12 DRAWINGS are those listed in the Index to Specifications and Drawings with all addenda thereto.

2.1.13 WRITTEN NOTICE: Written notice shall be considered as served when delivered in person or sent by registered mail to the individual, firm or corporation or to the last business address of such known to him who serves the notice.

a. Change of Address: It shall be the duty of each party to advise the other parties to the Contract as to any change in his business address until completion of the Contract.

2.1.14 ACT OF GOD means an earthquake, flood, cyclone or other cataclysmic phenomenon of nature. Rain, wind, flood or other natural phenomenon of normal intensity for the locality shall not be construed as an Act of God and no reparation shall be made to the Contractor for damages to the work resulting therefrom.

Fig. 9-3 (Continued.)

SECTION 2.2 DRAWINGS, SPECIFICATIONS AND RELATED DATA

2.2.01 INTENT OF DRAWINGS AND SPECIFICATIONS: The intent of the Drawings and Specifications is that the Contractor furnish all labor and materials, equipment and transportation necessary for the proper execution of the work unless specifically noted otherwise. The Contractor shall do all the work shown on the Drawings and described in the Specifications and all incidental work considered necessary to complete the project in a substantial and acceptable manner, and to fully complete the work or improvement, ready for use, occupancy and operation by the Owner.

2.2.02 CONFLICT: If there be conflicting variance between the Drawings and the Specifications, the provisions of the Specifications shall control. In case of conflict between the General Conditions of the Contract or any modifications thereof and the Detailed Specification Requirements, the Detailed Specification Requirements shall control.

2.2.03 DISCREPANCIES IN DRAWINGS: Any discrepancies found between the Drawings and Specifications and site conditions or any errors or omissions in the Drawings or Specifications shall be immediately reported to the Engineer, who shall promptly correct such error or omission in writing. Any work done by the Contractor after his discovery of such discrepancies, errors or omissions shall be done at the Contractor's risk.

2.2.04 ADEQUACY OF DRAWINGS AND SPECIFICATIONS: Responsibility for adequacy of the design and for sufficiency of the Drawings and Specifications shall be borne by the Owner. The complete requirements of the work to be performed under the Contract shall be set forth in Drawings and Specifications to be supplied by the Owner through the Engineer or by the Engineer as representative of the Owner. Drawings and Specifications furnished shall be in accordance with the Contract Documents and shall be true and accurate developments thereof.

2.2.05 ADDITIONAL INSTRUCTIONS: Further instructions may be issued by the Engineer during the progress of the work by means of Drawings or otherwise to make more clear or specific the Drawings and Specifications or as may be necessary to explain or illustrate changes in the work to be done.

2.2.06 COPIES OF DRAWINGS AND SPECIFICATIONS FURNISHED: Except as provided for otherwise, all required copies of Drawings and Specifications necessary for the execution of the work shall be furnished to the Contractor without charge.

2.2.07 DRAWINGS AND SPECIFICATIONS AT JOB SITE: One complete set of all Drawings and Specifications shall be maintained at the job site and shall be available to the Engineer at all times.

2.2.08 OWNERSHIP OF DRAWINGS AND SPECIFICATIONS: All original or duplicated Drawings and Specifications and other data prepared by the Engineer shall remain the property of the Engineer, and they shall not be re-used on other work, but shall be returned to him upon completion of the work.

2.2.09 DIMENSIONS: Figured dimensions on the plans will be used in preference to scaling the Drawings. Where the work of the Contractor is affected by finish dimensions, these shall be determined by the Contractor at the site, and he shall assume the responsibility therefor.

2.2.10 MODELS: All models prepared for this work shall become the property of the Owner at the completion of the work.

2.2.11 SAMPLES: All samples called for in the Specifications or required by the Engineer shall be furnished by the Contractor and shall be submitted to the Engineer for his approval. Samples shall be furnished so as not to delay fabrication, allowing the Engineer reasonable time for the consideration of the samples submitted.

    a. Samples for Tests: Contractor shall furnish such samples of material as may be required for examination and test. All materials and workmanship shall be in accordance with approved samples. All samples of materials for tests shall be taken according to methods provided in the Specifications.

2.2.12 SHOP DRAWINGS: The Contractor shall provide shop drawings, settings, schedules and such other drawings as may be necessary for the prosecution of the work in the shop and in the field as required by the Drawings, Specifications or Engineer's instructions. Deviations from the Drawings and Specifications shall be called to the attention of the Engineer at the time of the first submission of shop drawings and other drawings for approval. The Engineer's approval of any drawings shall not release the Contractor from responsibility for such deviations. Shop drawings shall be submitted according to the following schedule:

    a. Three copies shall be submitted at least thirty (30) days before the materials indicated thereon are to be needed, or earlier if required to prevent delay of the work.

    b. The Engineer shall, within fourteen (14) days of the submittal of any shop drawings, return one copy to the Contractor marked with all corrections and changes.

CONSULTING ENGINEERS COUNCIL
General Conditions of the Contract
Copyright 1958 — 5th Printing

2.2

Fig. 9-3 (Continued.)

c. The Contractor shall then correct the shop drawings to conform to the corrections and changes requested by the Engineer.

d. Following completion of such corrections and changes, the Contractor shall furnish the Engineer two copies of the shop drawings conforming to the required corrections and changes.

2.2.13 QUALITY OF EQUIPMENT AND MATERIALS: In order to establish standards of quality, the Engineer has, in the detailed Specifications, referred to certain products by name and catalog number. This procedure is not to be construed as eliminating from competition other products of equal or better quality by other manufacturers where fully suitable in design.

a. The Contractor shall furnish the complete list of proposed desired substitutions prior to signing of the Contract, together with such engineering and catalog data as the Engineer may require.

b. The Contractor shall abide by the Engineer's judgment when proposed substitute materials or items of equipment are judged to be unacceptable and shall furnish the specified material or item of equipment in such case. All proposals for substitutions shall be submitted in writing by the General Contractor and not by individual trades or material suppliers. The Engineer will approve or disapprove proposed substitutions in writing within a reasonable time. No substitute materials shall be used unless approved in writing.

2.2.14 EQUIPMENT APPROVAL DATA: The Contractor shall furnish one copy of complete catalog data for every manufactured item of equipment and all components to be used in the work, including specific performance data, material description, rating, capacity, working pressure, material gage or thickness, brand name, catalog number and general type.

a. This submission shall be compiled by the Contractor and approved by the Engineer before any of the equipment is ordered.

b. Each data sheet or catalog in the submission shall be indexed according to specification section and paragraph for easy reference.

c. After written approval, this submission shall become a part of the Contract, and may not be deviated from except upon written approval of the Engineer.

d. Catalog data for equipment approved by the Engineer does not in any case supersede the Engineer's Contract Documents. The approval of the Engineer shall not relieve the Contractor from responsibility for deviations from Drawings or Specifications, unless he has in writing called the Engineer's attention to such deviations at the time of submission, nor shall it relieve him from responsibility for errors of any sort in the items submitted. The Contractor shall check the work described by the catalog data with the Engineer's Contract Documents for deviations and errors.

e. It shall be the responsibility of the Contractor to insure that items to be furnished fit the space available. He shall make necessary field measurements to ascertain space requirements, including those for connections, and shall order such sizes and shapes of equipment that the final installation shall suit the true intent and meaning of the Drawings and Specifications.

f. Where equipment requiring different arrangement of connections from those shown is approved, it shall be the responsibility of the Contractor to install the equipment to operate properly, and in harmony with the intent of the Drawings and Specifications, and to make all changes in the work required by the different arrangement of connections.

2.2.15 SURVEYS: Unless otherwise specified, the Owner shall establish all base lines for the location of the principal component parts of the work together with a suitable number of bench marks adjacent to the work. Based upon the information provided by the Owner, the Contractor shall develop and make all detail surveys necessary for construction, including slope stakes, batter boards, stakes for pile locations and other working points, lines and elevations. The Contractor shall have the responsibility to carefully preserve bench marks, reference points and stakes, and, in the case of destruction thereof by the Contractor or resulting from his negligence, the Contractor shall be charged with the expense and damage resulting therefrom and shall be responsible for any mistakes that may be caused by the unnecessary loss or disturbance of such bench marks, reference points and stakes.

CONSULTING ENGINEERS COUNCIL
General Conditions of the Contract
Copyright 1958 — 5th Printing

2.3

Fig. 9-3 (Continued.)

SECTION 2.3 ENGINEER-OWNER-CONTRACTOR RELATIONS

2.3.01 ENGINEER'S RESPONSIBILITY AND AUTHORITY: All work shall be done under the general supervision of the Engineer. The Engineer shall decide any and all questions which may arise as to the quality and acceptability of materials furnished, work performed, rate of progress of work, interpretation of Drawings and Specifications and all questions as to the acceptable fulfillment of the Contract on the part of the Contractor.

2.3.02 ENGINEER'S DECISIONS: All claims of the Owner or the Contractor shall be presented to the Engineer for decision which shall be made in writing within a reasonable time. All decisions of the Engineer shall be final except in cases where time and/or financial considerations are involved, which shall be subject to arbitration.

2.3.03 SUSPENSION OF WORK: The Engineer shall have the authority to suspend the work, wholly or in part, for such period or periods, as he may deem necessary, due to unsuitable weather, or such other conditions as are considered unfavorable for prosecution of the work, or failure on the part of the Contractor to carry out the provisions of the Contract or to supply materials meeting the requirements of the Specifications. The Contractor shall not suspend operation without the Engineer's permission.

2.3.04 ARBITRATION: Should there be any dispute or any questioned decision of the Engineer which is subject to arbitration, it shall be promptly submitted to arbitration upon demand by either party to the dispute. The Contractor shall not delay the work because arbitration proceedings are pending unless he shall have written permission from the Engineer so to do and such delay shall not extend beyond the time when the arbitrators shall have opportunity to determine whether the work shall continue or be suspended pending decision by the arbitrators of such a dispute. Any demand for arbitration shall be in writing and shall be delivered to the Engineer and any adverse party either by personal delivery or by registered mail addressed to the last known address of each within ten (10) days of receipt of the Engineer's decision, and in no event after final payment has been made and accepted, subject, however, to any express stipulation to the contrary in the Contract Documents. Should the Engineer fail within a reasonable period to make a decision, a demand for arbitration may then be made as if the Engineer's decision had been rendered against the party demanding arbitration.

    a. No one shall be qualified to act as an arbitrator who has, directly or indirectly, any financial interest in the Contract or who has any business or family relationship with the Owner, the Contractor, or the Engineer. Each arbitrator selected shall be qualified by experience and knowledge of the work involved in the matter to be submitted to arbitration.

    b. Arbitration shall be in accordance with the procedure and standards of The American Arbitration Association.

2.3.05 INSPECTION OF WORK: All materials and each part or detail of the work shall be subject at all times to inspection by the Engineer, and the Contractor will be held strictly to the true intent of the Specifications in regard to quality of materials, workmanship, and the diligent execution of the Contract. Such inspection may include mill, plant, or shop inspection, and any material furnished under these Specifications is subject to such inspection. The Engineer shall be allowed access to all parts of the work and shall be furnished with such information and assistance by the Contractor as is required to make a complete and detailed inspection.

2.3.06 EXAMINATION OF COMPLETED WORK: If the Engineer requests it, the Contractor at any time before acceptance of the work shall remove or uncover such portions of the finished work as may be directed. After examination, the Contractor shall restore said portions of the work to the standard required by the Specifications. Should the work thus exposed or examined prove acceptable, the uncovering or removing, and the replacing of the covering or making good of the parts removed shall be paid for as Extra Work, but should the work so exposed or examined prove unacceptable, the uncovering, removing and replacing shall be at the Contractor's expense.

2.3.07 CONTRACTOR'S SUPERINTENDENCE: A qualified superintendent, who is acceptable to the Engineer, shall be maintained on the work and give efficient supervision to the work until its completion. The superintendent shall have full authority to act in behalf of the Contractor, and all directions given to the superintendent shall be considered given to the Contractor. In general, the Engineer's instructions shall be confirmed in writing and always upon written request from the Contractor.

2.3.08 LANDS BY OWNER: The Owner shall provide the lands shown on the Drawings upon which the work under the Contract is to be performed and to be used for rights of way for access. Any delay in furnishing these lands by the Owner shall be deemed proper cause for adjustment in the Contract Amount and in the time of completion.

CONSULTING ENGINEERS COUNCIL
General Conditions of the Contract
Copyright 1958 — 5th Printing

2.4

Fig. 9-3 (Continued.)

2.3.09 LANDS BY CONTRACTOR: Any additional land and access thereto not shown on the Drawings that may be required for temporary construction facilities or for storage of materials shall be provided by the Contractor with no liability to the Owner. The Contractor shall confine his apparatus and storage of materials and operation of his workmen to those areas described in the Drawings and Specifications and such additional areas which he may provide as approved by the Engineer.

2.3.10 PRIVATE PROPERTY: The Contractor shall not enter upon private property for any purpose without obtaining permission, and he shall be responsible for the preservation of all public property, trees, monuments, etc. along and adjacent to the street and/or right-of-way, and shall use every precaution necessary to prevent damage or injury thereto. He shall use suitable precautions to prevent damage to pipes, conduits, and other underground structures, and shall protect carefully from disturbance or damage all monuments and property marks until an authorized agent has witnessed or otherwise referenced their location and shall not remove them until directed.

2.3.11 ASSIGNMENT OF CONTRACT: Neither the Contractor nor the Owner shall sublet, sell, transfer, assign or otherwise dispose of the Contract or any portion thereof, or of his right, title or interest therein, or his obligations thereunder, without written consent of the other party.

2.3.12 REMOVAL OF CONSTRUCTION EQUIPMENT, TOOLS AND SUPPLIES: At the termination of this Contract, before acceptance of the work by the Engineer, the Contractor shall remove all of his equipment, tools and supplies from the property of the Owner. Should the Contractor fail to remove such equipment, tools, and supplies, the Owner shall have the right to remove them.

2.3.13 SUSPENSION OF WORK BY OWNER: The work or any portion thereof may be suspended at any time by the Owner provided that he gives the Contractor five (5) days' written notice of suspension, which shall set forth the date on which work is to be resumed. The Contractor shall resume the work upon written notice from the Owner and within ten (10) days after the date set forth in the notice of suspension. If the Owner does not give written notice to resume work within ten (10) days of the date fixed in the notice of suspension, the Contractor may abandon that portion of the work so suspended and shall be entitled to payment in accordance with Paragraph 2.7.11.

2.3.14 OWNER'S RIGHT TO CORRECT DEFICIENCIES: Upon failure of the Contractor to perform the work in accordance with the Contract Documents, including any requirements with respect to the Schedule of Completion, and after five (5) days' written notice to the Contractor and receipt of written approval from the Engineer, the Owner may, without prejudice to any other remedy he may have, correct such deficiencies.

2.3.15 OWNER'S RIGHT TO TERMINATE CONTRACT AND COMPLETE THE WORK: The Owner shall have the right to terminate the employment of the Contractor after giving ten (10) days' written notice of termination to the Contractor in the event of any default by the Contractor and upon receiving written notice from the Engineer certifying cause for such action. In the event of such termination, the Owner may take possession of the work and of all materials, tools and equipment thereon and may finish the work by whatever method and means he may select. It shall be considered a default by the Contractor whenever he shall:

a. Declare bankruptcy, become insolvent, or assign his assets for the benefit of his creditors.

b. Disregard or violate important provisions of the Contract Documents or Engineer's instructions, or fail to prosecute the work according to the agreed Schedule of Completion, including extensions thereof.

c. Fail to provide a qualified superintendent, competent workmen or sub-contractors, or proper materials, or fail to make prompt payment therefor.

2.3.16 CONTRACTOR'S RIGHT TO SUSPEND WORK OR TERMINATE CONTRACT: The Contractor may suspend work or terminate Contract upon ten (10) days' written notice to the Owner and the Engineer, for any of the following reasons:

a. If an order of any court, or other public authority caused the work to be stopped or suspended for a period of ninety (90) days through no act or fault of the Contractor or his employees.

b. If the Engineer should fail to act upon any Request for Payment within ten (10) days after it is presented in accordance with the General Conditions of the Contract.

c. If the Owner should fail to act upon any Request for Payment within thirty (30) days after its approval by the Engineer.

d. If the Owner should fail to pay the Contractor any sum within thirty (30) days after its award by arbitrators.

CONSULTING ENGINEERS COUNCIL
General Conditions of the Contract
Copyright 1958 — 5th Printing

2.5

Fig. 9-3 (Continued.)

2.3.17 RIGHTS OF VARIOUS INTERESTS: Wherever work being done by the Owner's forces or by other contractors is contiguous to work covered by this Contract, the respective rights of the various interests involved shall be established by the Engineer, to secure the completion of the various portions of the work in general harmony.

2.3.18 SEPARATE CONTRACTS: The Owner may let other contracts in connection with the work of the Contractor. The Contractor shall cooperate with other Contractors with regard to storage of materials and execution of their work. It shall be the Contractor's responsibility to inspect all work by other Contractors affecting his work and to report to the Engineer any irregularities which will not permit him to complete his work in a satisfactory manner. His failure to notify the Engineer of such irregularities shall indicate the work of other Contractors has been satisfactorily completed to receive his work. The Contractor shall not be responsible for defects of which he could not have known, which develop in the work of others after the work is completed. It shall be the responsibility of the Contractor to measure the completed work in place and report to the Engineer immediately any difference between completed work by others and the Drawings.

2.3.19 SUB-CONTRACTS: At the time specified by the Contract Documents or when requested by the Engineer, the Contractor shall submit in writing to the Owner for approval of the Engineer the names of the sub-contractors proposed for the work. Sub-contractors may not be changed except at the request or with the approval of the Engineer. The Contractor is responsible to the Owner for the acts and omissions of his sub-contractors, and of their direct and indirect employees, to the same extent as he is responsible for the acts and omissions of his employees. The Contract Documents shall not be construed as creating any contractual relation between any sub-contractor and the Owner. The Contractor shall bind every sub-contractor by the terms of the Contract Documents.

a. For convenience of reference and to facilitate the letting of Contracts and sub-contracts, the Specifications are separated into titled sections. Such separations shall not, however, operate to make the Engineer an arbiter to establish limits to the contracts between Contractor and sub-contractors.

2.3.20 WORK DURING AN EMERGENCY: The Contractor shall perform any work and shall furnish and install any materials and equipment necessary during an emergency endangering life or property. In all cases he shall notify the Engineer of the emergency as soon as practicable, but he shall not wait for instructions before proceeding to properly protect both life and property.

2.3.21 ORAL AGREEMENTS: No oral order, objection, claim or notice by any party to the others shall affect or modify any of the terms or obligations contained in any of the Contract Documents, and none of the provisions of the Contract Documents shall be held to be waived or modified by reason of any act whatsoever, other than by a definitely agreed waiver or modification thereof in writing, and no evidence shall be introduced in any proceeding of any other waiver or modification.

CONSULTING ENGINEERS COUNCIL
General Conditions of the Contract
Copyright 1958 — 5th Printing

2.6

Fig. 9-3 (Continued.)

SECTION 2.4 MATERIALS AND WORKMANSHIP

2.4.01 MATERIALS FURNISHED BY THE CONTRACTOR: All materials used in the work shall meet the requirements of the respective Specifications, and no material shall be used until it has been approved by the Engineer. All materials not otherwise specifically indicated shall be furnished by the Contractor.

2.4.02 MATERIALS FURNISHED BY THE OWNER: Materials specifically indicated shall be furnished by the Owner. The fact that the Owner is to furnish material is conclusive evidence of its acceptability for the purpose intended, and the Contractor may continue to use it until otherwise directed. If the Contractor discovers any defect in material furnished by the Owner, he shall notify the Engineer. Unless otherwise noted or specifically stated, materials furnished by the Owner, which are not of local occurrence, are considered to be f.o.b. the nearest railroad station. The Contractor shall be prepared to unload and properly protect all such material from damage or loss. The Contractor shall be responsible for material loss or damage after receipt of material at the point of delivery.

2.4.03 STORAGE OF MATERIALS: Materials shall be so stored as to insure the preservation of their quality and fitness for the work. When considered necessary, they shall be placed on wooden platforms or other hard, clean surfaces, and not on the ground, and/or they shall be placed under cover. Stored materials shall be located so as to facilitate prompt inspection. Private property shall not be used for storage purposes without the written permission of the owner or lessee.

2.4.04 CHARACTER OF WORKMEN: The Contractor shall at all times be responsible for the conduct and discipline of his employees and/or any sub-contractor or persons employed by sub-contractors. All workmen must have sufficient knowledge, skill, and experience to perform properly the work assigned to them. Any foreman or workman employed by the Contractor or sub-contractor who, in the opinion of the Engineer, does not perform his work in a skillful manner, or appears to be incompetent or to act in a disorderly or intemperate manner shall, at the written request of the Engineer, be discharged immediately and shall not be employed again in any portion of the work without the approval of the Engineer.

2.4.05 REJECTED WORK AND MATERIALS: All materials which do not conform to the requirements of the Contract Documents, are not equal to samples approved by the Engineer, or are in any way unsatisfactory or unsuited to the purpose for which they are intended, shall be rejected. Any defective work whether the result of poor workmanship, use of defective materials, damage through carelessness or any other cause shall be removed within ten (10) days after written notice is given by the Engineer, and the work shall be re-executed by the Contractor. The fact that the Engineer may have previously overlooked such defective work shall not constitute an acceptance of any part of it.

    a. Should the Contractor fail to remove rejected work or materials within ten (10) days after written notice to do so, the Owner may remove them and may store the materials.

    b. Correction of Faulty Work After Final Payment shall be in accordance with Paragraph 2.7.19.

2.4.06 MANUFACTURER'S DIRECTIONS: Manufactured articles, material and equipment shall be applied, installed, connected, erected, used, cleaned and conditioned as directed by the manufacturer unless herein specified to the contrary.

2.4.07 CUTTING AND PATCHING: The Contractor shall do all necessary cutting and patching of the work that may be required to properly receive the work of the various trades or as required by the Drawings and Specifications to complete the structure. He shall restore all such cut or patched work as directed by the Engineer. Cutting of existing structure that shall endanger the work, adjacent property, workmen or the public shall not be done unless approved by the Engineer and under his direction.

2.4.08 CLEANING UP: The Contractor shall remove from the Owner's property, and from all public and private property, all temporary structures, rubbish, and waste materials resulting from his operation or caused by his employees, and shall remove all surplus materials leaving the site smooth, clean and true to line and grade.

2.4.09 GUARANTY PERIOD: The Contractor shall warrant all equipment furnished and work performed by him for a period of one year from the date of written acceptance of the work.

    a. Correction of Faulty Work After Final Payment shall be as provided in Paragraph 2.7.19.

CONSULTING ENGINEERS COUNCIL
General Conditions of the Contract
Copyright 1958 — 5th Printing

Fig. 9-3 (Continued.)

SECTION 2.5 INSURANCE, LEGAL RESPONSIBILITY AND PUBLIC SAFETY

2.5.01 INSURANCE: The Contractor shall secure and maintain such insurance from an insurance company authorized to write casualty insurance in the State where the work is located as will protect himself, his sub-contractors, and the Owner from claims for bodily injury, death or property damage which may arise from operations under this Contract. The Contractor shall not commence work under this Contract until he has obtained all insurance required under this paragraph and shall have filed the certificate of insurance or the certified copy of the insurance policy with the Owner. Each insurance policy shall contain a clause providing that it shall not be cancelled by the insurance company without ten (10) days' written notice to the Owner of intention to cancel. The amounts of such insurance shall be not less than the following:

    a. Workmen's Compensation and Employer's Liability Insurance shall be secured and maintained as required by the State where the work is located.

    b. Public Liability, Bodily Injury, and Property Damage:
        1. Injury or death of one person: ....$ 50,000
        2. Injury to more than one person in a single accident: $200,000
        3. Property damage: ....$ 50,000

    c. Automobile and Truck Public Liability, Bodily Injury, and Property Damage:
        1. Injury or death of one person: ....$ 50,000
        2. Injury to more than one person in a single accident: $200,000
        3. Property damage: ....$ 50,000

2.5.02 INDEMNITY: The Contractor shall indemnify and save harmless the Owner from and against all losses and all claims, demands, payments, suits, actions, recoveries and judgments of every nature and description brought or recovered against him by reason of any omission or act of the Contractor his agents or employees, in the execution of the work or in the guarding of it. The Contractor shall obtain in the name of the Owner and shall maintain and pay the premiums for such insurance in such amount and with such provisions as will protect the Owner from contingent liability under this Contract and a copy of such insurance policy or policies shall be delivered to the Owner. Full compliance by the Owner with the terms and provisions of such insurance policy or policies shall be a condition precedent to the Owner's right to enforce against the Contractor any provisions of this article.

2.5.03 FIRE INSURANCE: In addition to such Fire Insurance as the Contractor elects to carry for his own protection, he shall secure and maintain in the name of the Owner policies upon such structures and material and in such amounts as shall be designated in SECTION 2.8—MODIFICATIONS OF THE GENERAL CONDITIONS. The policies shall be secured from a company which is satisfactory to the Owner and delivered to the Owner.

2.5.04 PERFORMANCE BOND: The Contractor shall, at the time of his execution of the Contract, furnish a corporate surety bond in the sum equal to the Contract Amount. The form of the bond shall be as the Owner may prescribe and with a Surety Company authorized to do business in the State where the work is located.

2.5.05 PATENTS AND ROYALTIES: If any design, device, material or process covered by letters patent or copyright is used by the Contractor, he shall provide for such use by legal agreement with the owner of the patent or a duly authorized licensee of such owner, and shall save harmless the Owner from any and all loss or expense on account thereof, including its use by the Owner.

2.5.06 PERMITS: All permits and licenses necessary for the prosecution of the work shall be secured by the Contractor.

2.5.07 LAWS TO BE OBSERVED: The Contractor shall give all notices and comply with all Federal, State and local laws, ordinances and regulations in any manner affecting the conduct of the work, and all such orders and decrees as exist, or may be enacted by bodies or tribunals having any jurisdiction or authority over the work, and shall indemnify and save harmless the Owner against any claim or liability arising from, or based on, the violation of any such law, ordinance, regulation, order or decree, whether by himself or his employees.

2.5.08 WARNING SIGNS AND BARRICADES: The Contractor shall provide adequate signs, barricades, red lights and watchmen and take all necessary precautions for the protection of the work and the safety of the public. All barricades and obstructions shall be protected at night by red signal lights which shall be kept burning from sunset to sunrise. Barricades shall be of substantial construction and shall be painted white or whitewashed to increase their visibility at night. Suitable warning signs shall be so placed and illuminated at night as to show in advance where construction, barricades, or detours exist.

CONSULTING ENGINEERS COUNCIL
General Conditions of the Contract
Copyright 1958 — 5th Printing

2.8

Fig. 9-3 (Continued.)

2.5.09 PUBLIC SAFETY AND CONVENIENCE: The Contractor shall at all times so conduct his work as to insure the least possible obstruction to traffic and inconvenience to the general public and the residents in the vicinity of the work, and to insure the protection of persons and property in a manner satisfactory to the Engineer. No road or street shall be closed to the public except with the permission of the Engineer and proper governmental authority. Fire hydrants on or adjacent to the work shall be kept accessible to fire-fighting equipment at all times. Temporary provisions shall be made by the Contractor to insure the use of sidewalks and the proper functioning of all gutters, sewer inlets, drainage ditches, and irrigation ditches, which shall not be obstructed except as approved by the Engineer.

2.5.10 CROSSING UTILITIES: When new construction crosses highways, railroads, streets or utilities under the jurisdiction of State, County, City or other public agency, public utility or private entity, the Contractor shall secure written permission from the proper authority before executing such new construction. A copy of this written permission must be filed with the Owner before any work is done. The Contractor will be required to furnish a release from the proper authority before final acceptance of the work.

2.5.11 SANITARY PROVISIONS: The Contractor shall provide and maintain such sanitary accommodations for the use of his employees and those of his sub-contractors as may be necessary to comply with the requirements and regulations of the local and State departments of health and as directed by the Engineer.

CONSULTING ENGINEERS COUNCIL
General Conditions of the Contract
Copyright 1958 — 5th Printing

2.9

Fig. 9-3 (Continued.)

SECTION 2.6 PROGRESS AND COMPLETION OF WORK

2.6.01 NOTICE TO PROCEED: Following the execution of the Contract by the Owner, written Notice to Proceed with the work shall be given to the Contractor. The Contractor shall begin and shall prosecute the work regularly and uninterruptedly thereafter (unless otherwise directed in writing by the Owner) with such force as to secure the completion of the work within the time stated in the Proposal.

2.6.02 CONTRACT TIME: The Contractor shall complete, in an acceptable manner, all of the work contracted for in the time stated in the Proposal. Computation of Contract Time shall commence on the seventh (7th) day following the date of mailing, by regular mail, of the Notice to Proceed and every calendar day following, except as herein provided, shall be counted as a working day.

2.6.03 SCHEDULE OF COMPLETION: The Contractor shall submit, at such times as may reasonably be requested by the Engineer, schedules which shall show the order in which the Contractor proposes to carry on the work, with dates at which the Contractor will start the several parts of the work, and estimated dates of completion of the several parts.

2.6.04 CHANGES IN THE WORK: The Owner may, as the need arises, order changes in the work through additions, deletions or modifications without invalidating the Contract. Compensation and time of completion affected by the change shall be adjusted at the time of ordering such change.

2.6.05 EXTRA WORK: New and unforeseen items of work found to be necessary and which cannot be covered by any item or combination of items for which there is a Contract price shall be classed as Extra Work. The Contractor shall do such Extra Work and furnish such materials as may be required for the proper completion or construction of the whole work contemplated upon written order from the Owner as approved by the Engineer. In the absence of such written order, no claim for Extra Work shall be considered. Extra Work shall be performed in accordance with these Specifications where applicable and work not covered by the Specifications or special provisions shall be done in accordance with the best practice as approved by the Engineer. Extra Work required in an emergency to protect life and property shall be performed by the Contractor as required.

2.6.06 EXTENSION OF CONTRACT TIME: A delay beyond the Contractor's control occasioned by an Act of God, or act or omission on the part of the Owner or by strikes, lockouts, fire, etc., may entitle the Contractor to an extension of time in which to complete the work as determined by the Engineer, provided, however, that the Contractor shall immediately give written notice to the Engineer of the cause of such delay.

2.6.07 USE OF COMPLETED PORTIONS: The Owner shall have the right to take possession of and use any completed or partially completed portions of the work, notwithstanding that the time for completing the entire work or such portions may not have expired; but such taking possession and use shall not be deemed an acceptance of any work not completed in accordance with the Contract Documents. If such prior use increases the cost of or delays the completion of uncompleted work or causes refinishing of completed work, the Contractor shall be entitled to such extra compensation, or extension of time or both, as the Engineer may determine.

CONSULTING ENGINEERS COUNCIL
General Conditions of the Contract
Copyright 1958 — 5th Printing

2.10

Fig. 9-3 (Continued.)

SECTION 2.7 MEASUREMENT AND PAYMENT

2.7.01 DETAILED BREAKDOWN OF CONTRACT AMOUNT: Except in cases where unit prices form the basis for payment under the Contract, the Contractor shall within ten (10) days of receipt of Notice to Proceed, submit a complete breakdown of the Contract Amount showing the value assigned to each part of the work, including an allowance for profit and overhead. Upon approval of the breakdown of the Contract Amount by the Engineer, it shall be used as the basis for all Requests for Payment.

2.7.02 REQUESTS FOR PAYMENT: The Contractor may submit periodically but not more than once each month a Request for Payment for work done and materials delivered and stored on the site. The Contractor shall furnish the Engineer all reasonable facilities required for obtaining the necessary information relative to the progress and execution of the work. Payment for materials stored on the site will be conditioned upon evidence submitted to establish the Owner's title to such materials. Each Request for Payment shall be computed from the work completed on all items listed in the Detailed Breakdown of Contract Amount, less 10% to be retained until final completion and acceptance of the work, and less previous payments. Where unit prices are specified, the Request for Payment shall be based on the quantities completed.

2.7.03 ENGINEER'S ACTION ON A REQUEST FOR PAYMENT: Within ten (10) days of submission of any Request for Payment by the Contractor, the Engineer shall:

   a. Approve the Request for Payment as submitted.

   b. Approve such other amount as he shall decide is due the Contractor, informing the Contractor in writing of his reasons for approving the amended amount.

   c. Withhold the Request for Payment, informing the Contractor in writing of his reasons for withholding it.

2.7.04 OWNER'S ACTION ON AN APPROVED REQUEST FOR PAYMENT: Within thirty (30) days from the date of approval of a Request for Payment by the Engineer, the Owner shall:

   a. Pay the Request for Payment as approved.

   b. Pay such other amount in accordance with Paragraph 2.7.05 as he shall decide is due the Contractor, informing the Contractor and the Engineer in writing of his reasons for paying the amended amount.

   c. Withhold payment in accordance with Paragraph 2.7.05 informing the Contractor and the Engineer of his reasons for withholding payment.

2.7.05 OWNER'S RIGHT TO WITHHOLD PAYMENT OF AN APPROVED REQUEST FOR PAYMENT: The Owner may withhold payment in whole or in part on an approved Request for Payment to the extent necessary to protect himself from loss on account of any of the following causes discovered subsequent to approval of a Request for Payment by the Engineer:

   a. Defective work.

   b. Evidence indicating the probable filing of claims by other parties against the Contractor.

   c. Failure of the Contractor to make payments to sub-contractors, material suppliers or labor.

   d. Damage to another contractor.

2.7.06 INTEREST ON UNPAID REQUESTS FOR PAYMENT: Should the Owner fail to pay an approved Request for Payment within thirty (30) days from the date of approval by the Engineer, and should he fail to inform the Engineer and the Contractor in writing of his reasons for withholding payment, the Owner shall pay the Contractor interest on the amount of the Request for Payment at the rate of six per cent (6%) per annum until payment is made.

2.7.07 RESPONSIBILITY OF THE CONTRACTOR: Unless specifically noted otherwise, the Contractor shall furnish all materials and services and perform all the work described by the Contract Documents or shall have all materials and services furnished and all the work performed at his expense. It shall be the Contractor's responsibility to pay for:

   a. Replacement of survey bench marks, reference points and stakes provided by the Owner under Paragraph 2.2.15.

   b. Lands by Contractor provided in accordance with Paragraph 2.3.09.

   c. Insurance obtained in accordance with Paragraphs 2.5.01 and 2.5.02.

   d. Fire Insurance obtained in accordance with Paragraph 2.5.03.

   e. Performance Bond obtained in accordance with Paragraph 2.5.04.

   f. Royalties required under Paragraph 2.5.05.

   g. Permits and Licenses required of the Contractor and all sub-contractors.

CONSULTING ENGINEERS COUNCIL
General Conditions of the Contract
Copyright 1958 — 5th Printing

2.11

Fig. 9-3 (Continued.)

2.7.08 PAYMENT FOR UNCORRECTED WORK: Should the Engineer direct the Contractor not to correct work that has been damaged or that was not performed in accordance with the Contract Documents, an equitable deduction from the Contract Amount shall be made to compensate the Owner for the uncorrected work.

2.7.09 PAYMENT FOR REJECTED WORK AND MATERIALS: The removal of work and materials rejected under Paragraph 2.4.05 and the re-execution of acceptable work by the Contractor shall be at the expense of the Contractor, and he shall pay the cost of replacing the work of other contractors destroyed or damaged by the removal of the rejected work or materials and the subsequent replacement of acceptable work.

    a. Removal of rejected work or materials and storage of materials by the Owner in accordance with Paragraph 2.4.05 shall be paid by the Contractor within thirty (30) days after written notice to pay is given by the Owner. If the Contractor does not pay the expenses of such removal and after ten (10) days' written notice being given by the Owner of his intent to sell the materials, the Owner may sell the materials at auction or at private sale and shall pay to the Contractor the net proceeds therefrom after deducting all the costs and expenses that should have been borne by the Contractor.

2.7.10 PAYMENTS FOR EXTRA WORK: Written notice of claims for payments for Extra Work shall be given by the Contractor within ten (10) days after receipt of instructions from the Owner as approved by the Engineer to proceed with the Extra Work and also before any work is commenced, except in emergency endangering life or property. No claim shall be valid unless so made. In all cases, the Contractor's itemized estimate sheets showing all labor and material shall be submitted to the Engineer. The Owner's order for Extra Work shall specify any extension of the Contract Time and one of the following methods of payment:

    a. Unit prices or combinations of unit prices which formed the basis of the original Contract.

    b. A lump sum based on the Contractor's estimate, accepted by the Owner, and approved by the Engineer.

    c. Actual cost plus 15% for overhead and profit.

2.7.11 PAYMENT FOR WORK SUSPENDED BY THE OWNER: If the work or any part thereof shall be suspended by the Owner and abandoned by the Contractor as provided in Paragraph 2.3.13, the Contractor will then be entitled to payment for all work done on the portions so abandoned, plus 15% of the value of the abandoned work to compensate for overhead, plant expense, and anticipated profit.

2.7.12 PAYMENT FOR WORK BY THE OWNER: The cost of the work performed by the Owner in removing construction equipment, tools and supplies in accordance with Paragraph 2.3.12 and in correcting deficiencies in accordance with Paragraph 2.3.14 shall be paid by the Contractor.

2.7.13 PAYMENT FOR WORK BY THE OWNER FOLLOWING HIS TERMINATION OF THE CONTRACT: Upon termination of the Contract by the Owner in accordance with Paragraph 2.3.15, no further payments shall be due the Contractor until the work is completed. If the unpaid balance of the Contract Amount shall exceed the cost of completing the work including all overhead costs, the excess shall be paid to the Contractor. If the cost of completing the work shall exceed the unpaid balance, the Contractor shall pay the difference to the Owner. The cost incurred by the Owner, as herein provided, and the damage incurred through the Contractor's default, shall be certified by the Owner, and approved by the Engineer.

2.7.14 PAYMENT FOR WORK TERMINATED BY THE CONTRACTOR: Upon suspension of the work or termination of the Contract by the Contractor in accordance with Paragraph 2.3.16, the Contractor shall recover payment from the Owner for the work performed, plus loss on plant and materials, plus established profit and damages, as approved by the Engineer.

2.7.15 PAYMENT FOR SAMPLES AND TESTING OF MATERIALS: Samples furnished in accordance with Paragraph 2.2.11 shall be furnished by the Contractor at his expense.

    a. Testing of samples and materials furnished in accordance with Paragraph 2.2.11 shall be arranged and paid for by the Owner.

2.7.16 RELEASE OF LIENS: The Contractor shall deliver to the Owner a complete release of all liens arising out of this Contract before the retained percentage or before the final Request for Payment is paid. If any lien remains unsatisfied after all payments are made, the Contractor shall refund to the Owner such amounts as the Owner may have been compelled to pay in discharging such liens including all costs and a reasonable attorney's fee.

CONSULTING ENGINEERS COUNCIL
General Conditions of the Contract
Copyright 1958 — 5th Printing

2.12

Fig. 9-3 (Continued.)

2.7.17 ACCEPTANCE AND FINAL PAYMENT: When the Contractor shall have completed the work in accordance with the terms of the Contract Documents, the Engineer shall certify his acceptance to the Owner and his approval of the Contractor's final Request for Payment, which shall be the Contract Amount plus all approved additions less all approved deductions and less previous payments made. The Contractor shall furnish evidence that he has fully paid all debts for labor, materials, and equipment incurred in connection with the work, following which the Owner shall accept the work and release the Contractor except as to the conditions of the Performance Bond, any legal rights of the Owner, required guarantees, and Correction of Faulty Work after Final Payment, and shall authorize payment of the Contractor's final Request for Payment. The Contractor must allow sufficient time between the time of completion of the work and approval of the final Request for Payment for the Engineer to assemble and check the necessary data.

2.7.18 TERMINATION OF CONTRACTOR'S RESPONSIBLITY: The Contract will be considered complete when all work has been finished, the final inspection made by the Engineer, and the project accepted in writing by the Owner. The Contractor's responsibility shall then cease, except as set forth in his Performance Bond, as required by the Guaranty Period in accordance with Paragraph 2.4.09 and as provided in Paragraph 2.7.19.

2.7.19 CORRECTION OF FAULTY WORK AFTER FINAL PAYMENT: The approval of the final Request for Payment by the Engineer and the making of the final payment by the Owner to the Contractor shall not relieve the Contractor of responsibility for faulty materials or workmanship. The Owner shall promptly give notice of faulty materials or workmanship and the Contractor shall promptly replace any such defects discovered within one year from the date of written acceptance of the work. The Engineer shall decide all questions arising under this paragraph, and all such decisions shall be subject to arbitration.

CONSULTING ENGINEERS COUNCIL
General Conditions of the Contract
Copyright 1958 — 5th Printing

2.13

Fig. 9-3 (Continued.)

QUESTIONS

1. What are standard general conditions?
2. What are some of the advantages in the use of standard general conditions?
3. Name four important types of insurance.
4. Who are the principals in a three-man arbitration committee?
5. Who pays the premium for a guaranty bond covering faithful performance of the contract if the bond is required by instructions given subsequent to the submission of bids?
6. What is the relationship of special conditions to general conditions?

10 Trade Sections

The trade section describes a certain part of the construction project that would be difficult to show in working drawings. It gives information in the following order:

1. The relation of the particular trade section to all other sections
2. What is to be installed
3. How it will be installed
4. Where it is to be installed
5. Controls

PART OF THE CONTRACT DOCUMENTS

The trade sections are made part of the contract documents under the simple term "specifications." This is spelled out in Article 6 of AIA Form A-1, Form of Agreement for Use When a Stipulated Sum Forms the Basis of Payment [1] "Article 6. THE CONTRACT DOCUMENTS--The General Conditions of Contract, the Specifications and the Drawings, together with this Agreement, form the contract, and they are fully a part of the Contract as if hereto attached or herein repeated."

Responsibilities. The specifications are listed along with the other contract documents, and it is the contractor's responsibility to read them and know their contents before he signs the agreement with the owner. It is the architect's responsibility to identify all the documents when the agreement is signed in order that there will be no misunderstanding at a later date. If any part of the project is omitted or not fully described, Article 2 of the general conditions spells out the intent of the documents: "Article 2. EXECUTION, CORRELATION AND INTENT OF DOCUMENTS—The Contract Documents shall be signed in duplicate by the Owner and the Contractor. In case either the Owner or Contractor or both fail to sign the General Conditions, Drawings or Specifications, the Architect shall identify them."

This article of the general conditions also covers the use of technical language and definitions in the trade sections.

[1] By permission of the American Institute of Architects.

Relationship to General Conditions. A statement is usually made at the beginning of each trade section tying that particular section to all the general conditions. Such a statement, appearing at the beginning of each trade section, has been held in some cases to be as valid as if the entire general conditions were repeated herein.

Article 2 of the AIA general conditions states that "the General Conditions shall be made a part of each section of the Specifications." To rely on each subcontractor bidding on a portion of a construction project to read this statement and fully understand its implications is not a safe procedure. This danger is further complicated by the widespread practice of some prime contractors of splitting up a book of specifications and giving each subbidder only those parts related to his work. It is questionable, under these circumstances, whether the subcontractor could be expected to know the contents of the general conditions and be bound by them. In a recent court case in California, it was held that the subcontractor was not bound by the general conditions in that it was proved that the prime contractor had not furnished the subcontractor a copy of the general conditions or specifically warned him of this clause and its effect on his work. The elimination of this phase from the trade sections could result in litigation between the subcontractor and the contractor or liens filed against the owner and could be very costly to the owner.

Relationship to Special Conditions. The relationship between the trade sections and any special conditions of the contract documents should be very carefully considered. Each job has its special conditions, and these should be checked very carefully for their effect on each trade section. Trade sections from former jobs should be checked carefully against any special conditions before they are considered as guides for writing trade sections for a new job.

Relationship to Drawings. The drawings are complementary to the trade sections.

Anything shown on the drawings and not described in a trade section is considered as though it were both shown and described. Although Article 2 of the AIA general conditions defines this as binding, the selection of information to be shown on the drawings and that which is to be included in the trade section is very important. A policy should be set up in every office to be followed consistently in each section of the work. Information included in a trade section should not be duplicated on the drawings. Information shown on the drawings should not duplicate that which is in the specifications. A specification is a bill of particulars, and the trade section should be an amplification and extension of the drawings. Duplication in a trade section of material on the drawings can easily lead to contradictions and confusion. A bidder can only assume that this condition will be carried over on the job, and he will make his bid higher to take care of this eventuality. This makes for higher costs to the owner and leads to misunderstandings.

FORMAT FOR TRADE SECTIONS

Each trade section of a set of specifications should follow the same general outline or format. Uniformity in the presentation of the necessary information is important for several reasons: (1) The specifications writer, in following a definite procedure, is less likely to overlook items of information that should be included; (2) the contractor and estimator will soon become acquainted with the general arrangement of each trade section and will be able to find specific information quickly; and (3) the guide specification can be used as a checklist during the design stage of the project.

SPECIFICATION GUIDES

Following is an example of a guide prepared for the specifications writers of a large office handling all phases of building design, including civil, structural, mechanical, and architectural design:

In order to present a uniform appearance of all sections of our specifications, the specifications section has prepared a guide to assist those who are preparing the individual sections. We believe the use of this format will save time in the preparation of specifications and will help specifications writers avoid some of the duplications, omissions, and conflicts that can easily occur.

This material is presented as a guide only and will have to be expanded or altered, in many instances, to fit individual sections or trades. Not all headings will apply, but care should be used that the arrangement of content follows this general pattern.

The uniform arrangement of each section will be of value to the contractor bidding on the job and will help in the subsequent control by our supervision section. The format, in outline form, could be used during the planning stages of a new project as a checklist in the development of job criteria.

Format for Specifications

Documents	No numbers
Trade sections	Numbered
Main headings	Numbered
Subheadings	Small letters
Paragraphs	Number in parenthesis
Paragraphs subdivisions	Small letters in parenthesis

1. General
   a. Reference to General or Special Conditions.
   b. Cooperation with other trades; notification of readiness.
   c. Inspection and acceptance of other work.
   d. Tools, equipment, and scaffolding.
   e. Codes.
   f. Standards.
   g. Permits.
   h. Fees.
2. Work included in this section
   a. List individual items that could possibly have been included under another section.
   b. Use headings only. Be as brief as possible. Give no descriptions.
   c. Finish with a general statement of work intended to be covered in this section.
   d. Work to be furnished only.
   e. Work to be installed only.
3. Work not included in this section
   a. List items that could conceivably have been included in this section but are not.
   b. Use headings only. Do not note any specific sections where these items will be found.

c. Check and make a note of each item that is being excluded and be sure it is specifically included under the "work included" heading of the section where it WILL be covered.

d. Be specific. Do not use "etc.," "similar," "miscellaneous," "various," "necessary," or "such as."

e. Items that are not to be furnished under this section.

f. Items that are not to be installed under this section.

4. Samples
   a. List any special conditions, sizes, or number of samples to be furnished.
   b. General statement referring to applicable section of the General Conditions or Special Conditions.

5. Shop drawings
   a. Itemize any specific drawings required.
   b. General statement referring to applicable sections of the General Conditions or Special Conditions.

6. Delivery and storage of materials
   a. Certificates.
   b. Grade marks.
   c. Labels.
   d. Original cartons.
   e. Mixing locations.
   f. Prefabrication locations.
   g. Storage locations.
   h. Access to storage locations.
   i. Maintenance of storage locations.
   j. Protection of materials.
   k. When delivered.
   l. Time of delivery.

7. Materials
   a. List acceptable manufacturers. Each Trade Section of the Specifications should include the following statement: "Unless otherwise specified, materials furnished under this section shall be as manufactured or distributed by the following." Give city and state of source or nearest distributor, if necessary.
   b. List designated Federal specifications or standards for each material specified in this section.
   c. State quality, color, or pattern groupings to be selected by Architect from a particular group. NOTE: Check price groupings.
   d. List each material. Do not use any

of the following: "or equal," "approved equal," "equal to," "similar," or other indefinite phrases. Substitutions are handled in the General Conditions. If possible, describe a material completely, clearly, and concisely without using trade names or company names.

e. Schedules, including general notes on use of schedule, types or locations, and key to symbols used in this schedule.

8. Tests
   a. Inspections.
   b. Laboratories.

9. Inspections
   a. What?
   b. Who?
   c. When?
   d. Where?

10. Subsurface
    a. Work to be done by other trades.
    b. Painting and back painting.
    c. Shop coats.
    d. Acceptance and inspection of subsurface.

11. Installation
    Describe installation of each material or piece of equipment.

12. Finish
    General statement of finish.

13. Protection
    a. Work in place.
    b. Responsibility.
    c. Curing.
    d. Work of other trades.

14. Adjustments
    a. Final adjustments.
    b. Operational tests.

15. Labeling.
    a. Type
    b. Who is responsible.

16. As-built drawings.
    This is covered in a general way in the General Conditions. If you want to be more specific, you must so state.

17. Warranty-guaranty
    NOTE: A one-year guaranty is included in the General Conditions. Include only those exceeding one year.

18. Cleanup
    General Conditions cover final cleanup, washing, waxing, and polishing. Only if special cleanup is needed will this item be included.

SCOPE PARAGRAPH

The inclusion of a paragraph labeled "scope" at the first of each trade section is a practice followed by many specifications writers. They feel that they can here present a summary of the items they expect to cover in this section for quick reference by the estimator. Others feel that the inclusion of this paragraph is unnecessary and may even be dangerous. They contend that the heading itself gives the scope of the section. For example, if the heading is "concrete," nothing more is needed. The specifications writer can proceed to specify in detail exactly each item that is to be covered. If he attempts to summarize all items that may be involved in a trade section, he may leave out items of this summary or disregard items that should have been included. This could be a point of controversy or the basis of a claim for extras. The contractor could claim that if the particular item has not been included in the scope paragraph, he does not have to furnish it.

Work Included. The scope heading is sometimes modified and divided into two parts, "work included" and "work excluded." The major sections of the work to be included are then listed under the "work included" subheading, and those items not included in the section are listed under "work excluded." The description of the work included could be stated in general terms, for example:

1. Scope
   Provide all materials and equipment and perform all operations required to complete sheet-metal work, as indicated on the drawings and specified herein.
2. Work excluded
   a. Metal louvers for doors
   b. Sheet-metal work for heating and ventilating systems
   c. Flashings for plumbing vents, ducts, and mechanical equipment
   d. Piping extending through roofs
   e. Aluminum roof deck for covered passageways

The scope paragraph covers the work included in a general way and specifically excludes items that are not included in this section. The same type of information could be included under the two headings "work included in this section" and "work not in this section," as in the following:

3. Work included in this section
   a. All glass and glazing except as specifically excluded
   b. Mirrors
   c. Mirror trim and backing
   d. Setting of metal glazing beads
   e. Setting of cement asbestos, hardboard panels
4. Work not in this section
   a. Furnishing of wood stops
   b. Fire-extinguisher glass
   c. Glass in swinging doors
   d. Furnishing of metal glazing beads
   e. Cleaning of glass
   f. Furnishing of cement asbestos and hardboard

Work Excluded. Note that the second heading is not "work excluded" because this could be interpreted as excluding these items from the entire project. What is really meant is that while they are a part of the project, they have been included in another section. Even though the items not shown in this section may not occur in another section, if they are shown on the drawings it would still be the general or prime contractor's responsibility to furnish them. They are not excluded. The reader will notice that some items are installed under this section but furnished by others. The inclusion or exclusion of these items must be carefully thought out, and they must be included or excluded according to the trade practices of the particular locale of the project, type of project, and union jurisdictional agreements. Inasmuch as a particular section may be used by subcontractors in preparing a bid for the general contractor, extreme care should be taken to include in each section only work usually done and material usually furnished by that particular subcontractor. If a doubt exists as to who will do a part of the work, it is better to separate the work into two sections than to have two subcontractors submitting bids on portions of a section.

INSPECTION AND TESTS

Some of the work will require inspections or tests during the process of construction, and although the procedures to be followed are specified in a general way in the general conditions or special conditions, each section must specify exactly what tests or inspections will be required in the particular section. In order to make a cost estimate of a phase of the work, the contractor must be able to anticipate the number and type of tests that will be required. A statement such as the following does not give the contractor the information he needs to make a realistic cost estimate, and he can only assume that the engineer or architect will be entirely unreasonable and raise his bid accordingly: "Tests will be required from time to time as the work progresses, when in the opinion of the Engineer, such tests are necessary." Even though the required tests are to be paid for by the owner, the loss of time, additional labor, and possible delays could be definite cost factors to be considered by the contractor in the preparation of his bid.

COOPERATION BETWEEN TRADES

A construction project is a complicated and intricate procedure requiring the cooperation and integration of the work of many trades. Each trade must know its relationship with others on the job. A project can show a profit or loss for the general contractor depending on the degree of cooperation between the various individuals making up the crews of each subcontractor. Who will furnish such items as backing needed by the mechanical trades for the hanging of the plumbing fixtures? Who will cut holes through wood, steel, or concrete for pipes? Who will dig trenches to receive pipes? Who will guarantee the accuracy and prepare the surfaces of floors, walls, and ceilings to receive finished materials? The timing and coordination of all work to be done is of the utmost importance.

Time Element. The practice of having crews of one trade waiting for the work of another trade to be completed is time-consuming and costly. A statement such as the following should be included in the appropriate section: "This Contractor shall furnish and deliver complete, as needed, all materials to other trades as required to be furnished under this section."

The following is from a sheet-metal section: "Reglets--Furnish reglets, with setting instructions. These items shall be supplied to the job site in time to be set in forms before concrete is poured."

ITEMS FURNISHED BY OTHERS

Some items must be furnished to manufacturers considerably before the work under a particular section is under way. The supplier of these items must be warned that this is a part of his responsibility. Templates and setting diagrams are needed in some types of work to assure a proper fit of the finished product. Manufacturers of hollow metal doors must be supplied with hardware templates well in advance of door installation because the cutouts for hardware must be made during the manufacturing process. All these items must be anticipated by the specifications writer and noted in the appropriate trade section. Many items of the work are affected by the work of the other trades. Roof decking affects the final roofing. The construction and finish of subfloors affect finish flooring. The application of grounds or metal screeds influences the finish plaster. Many times, when failures occur, the applicator of the finish material maintains that his work is good and that what was under it or next to it caused the failure. Where this is likely to occur, the installer of the finish material can rightly be made responsible for the final appearance by the inclusion of a statement such as the following: "The Contractor shall inspect all areas or surfaces adjacent to or affecting his work, and all unsatisfactory conditions shall be reported to the Architect in writing. No material in this section shall be applied until such defects or conditions have been corrected."

SCAFFOLDING

Scaffolding, work platforms, lifts, hoists, cranes, ladders, and barricades should be considered. Will these be furnished by the general contractor for the use of all trades? Will each trade furnish its own? These questions can be answered only by studying the particular job conditions and local trade practices. If this is not spelled out in the trade section, each subcontractor can only assume that he will be required to furnish these items and he will increase his bid to take care of the possibility or eliminate them from his estimate and charge an extra fee if he is required to furnish them.

STORAGE OF MATERIALS

Who will designate storage areas for each trade? What provision will be made for protection from weather? Various materials should be stored on the job site for a given period of time to allow for stabilization of moisture content. A statement such as the following should be included: "All lumber and timbers used for permanent structural purposes shall be air-seasoned for at least sixty days on the job site before being installed in the work."

DELIVERY OF MATERIALS

Some materials should not be delivered to the job site or stored on the job until certain processes have been completed, and a statement such as the following may be necessary: "Do not bring interior finish, including doors and cabinet work, into building until plaster is thoroughly dry."

Bulk Delivery. If a material has been delivered to a job in bulk form or has been removed from the original cartons, it is, in many instances, difficult for an inspector on the job to determine whether the proper product has been furnished. The specifications writer must state that the product should be delivered in unopened original containers, and he sometimes requires a certificate from the supplier stating the exact grade furnished. The Tile Council of America recommends that in order to assure proper quality, the following be inserted in the appropriate trade section: "Tile shall be delivered to the work in unopened cartons sealed with a grade seal bearing the name of the manufacturer and the words "standard grade" printed thereon. Keep grade seals intact and cartons dry until tiles are used. Furnish manufacturer's master grade certificate before installation."

Lot Numbers. In addition to ceramic tile, such items as resilient floor tiles, acoustical ceiling tiles, prefinished paneling, and similar items should be covered in a like manner. Although most reputable manufacturers usually maintain a close control over color and textures of materials, material from one day's run may differ from that of the next month or year. To assure that all tile or sheets of material will match, it is sometimes necessary to include a statement such as the following, taken from a resilient-flooring specification: "All material shall be delivered in the manufacturer's original sealed containers, identified with the manufacturer's name and with the grade, lot number, and date of manufacture on each container."

Labels. Care must be taken by the specifications writer that a clause requiring labels does not work a hardship on the contractor or present a requirement that cannot be met. The following was taken from a glass and glazing section: "All glass shall be new and comply with related provisions of Federal Specifications DD-G-451a, or as herein modified. Each sheet shall bear the manufacturer's label showing type and grade. Labels shall not be removed until approved by the Architect."

For purposes of product and quality identification, all glass is factory-labeled. Orders placed at the factory for individual projects are glazed with labels. However, labels may be trimmed off when requirements are cut from local stock. It is common practice to cut large sheets of plate, heavy sheet, and rough rolled glass into small lights. Since only one label is affixed to the large sheet, the balance of the order will be delivered to the job unlabeled, and in this case the burden of proof of identification is on the supplier. On completion of the job, the architect may ask to review the glazing contractor's files for confirmation of adherence to the specifications. He cannot expect a manufacturer's label on each small piece of glass.

SAMPLES

Article 8 of the AIA general conditions, Document No. A201, states: "The Contractor shall furnish for approval all samples as directed. The work shall be in accordance with the approved samples." It is therefore the specifications writer's responsibility to state exactly what samples will be required in each section. The trade section must also give size, shape, methods of shipping and storage, methods of approval or rejection of samples, and any other necessary information on the furnishing, testing, or handling of the samples covered in the particular trade section. The following, from a painting section, is an example:

1. Submit, for preliminary approval, sample panels 8" X 12" showing each coat, type of finish, and color, using materials specified. Each coat of paint shall be tinted toward the finish color by making the coats a slightly different shade. Submit samples at least two weeks in advance of commencing work.
2. Before application of final color or finish, prepare large sample panels (minimum 4'-0" X 6'-0") for Architect's approval. Apply samples at the job site, directly to surfaces to be finished. Mod-

ify samples as directed, until approved. Do not proceed with remainder of the work until approval has been given. Finish work must match approved samples.

The description of samples may necessitate a detailed statement, such as the one shown above, or a more general one, as follows: "The Contractor shall submit samples, in accordance with the applicable provisions of the General Conditions and the Special Conditions, of each type of material or finish to be installed under this section."

SHOP DRAWINGS

Article 5 of the AIA general conditions, Document No. A201, states in part: "The Contractor shall check and verify all field measurements and shall submit with such promptness as to cause no delay in his work or in that of any contractor, three copies, checked and approved by him of all shop or setting drawings and schedules required for the work of the various trades."

It is now the responsibility of the specifications writer to identify, in the trade sections, what will be required. The general form, number, and method of approval are described in the general conditions; however, the specific shop drawings which will be required under a particular section must be specified. These drawings may consist of manufacturer's literature or may require detailed setting, joining, fabrication, and installation details. If the time of submission is an important item, the date when they must be submitted should be specified. The following is from a section on kitchen equipment: "Submit shop drawings of work specified in accordance with the General Conditions section. Submit manufacturer's catalogs showing cuts of complicated equipment and detailed description of all equipment to be installed."

AS-BUILT DRAWINGS

In addition to the shop drawings some sections of the work may require as-built drawings to be furnished at the end of the job. Usually this is required only in the mechanical sections. Electrical runs, piping diagrams, and air-conditioning ducts are located on these drawings as an aid to future maintenance. The general contractor may be asked to provide as-built drawings for the entire project.

Pipes, ducts, valves, and controls are labeled, painted, or designated in some manner on most public buildings and large, complex building projects. The drawings required, labeling, and identification of items are specified in the appropriate trade section.

PROTECTION OF WORK

Protection of work must be considered from several standpoints. The protection of adjacent surfaces must be specified. The Associated Brick Manufacturers of Southern California recommend the following: "Protection—Protect all sills, ledges, offsets, and other materials from droppings or mortar during construction. Protect the tops of all unfinished masonry from rain by using water-repellent covering. Protect the surfaces of walls, piers, pilasters, or columns from mortar droppings or splashes." This covers the splashing of mortar while laying brick but does not cover the damage caused by the mixing, carrying, or storage of masonry materials. Damage caused by these operations could be very extensive and must be covered. The California Lathing and Plastering Association recommends that the following be included in the plastering section: "Protection—The lathing and plastering contractor shall provide, install, and maintain all protection necessary to preserve the work of other trades free from damage due to lathing and plastering operations (except as otherwise set forth in paragraph 2.21 of this section)."

EXCLUSION CLAUSES

Paragraph 2.21, referred to above, specifically relieves the plastering contractor of any responsibility for the following: "2.21—Protection of all floor areas for duration of work whether or not the working surface constitutes the finish floor or is to receive a covering." If this exclusion clause is to be used, the specifications writer must then include protection in a section devoted to the general contractor's work. It would be better to eliminate this exclusion clause entirely. The payment for, or repair of, damage done to other work caused by a particular trade, where the protection is not adequate, can be an important item and must be covered where necessary.

BUILDING CODES AND ORDINANCES

These directly affect the work of many

trade sections. Certain standards of performance and quality are required by local, state, and--in some instances--national bodies. It must be realized that these standards are minimum requirements and that the quality desired may exceed this minimum. Three statements are therefore needed in the trade section involved. The first states which ordinances, codes, and regulations are to be considered minimum requirements; the second states that those restrictions specified which exceed the requirements of the code or ordinance shall govern; and the third states that nothing in the plans or specifications shall be deemed as authority to violate ordinances. The inclusion of this third statement is questionable because it implies that there may be items in the drawings and specifications that are contrary to ordinances and that the designer or specifications writer has not checked his work or does not know the code. This puts the contractor in the position of having to check the contract documents to see whether someone has made a mistake. This portion may be stated briefly as follows: "Ordinance Requirements—Refer to "Legal Requirements" in the General Conditions. All work done shall be in accordance with the Los Angeles County Electrical Ordinance, except that where the requirements of the Specifications exceed those of the ordinance, the Specifications shall govern." Specific codes, rules, and safety orders may be enumerated as follows:

Surveys, Permits, Codes, Safety Orders
1. Refer to sections entitled General Conditions and Special Conditions.
2. All work and materials shall be in full accordance with the latest rules and regulations of:
   a. Title 8 - General Industrial Safety Orders.
   b. State Fire Marshal.
   c. U.B.F.U.
   d. Uniform Building Code.
   e. County Air Pollution Control Board.
   f. Title 19 - Public Safety: Fire and Panic Safety Standards.
   g. Other applicable laws, regulations, local codes, and ordinances.
3. Nothing in these drawings or specifications shall be construed to permit work not conforming to these codes.

The necessity of including such a detailed and comprehensive statement is questionable if the designer and the specifications writer are competent. The drawings and specifications should conform to these codes, and the only justification for including such a statement would be to cover items not shown or specified. This could also evidence a laziness on the part of the specifications writer: He has not troubled to look up the codes.

BUILDING PERMITS

The architect usually applies for the building permit, which is paid for by the general contractor. This is covered in the AIA general conditions, Article II. However, specialized permits and licenses necessary for certain portions of the work, such as plumbing and electrical work, may be obtained by subcontractors for their portion of the work. The cost of these permits or licenses is then included in the subbid to the general contractor. A statement will then be included in the trade section such as the following: "The contractor shall secure and pay for all permits, inspections fees, meters, and service utility extensions required under this section as part of this contract." Notice that the designation "subcontractor" is not used, but simply "contractor." This gives the general contractor the choice of either requiring his subcontractor to apply and pay for these items or doing so himself.

SPECIAL INFORMATION

Some sections of the specifications, particularly the mechanical sections, require the inclusion of special information covering such items as balancing of air-conditioning systems at the completion of the job, adjusting of thermostats, regulating of lighting equipment, operation manuals, instruction of employees, spare parts, and other miscellaneous aspects of the work. The specifications writer must, in most cases, consult experts in the particular field to ensure the completeness and accuracy of these sections.

FINAL CLEANUP

This is the responsibility of the general contractor and is covered in the last article of the AIA general conditions. However, the rough or preliminary cleanup is usually noted in the trade section, for example: "At completion of the work, remove from the property all tools, equipment, surplus materials, and debris resulting from lathing and plastering operations. Leave premises neat and broom clean."

SPECIAL CLEANUP

The glass and glazing, ceramic tile, architectural metals, terrazzo, masonry, painting, and several other sections require special attention as to cleaning and cleanup. For example, the cleaning of glass is many times specifically excluded from the glass and glazing section and is specified under the painting section. Special provision should be made for the cleaning of sand-blasted and acid-etched glass as soon as possible after the glass is in place. Excess putty and paint should be removed promptly from this specially processed glass. It is important that this be done before the drying oils can harden through exposure to air. The cleaning cannot wait for the entire glazing to be complete but must be a close follow-up while the job is in progress. A check with the glass manufacturer will give the specifications writer the exact cleaning procedure.

GUARANTY

In some cases, it is unnecessary to include these clauses in the trade sections. A guaranty is an undertaking to answer for another's liability—a provision to answer for the performance of some duty in case of the failure of some person who is liable for such performance. Article 20 of the AIA general conditions states in part: "The contractor shall guarantee to remedy any defects due to faulty materials or workmanship and pay for any damage to other work resulting therefrom, which shall appear within a period of one year from the date of final payment. . . ."

The word "guarantee" here means that the general contractor, acting as a third party or "surety" will make good all work done by any one working for him. Article 30 of the AIA general conditions states that the owner may require the contractor to furnish a "guaranty bond." This requires the contractor to secure a surety (or someone who will pay for work to be done if the contractor defaults). The surety is then the third person, making Article 20 effective.

WARRANTY

This is a statement of fact. The contractor warrants his work to be as required by the plans and specifications. A manufacturer warrants that his product is of the quality specified. This does not imply a responsibility to make good for any failure in the future. Only a third party, called the "surety," gives the owner a guaranty to make good any failure in the performance of the contractor.

GUARANTY BONDS

The furnishing of guaranty bonds for each section of the specifications can be an expensive item, so unless something other than the one-year guaranty required in the general conditions is desired, the clause is not included in each trade section.

ALLOWANCES

In some sections of the work, particularly in residences, it is not possible or desirable to complete the selection of certain items at the start of the job. In this instance, an "allowance" is placed in that particular section for bidding purposes. The specifications writer then estimates the amount to be spent, and the owner, at the proper time, selects the exact items to be installed. If the items selected cost more than the allowance, the owner bears the extra cost. If the items cost less, the owner is entitled to a reduction of the contract price. The installation of these items must be covered in the specifications, and the cost of this installation is borne by the contractor. Finish hardware, wallpaper, patterned glass, and electrical fixtures are the common items so covered, for example:

Lighting Fixtures
An allowance of $125, not including flush lights, exterior lights, garden lights, or fluorescent lights, shall be made by the General Contractor. The lighting fixtures will be selected by the Owner and shall be installed by the Contractor.

or

Finish Hardware
a. The Contractor shall allow in his bid the sum of $125 for the purchase of finish hardware, which will be selected by the Owner.
b. Finish hardware shall be installed under the contract.

SCHEDULES

If an allowance is not made, these items and others like them must appear in some form of a schedule. These schedules are many times included on the drawings. The practice of including many schedules on the drawings can be an expensive way to present this information. It is obviously cheaper to have as much of this information typed as possible instead of requiring a draftsman to spend hours lettering it on the drawings. Certain information, however, is more conveniently included on the drawings from the standpoint of easy reference. This can be simplified by the use of symbols on the drawings, these symbols being in turn fully described in the specification trade section. As an example, each electrical fixture has been identified on the drawings as A, B, C, or D. Included at the end of the electrical section is the following:

Fixture Schedule

Type	Description	Catalog number and Manufacturer
A.	Incandescent concentric ring, 750/1000 watts	Soot-Black Corp. #RE-100S
B.	Incandescent, porcelain lamp holder	Whipple Co. #AL 3140
C.	Incandescent, ceiling-mounted, drum typed, enclosed globe	Soot-Black Corp. #LH-1110
D.	Incandescent, recess, with a corney drop lens, 150 watts	Whale Oil Lamp Co. #1608-DO-PB

This type of schedule could also be used for several other sections such as doors, windows, glass, tile, floor coverings, painting, plumbing, and others.

FINISH-HARDWARE SCHEDULES

The preparation of a finish-hardware schedule can be very difficult for a large job. On a small job, an allowance is usually used, and the owner selects the hardware then needed. However, for the more complex jobs, this schedule is often prepared with the help of a hardware consultant who is familiar with the thousands of specialized items available. The hardware consultant, who usually works for a single supplier of hardware, assists in the preparation of this section and lists his own line of products along with comparable products of other distributors. The hardware schedule can be set up in one of two ways. In the first, each door is numbered and enumerated in the schedule, and each item is then listed for these doors. As an example:

1. Exterior doors 1, 2, 3, & 4 from kindergartens
   5, 6, 7, 8, & 9 from classrooms
   1, 2, & 3
   Unichecks—1-1/2" offset X top pivot M19 Non-Hold
   Locksets—OK 7616 ML GMK
   Kick plates—OK 2840, 10" X 2" less door width
   Door holders—W707
2. Interior doors 16 from custodian 14
   Butts—A 2714-1/2CD 4X4
   Lockset—OK 7637 ML GMK
   Door holder—GJ 324-26D

Some offices and some clients have set up door types that require a particular set of hardware. They then can include this list in every set of specifications and identify each door on the drawings, for example:

Group Q	
Butts	STA 714-1/2 PC 4-1/2 X 4-1/2
Flush bolts	116—12-1/2
Door pulls	7875-1/2 HMR X 1882 fixed
Door holders	G.J. 44

Group R	
Butts	STA 714-1.2 PC 4-1/2 X 4-1/2
Lockset	7837 HMR X 1882 GMK
Door stop	67-1/2

The specifications writer must check the drawings very carefully with this type of schedule. It is quite difficult to change such a schedule because the drawings must be changed and not simply the schedule in the specifications.

SUPPLEMENTAL INFORMATION

The trade sections have been discussed in some details. However, this discussion was necessarily limited in scope, and each trade section requires careful study and analysis to determine what miscellaneous information must be included. Job size, type of construction, type of client, whether Federal government, local government, school board, large corporation, small business, or residential, influence the form to be used, and the amount of material to be included. Regional trade practices and national and local union jurisdiction regulations affect the trade sections. While the inclusion of this type of information is extremely important, the actual specifications of materials, processes, and installation methods make up the bulk of the trade section. The specification of materials and installation will here be considered separately, although they are exactly integral parts of each section.

QUESTIONS

1. What is the relationship of a trade section and the general conditions?
2. How can a large office, with many specifications writers, establish a uniform format for trade sections?
3. What is a better term than "work excluded" when used in a trade section?
4. What information must be included in trade sections that describe two items of work which will adjoin?
5. If grade labels have been removed from glass delivered to the site, how can the architect assure himself that the glass delivered was as specified?
6. If the working drawings show details and location of a particular item, explain very briefly what the specification should include.

CHAPTER 11 Specification of Materials and Processes

Specifications are word descriptions of materials and of methods of installation and job conditions that affect those particular materials. Before we can form these word descriptions of materials, we must know for whom they are written. The owner, for the most part, does not have the ability to interpret the technical terms used in a modern building project and is interested in the final effect and the use of the building. He has entrusted the architect with the assembling of the details in such a manner as to achieve this effect. He is therefore not primarily interested in these details. The architect directs the assembling of these details, and he also directs the writing of specifications and decides what is to be included in them. The general contractor must know the extent of the project in order to break it down into those parts he will do himself and those parts he will sublet. His estimator must be able to take off accurate quantities and assign costs for the quality of the workmanship and materials that will make up the job. The subcontractors and their estimators must be able to determine the extent of their responsibilities and prepare an accurate bid for the prime contractor. Materials dealers, suppliers, and manufacturers must have a clear, concise, and accurate description of the materials they will be expected to furnish. The contractor's and architect's superintendents must have a well-defined guide to follow during the process of construction. As mentioned before, the specifications are legal documents and may be used as evidence in a court of law or before a board of arbitration.

DIMENSIONS

Although the specifications usually do not give dimensions, the size or thickness of a material should be carefully specified in the trade sections, for example: "The door and curb shall be formed of .125" 6003-H-14 aluminum. Mirrors shall be registered safety mirrors or silvering quality, 1/4"-thick polished plate glass. Maple flooring indicated hardwood or H. W. shall be 25/64" thick. Keene's cement finish shall be from 1/16" to 1/8" thick. Gypsum board shall be 1/2" thick and 4'-0" wide. Terrazzo topping shall be not less than 5/8" thick."

QUALITY

A material to be used in a project must be clearly indicated. Let us consider the following words and phrases: "the best quality," "a good grade of," "the best grade of," "Class A," "smooth," "an acceptable quality of," "of selected," "an approved type of." Are these clear, concise measures of quality or are they merely a matter of someone's judgment? A materials dealer may have a limited stock or the franchise to deal in only a part of a manufacturer's line of merchandise, so he will want to furnish the best of that which he handles. The subcontractor, in some cases, may wish to furnish a product that will net him the largest profit, or it may be that the best quality of a material usually installed by his crew is not what is wanted by the general contractor to match other work on the project. The general contractor wants quality that will fit into the entire project with the greatest ease. This is what he will consider the best quality, although it may not be what the trained architect or specifications writer, judging from past experience, believes to be the best. The architect or specifications writer, in considering the quality or grade of a material and its relation to cost, may feel that the best material is one that fits the owner's budget. To the owner, the best quality could mean the most expensive, the most elaborate, or the flashiest material that can be purchased or manufactured, and that is what he believes is going to be installed in his building. It says in the specifications that the best, smoothest, and slickest Grade A material shall be used, so the only material he will select or approve is that which, in his untrained opinion, meets his requirements. The contractor, in preparing his bid for the project, must guess what the owner or architect is likely to approve. Unless he knows the architect's tastes, budget, and way of doing business from past experience, he has one of two alternatives. Not knowing what the architect or the owner will choose, select, approve, reject, or be satisfied with, he may select an item from which he can make the most profit and assume that the architect will approve it; or he can figure into his bid the most expensive material he can imagine. In this situation, he would need psychic knowledge of the exact quality of material which will be required in order to make an honest, exact, and realistic bid.

FINISH

The installation method and finish expected on work must also be carefully specified. Phrases such as the following are not enough to assure a satisfactory installation: "in a workmanshiplike manner," "according to accepted practices," "well cleaned," "well nailed," "a close fit," "in proper position," "well graded," "well mixed," "well overlapped," "well flashed," "clean," "dry," "wet," "smooth," "rough," "adequate," "approved," and "acceptable." Will the inspector on the job be able to judge these qualities from the above descriptions? When we speak of a workmanshiplike manner, are we thinking of the old-time cabinetmaker who could spend days turning out a hand-carved post or an intricately paneled wall, or are we considering a present-day finish carpenter who, because of our wage structure, must turn out a given volume of work each day? Is a well-cleaned aluminum surface one which has been treated and cleaned in such a manner as to remove all traces of oxide and foreign material and so provide a perfect surface for finishing, or does this description indicate merely that a laborer should knock off any plaster that may have splattered on it? Does it mean that a laborer should scrub a newly tiled surface with a coarse cleanser or acid until he has damaged it? A well-nailed subfloor under a 5/8" oak floor is something different from a well-nailed subfloor under an all-vinyl partially transparent resilient floor covering.

PRECISE DEFINITIONS

We must, then, spell out exactly what we mean if we expect to accomplish a given result. This can be illustrated by considering instructions for the treatment of just a small part of a building — the metal finish, for ex-

ample. Too often a statement such as the following is made: "All exposed metal sections shall be weather- and corrosion-resistant." This generalized statement is vague and leaves too much leeway regarding finish. In fact, it would permit any finish regardless of how inferior. Under this specification, the exposed sections could even be a mill finish or, in other words, raw, unprotected aluminum metal. After all, aluminum is resistant to weather in its bare state to a certain degree. Contrast that approach with a typical firm specification like this: "Aluminum handrail shall have Alcoa Aluminite 215C1 treatment with a minimum coating thickness of .008" and a minimum coating weight of 35 mg psi. Random checks of the production work shall be made by an appropriate procedure to determine the coating thickness and quality of seal. Results of such tests shall be notarized."

If we describe exactly what we want and define our terms, each person involved will know what is expected of him, and the inspector and superintendent on the job will have guideposts to follow. As an example, the author has seen a statement in painting specifications that all metal surfaces are to be cleaned and primed before the finish coats are to be applied. Is this specific? The following is an excerpt from a specification which can be checked in the field and which leaves no doubt in anyone's mind what is intended:

Wash all metal surfaces with mineral spirits to remove dirt or grease before applying finish. Where rust or scale is present, use a wire brush or sandpaper to clean the surface to bright metal before painting. Clean shop coats that have become marred with mineral spirits. Touch up abraded parts with specified primer as follows:

Ferrous metal—5037 LZI primer
Aluminum—5036 zinc chromate
Galvanized metal—7747 zinc dust; zinc oxide

It is not enough to say that a subfloor under resilient flooring should be well nailed. A statement such as the following is necessary: "Nail with 1-1/4" flathead No. 3 cadmium-plated, cement-coated drive screw nails; flush nail plywood starting in middle on 6" centers 1/2" in from the edge around the perimeter of each sheet of plywood."

There are accepted measures for smoothness of surfaces, thickness of coatings, and moisture content of materials. These should be used, and the method of testing should be designated. These methods should be accurately described in the specifications.

STANDARDS

Reference may be made to a standard method, for example, one described by a recognized testing laboratory or testing organization such as the ASTM. Instead of specifying "a white paint with good hiding power," we could specify "a white pigment in a linseed-oil vehicle graded 6 on the relative dry power scale as described in ASTM designation D 406-52.

DESCRIPTION OF MATERIALS

There are several approaches to describing a material or installation method. These could be divided into three broad categories and, further, into various combinations of the three.

THE PRESCRIPTION SPECIFICATION

If the exact materials to be used and a detailed description of the installation process are included, this is called a "prescription specification." The specifications writer describes exactly what basic material will be used, how they will be combined or fabricated, how they will be handled, and how they will be tested or controlled. The supplier's responsibility is relieved when he has complied with these criteria. The specifications can be checked by the inspector on the job site or in the fabrication plant before or during the erection process, and an accurate estimate can be made by the contractor. This approach assumes the competency of the specifications writer. Consultants called in to assist him in the preparation of these instructions, literature published by trade associations of manufacturers, or individual manufacturers will assist him in choosing a material or method that will accomplish the result the architect is looking for. Applied to concrete, for instance, this method would specify the type, size, grading, purity, and testing of the aggregate; the type of portland cement to be used and how it is to be stored, handled, and tested; the mixing water purity and testing; any admixtures to be used; and the mixing, proportioning, placing, curing, and testing of the concrete mixture. If the specifications writer has been clear, concise, and accurate in his description and the inspection has been thorough, the architect assumes that after a period of twenty-eight days the concrete will resist a compression stress of 2,000 lb, 2,500 lb, or 3,500 lb psi, whichever may be needed for a specific purpose.

PERFORMANCE SPECIFICATION

The specifier may, at times, feel unqualified to act as an expert in a particular method of installation or in the selection of a specific material to accomplish a given result. He is interested only in performance. He feels that he should not be bothered with the selection of materials and the determination of proportions to assure that a material will do what it is supposed to do. He may feel, with some justification, that it is the producer of this product who, through specialization in a small phase of the work of the building industry, has become an expert on the ways and means of accomplishing satisfactory results. He will then be inclined to write what is referred to as a "performance specification."

SPECIFYING END RESULTS

In a performance specification, the end result is specified, and it is up to the supplier to accomplish this result in any way he sees fit. Under suitable conditions, judiciously administered, the responsible producer is willing to do so. A guaranteed strength or result, however, is the source of much uncertainty in estimating costs. As an example, the amount of each of the various materials that go into a mix of concrete can be calculated and, using a given set of conditions, will result in a concrete structure of the required characteristics. This may even be proved by tests of this mixture made by a laboratory under a particular set of conditions. The contractor, in using this formula, though successful in the past, is making a guess as to how it will react or wear under a new set of conditions. The inspector on the job must take the producer's word that the product will react or wear in a particular manner—that it will come up to tests and provide the strength, wearing qualities, or finish desired at some future date. Core tests or concrete cylinders may be tested twenty-eight days after they are made, and, if they are faulty, the producer or the contractor may be held responsible. However, by that time the construction project has progressed, and it may not be economically feasible to remove or replace the faulty materials.

PRESCRIPTION PLUS PERFORMANCE

There is a third approach to this problem which is in reality a combination of the two described. This method could be called "prescription plus performance." Basic materials and the steps of fabrication are outlined in a broad manner that has been proved through experience, laboratory tests, or engineers' calculations to fit the particular set of circumstances to be encountered. This is coupled with the results expected and a guaranty is furnished by the contractor that the results will be satisfactory. Fabrication techniques will vary with the facilities and practices of the individual fabricators and the precise methods to be used. As long as they follow accepted practices and can be checked, the choice can be left to the fabricator's discretion, providing he accepts the responsibility of meeting the specified standard of performance and appearance. The specification of products where trade names are not used should contain guaranty clauses that are rigid but not unreasonable. This would be helpful in eliminating the bidder who might bid strictly on price in the hope of finishing the job before the results of his work can be proved faulty. These guaranties, however, must be enforced consistently and insisted upon to the letter in order to be effective.

OPEN, RESTRICTED, AND CLOSED SPECIFICATIONS

A further division can be made in the method to be used in describing a material or a method of installation. The specification can be "open," "restricted," or "closed." An open specification never names a specific item of equipment, a trade name, or a proprietary name. The specification may give the chemical or physical makeup of a product, the tests it must comply with, or the results expected from it, but it must never designate a specific manufacturer's name. Closed specifications designate a particular brand by the use of a trade name or proprietary name, giving catalog number, manufacturer, and sometimes a distributor at a particular address from whom the item is to be purchased. Restricted specifications, sometimes called "bidders choice," are those in which the material is described and then pinned down by limiting the choice to the products of two or more manufacturers or distributors. The catalog number or proprietary name of each is then specified, and the contractor may choose from this approved list.

OPEN SPECIFICATIONS

Any manufacturer or supplier who wishes to submit a bid may do so under an open specification. Open specifications are generally used on work for public agencies, many of which are required by law to use them. While the intent of these laws may be admirable and effective in preventing graft, kickbacks, and favoritism, it is next to impossible to write absolutely open specifications for any but the simplest projects. Basic materials are more adaptable to open specifications than equipment is. Concrete, steel, sand, or aluminum can be described without regard to manufacturers. Many specifiers use open specifications for materials of this type, even on work for private clients. A complex material or process must be described in enough detail to permit the contractor to bid, and this means that the type of equipment to be used must be basically established, thereby automatically eliminating some suppliers. Although some architects and specifications writers dislike open specifications because they feel that such specifications do not give them a firm control over the quality of the products, others contend that the open specification allows more chance for true competitive bidding which results in a lower cost to the owner. They feel that it allows the "little man" or the new product an equal chance with old and well-advertised products. The specifications writer must realize that the preparation of open specifications and control of the work or items furnished on the job can involve considerable expense for the architect. The checking and testing of proposed material to be used under open specifications can be very time-consuming. The possible variances in weight, size, or placement of machinery can affect the basic design of a building and necessitate extensive alterations of the drawings to accommodate a particular item chosen to be installed by the contractor. A true open specification is one in which acceptable minimum standards are spelled out, and such requirements can be met by several manufacturers within the limitations of the design, whether or not their names are mentioned.

Disadvantages of Open Specifications. Open specifications are by their nature usually wordy, and the specifications writer must spend valuable time writing, and the contractor reading, to assure a complete description of the product. The architect or specifications writer who has carefully studied or had experience in the use of the products of several manufacturers and has assured himself that their products will accomplish the desired effect can simplify and shorten the specifications by naming manufacturers, proprietary names, trade names, or catalog numbers without eliminating competition. The restricted specification can list those manufacturers whose products will be acceptable and then describe the product as in an open specification or designate specific items as manufactured by each, for example: "Materials furnished under this section shall be as manufactured by one of the following: (1) Jones Cork Co., (2) Smith Corp., (3) A & S Gypsum Co., and (4) Northern Division of Star Co. Edging shall be No-Edge Type 114-A as manufactured by B & F Metals Co., distributed by Williams & Co., Azusa, California, or Tudor Type A-309-H as manufactured by Hobbs Co., distributed by G & B Co., Los Angeles, California."

RESTRICTED SPECIFICATIONS

A method which describes a material or method and then limits the contractor's choice to two or more specific products or suppliers can be referred to as a "restricted specification" or "bidder's choice." The restricted specification contains some of the disadvantages of the open specification but is preferred by many architects as well as suppliers. If the contractor is given a choice of several products or installation methods, problems arise in the design of adjacent or adjoining surfaces and structures. The designer must know what equipment is to be installed in order to provide the necessary space, details, and connections. The possible use of several manufacturers' products must be carefully considered. Care must be taken and, in many instances, extensive research performed to ascertain that those several products named by manufacturer, trade name, or catalog number are in reality equal in quality and in price. To include one brand that is lower in price—which usually means lower in quality too—in a list of several specified as approved, is in

effect eliminating competition as effectively as though a strictly closed specification were written. The specifications writer, surely, is not naïve enough to hope that the contractor will choose to install any but this item. The list of several possible brands must be chosen very carefully in order for there to be a choice. Each manufacturer has certain features (usually patented) in his product that are not a part of his competitors' products. If the specifications writer has used this manufacturer's standard specifications as a guide or, as too often happens, has copied these recommendations, he can eliminate all the competition he wished to promote. The rival manufacturers named in the restricted clauses must pay royalties for the use of the patented feature or risk the possibility of litigation for infringement on patent rights. This could be a major item to the owner, as Article 10, Royalties and Patents, of the AIA general conditions states in part: ". . .the owner shall be responsible for all such loss when a particular process or the product of a particular manufacturer or manufacturers is specified. . . ." The restricted specification does have a number of advantages and can be used effectively to promote competition with its resulting lower bids.

CLOSED SPECIFICATIONS

Some architects, engineers, and suppliers insist that closed specifications eliminate competition and result in higher prices, although this is not necessarily so. When the specification is written, the selection of a particular product has been made from information furnished the architect before this time. Manufacturers' representatives have competed in selling the advantages of their products in both price and adaptability, and these advantages have been weighed and a decision reached. It is a matter of timing. The manufacturer, not named, has not convinced the specifier that his product will do the best job for the owner. During the design stage of a project, all specifications are open. The architect is the agent of the owner and, as such, has been given the authority to select and specify the many items that will make up the completed project. It is his duty to his client to insist on the particular product that will be the most satisfactory. Each contractor who is bidding the job knows exactly what must be furnished and knows that his materials cost will be similar to that of every other contractor. He cannot lower his bid by cutting corners, substituting inferior materials, or bid shopping or through kick-backs or deals between salesmen and contractors. He can lower his costs and subsequent bid only by being more efficient in the handling and installation of the product. The complete and positive definition permits the designer accurately to set room dimensions, foundations, fastenings, surfaces, and fittings. The architect can complete his drawings before the bids are let and take advantage of any special features offered by a product. The owner has a choice of the material he prefers and is relieved of the possibility of extras occasioned by additional work necessary to fit an "off brand" or unique piece of equipment into the project. Is it not more logical to follow the old adage and "call a spade a spade"?

SUBSTITUTIONS

The alleged disadvantages of, or opposition to, either the restricted or the closed specification can be minimized if a method for substituting alternate brands or installation methods is incorporated into the specifications. The method to be used by the contractor for making substitutions and the architect's approval or rejection of these requests must be carefully considered and clearly spelled out in the general conditions or special conditions. The AIA general conditions do not cover this point, and if the AIA forms are used, the information must be included in the special conditions. Some architects have felt that any request for substitutions should be submitted and a decision reached before the final bid is made. They then insert the requirement that requests for substitutions be received by the architect seven or ten days before bids are due. The architect can then analyze the material and, if he wishes to allow the substitution, send this information to all bidders in the form of an addendum which adds the material to the accepted list of products. In this manner, all bidders have the same advantage, and the architect and the contractor know exactly what will be accepted after the bids are opened.

SUBSTITUTIONS AFTER BID

Requiring all contractors bidding on a project to submit their substitution proposals during the bidding period creates certain problems. For an office handling a large volume of work or a project being bid by several con-

tractors, the checking, testing, and evaluation of requests and the writing of addenda can be an almost impossible task. To the contractor, who is usually pressed for time during the bidding period, the time-consuming paper work involved in submitting the requests of all his subbidders and notifying them of decisions can be a serious problem.

BASE-BID ALTERNATES

The requests for substitutions may be submitted with the contractor's proposal as alternatives to his base bid. The instructions for making the alternative proposals are then included in the agreement as well as in the general conditions or the special conditions. In an effort to eliminate the necessity of having to check and evaluate the many requests for substitutions during the bidding period and still allow the possibility of change, the clause is changed to permit the contractor who is awarded the contract a definite period AFTER the award in which to submit requests for substitutions. All these instructions should contain this information and require the contractor to state the amount to be added to, or deducted from, the contract price if the substitution is permitted. This new price becomes a part of the contract. The following excerpts from supplemental general sections prepared by an architect illustrate two methods of approach in handing this problem:

Substitution of Materials or Equipment

Materials and equipment designated in these specifications are given as standards; however, this implies no rights on the part of the Contractor or his subcontractors to substitute other materials for those specified, except in the manner herein described.

If the Contractor desires to make substitutions, he shall so state in his bid, showing first his bid for the installation of all materials and equipment as specified and second the deduction from, or addition to, the contract price which he will make if the proposed substitutions are permitted. He shall list the materials he desires to substitute, stating the material each is substituted for. If no substitutions are proposed or if proposed substitutions are not approved by the Architect, no deviation from the materials specified will be permitted unless in pursuance of a change order signed by the Owner and approved by the Architect.

Proposed substitutions shall fulfill, to the satisfaction of the Architect, the fundamental requirements and identical purposes of those specified. The Architect's approval of substitutions shall not be held to have relieved the Contractor of responsibility for the proper joining of the various parts of the work nor from such guaranties and maintenance provisions as may be specified herein.

Substitutions

1. Reference in the specifications or on the drawings to specific manufacturers' products or to trade names is for the purpose of establishing the standards of quality demanded. Such references are not intended to be restrictive, and, except where a specific product is necessary to match existing materials or items, the Contractor may apply to the Architect for permission to substitute materials or items other than those specified or implied.

2. Any request to substitute materials or products other than those specified shall be submitted to the Architect for consideration within twenty (20) days after the signing of the contract. Requests received after this time will be automatically rejected. Furnish five (5) copies of each submittal. Submittal shall show name of manufacturer, trade name, quality of material, amount to be added or subtracted from base bid, and all other pertinent information necessary to completely identify the material. Where applicable, furnish catalog cuts, photographs, samples, details of construction, independent laboratory test reports, operating data, and maintenance characteristics.

3. Should the Contractor desire to substitute a new item for a rejected item, such substitution should be made within ten (10) days after rejection, or material as originally specified shall be provided. It shall be the Contractor's responsibility to coordinate any work affected by substitutions.

QUESTIONS

1. Discuss briefly the term "or equal."
2. Define a prescription specification.
3. Define an open specification.
4. Define a closed specification.
5. What is a restricted specification?

CHAPTER 12 Specifications Words and Phrases

The specifications are a part of the contract documents and, as such, must be written with extreme care. The language used must be clear, exact, and in sufficient detail to meet all reasonable interpretations. It must be simple enough to be understood by the workmen on the job who may have a relatively small vocabulary. If the mechanic cannot understand what is wanted, he cannot do the job. Technical terms, if used, should be used in the sense which they have acquired through local usage. Instructions should be in sufficient detail to enable the contractor to ascertain exactly who will be required to do what. The specifications are legal documents, and each word, phrase, sentence, and punctuation mark may come under the scrutiny of a court of law or an arbitration board. Legal phraseology has been built up over a period of many years, and during this time the language has become more and more involved.

LONG WORDS

Long hyphenated words, or words such as "hereinbefore" and "hereinafter, " stilted legal phraseology, and complicated, compound sentences may impress the owner, but the very complexity of the writing may be interpreted in an entirely unforeseen way. The specifications writer is apt to assume that words have a single and definite meaning. He may be greatly surprised to find that the language he has used, which conveyed to his mind a very definite idea, is susceptible to numerous other interpretations. It is not necessary to use long phrases. The specifications writer need only be clear, concise, and correct.

REPETITION

In most writing it may be desirable to substitute words which are more or less synonymous in order to avoid constant repetition of a word, but, because few words are exactly synonymous, the specifications writer must choose the word that conveys the exact meaning he desires and use it as many times as necessary.

INVOLVED DESCRIPTIONS

Philadelphia architect David H. Morgan, a Fellow of the AIA, in an address before the Delaware Valley chapter of the CSI, pointed up this problem in a very forceful manner.

How many times have you written letters and clauses that, when cold, and after time lapses, have inevitably brought forth in astonishment, "Did I ever say and write THAT—it's not what I intended. " This, in my opinion, is attributable in a great degree to the polyglot assembly called the English language. If we could write specifications in a root language such as Sanskrit or Latin or Celtic, I'm sure a substantial quantity of our troubles would disappear. And to prove this, I cite a base which my good friend Ben John Small uses to illustrate "Federalese" (a dignified term for bureaucratic double talk). It appears that a New York City plumber wrote to the Bureau of Standards that he had found hydrochloric acid good for cleaning out clogged drain pipes. The Bureau's response was: "The efficacy of hydrochloric acid is indisputable but the corrosive residue is incompatible with metallic permanence. " The plumber wrote back he was glad. The Bureau replied, "We cannot assume responsibility for the production of toxic and noxious residue with hydrochrolic acid and suggest you use an alternative procedure. " By return mail, the plumber told how glad he was the Government thought his idea was okay. In desperation, the Bureau broke down and wrote the plumber in plain language: "For heaven's sake, don't use hydrochloric acid. It eats hell out of the pipes. "

In specifications writing, punctuation must be used very carefully and cautiously. Commas, semi-colons, periods cause quite a bit of trouble. Sharp contractors and their sharper lawyers have a field day when a punctuation mark is misplaced. I recall one comma cost our office $3,500.00 some years ago.[1]

CONTROVERSIAL PHRASES

There are several words, clauses, and sentences whose use in specifications is somewhat controversial. The specifications writer must know the meanings and understand the implications thoroughly before using these phrases in specifications. Probably the phrase "or equal" is the most discussed phrase whenever specifications writers meet to discuss the problems involved in specifications writing. Many articles have been written by architects and specifications writers on the subject of the "or equal" clause. The AIA, several engineering associations, and most specifications writers have taken a stand for its elimination. However, it is still being used, and there are many who insist that it belongs in a set of specifications.

Let us first consider the definition of "equal": identical, neither more or less; exactly the same in measure, quantity, number; like in value or quantity. How would this apply to the products of several manufacturers? Do two or more companies in competition produce identical products? In order to promote its particular product, a company does not claim that it produces an article which is exactly the same as that which is produced by a competitor, but one which is unique, better suited, or of a higher quality. If each salesman points out that his product is better than his competitors', then the phrase "or equal" cannot be used in specifications. What we must use is the questionable phrase "just as good or better" or the word "substitute." Consider the word "substitute"—that which is used in place of something else. There is no inference of equality here. Who will be the judge of what is equal? If the manufacturer maintains that his product is better, who will judge the equality of two different products? A statement may be placed in the specifications that products shall be "judged equal in the opinion of the architect." This is basing the choice of materials not on facts but on opinions. The architect or engineer has chosen, in the first place, the material that is best suited for the particular job at hand. Why is there a need for reconsideration?

An owner should have the right to choose what he wishes to purchase. Consider the following example: You go into an automobile agency and select a deluxe model of a particular make, model, and year with a specified group of accessories. The next day the dealer delivers a "just as good" but less expensive model saying, "This model is equal. It has a motor, four wheels, heater, radio, etc., all you specified except the brand name." Would you stand for this? Why should an owner accept another product to be placed in his building when he has already made a selection?

Proponents of the use of the "or equal" clause claim that unless it is included in the specifications, competitive bidding is eliminated, which raises costs. However, the use of this clause usually results in a lowering of quality rather than a rise in costs. The architect or engineer who has investigated all products and established their relative costs before the specifications are written and then has chosen one or more that will be satisfactory has not eliminated competition.

VAGUE PHRASES OR ESCAPE CLAUSES

Many, in lieu of obtaining and giving specific instructions which would define exactly what is required of the contractor, use vague phrases or escape clauses. Following is a list of such phrases taken from actual specifications:

As approved by the Architect.
To the entire satisfaction of the Architect.
In the judgment of the contracting office.
Unless otherwise directed by the Engineer.
At the discretion of the Engineer.
As directed by the Architect.
Photographs shall be taken when and where directed by the contracting officer.
In the opinion of the Architect.
To furnish. . .if directed by the Engineer.
All reasonable requests of the contracting officer shall be complied with.

The use of the above phrases would be greatly curtailed if the specifications writer would remember that the word "satisfaction" is de-

[1] D. H. Morgan, Questions and Answers on Construction Specifications, in Construction Specifier, Summer, 1957, p.27.

fined as "a personal feeling of pleasure or comfort generated by an award, a gift, or some emolument."

VERBS

Verb tense and mood in specifications are very important. Some authorities maintain that the same verb tense should be used throughout a set of specifications. However, this is not necessarily desirable and can cause unnecessary wordiness and confusion as to the exact meanings required. The proper tense and mood of the verb "to be," as used in specifications, are discussed in the following:

"shall": In spite of efforts of teachers to perpetuate the distinction between the words "shall" and "will," it is largely ignored by Americans. Specifications are commands to the contractor, and the imperative form of the verb "shall" must be used in describing the work the contractor is required to perform:
"The Contractor shall install. . . . "
"The Contractor shall inspect. . . . "
"The Contractor shall furnish. . . . "
"The Contractor shall submit. . . . "

"shall be": A positive statement giving the size, quality, or action that will be accepted: "Corner reinforcement shall be No. 100 Perf-a-Bead as manufactured by. . . . " "Rubber base shall be 1/8" thick." "Mirrors shall be registered safety mirrors of silvering quality." "Doors shall be mortised."

"will": "Will" is not a command; it states that something will happen in the future. When we say, "The lighting fixtures will be furnished by the Owner," we are stating this only as a matter of information. The specifications are commands only to the contractor: "The Contractor shall install fixtures, which will be furnished by the Owner," "Install toilet paper and towel holders, which will be furnished by the Owner,"

"must": Avoid the word "must" and instead use "shall." If "shall" is used in some places in the specifications and "must" in others, a difference in degree of responsibility is implied.

"to be": "To be," "is to be," "are to be," "should," and "should be" are indefinite forms of the verb, and, as we are writing specifics, they have no place in a set of specifications.

IMPERATIVE MOOD

The specifications are written as instructions directed to the general or prime contractor, and, in many instances, it is not necessary to use the verb "to be" in any form in these instructions. The instructions can be simplified if the imperative mood is used. The sentence, "The Contractor shall install toilet paper and towel holders, which will be furnished by the Owner" can be shortened without losing any of its force or understanding to the following: "Install toilet paper and towel holders furnished by the Owner."

The use of the imperative mood can eliminate many words and increase the ease of reading, and the sentence will still be as complete as though the verb "to be" were used. The material is made the subject of the sentence in this case.

PRONOUNS

The pronouns "he," "his," "this," "they," "their," "who," "it," and "which" should be used sparingly, if at all. It is better to repeat the noun. Use of pronouns can cause confusion as to the exact meaning. The following was taken from a plumbing specification: "All tests shall be carried out in the presence of a duly authorized plumbing inspector and a representative of the Architect, who shall be notified in advance by the Contractor." Who is going to be notified - the plumbing inspector, the architect, or the representative of the architect? Two short sentences and the elimination of the pronoun "who," instead of the compound sentence, would have cleared this up.

UNNECESSARY AND MISUSED WORDS

Many words and phrases used in specifications can be eliminated both for brevity and for clarity. Many words are used in such a manner as to be misleading and incorrect. Following is a list of the words most commonly misused:

"and/or": To define the use of this combination, let us consider what the courts have ruled. Florida Supreme Court (145 So. 217): "It is one of those inexcusable barbarisms which was sired by indolence and dammed by indifference, and has no more place in legal terminology than the vernacular of Uncle Remus in Holy Writ. I am unable to define how such senseless jargon becomes current.

The coiner of it certainly had no appreciation of terse and concise law English."

"or, and": The word "or" denotes a choice. Do we actually mean "Clean up and remove all tools, scaffolding, trash, or debris?" Use the word "and" unless a choice is intended.

"any, all, every": "Any" implies choice. It is indefinite. Use the word "all" only if necessary. "All" and "every" usually are not needed and can be eliminated. "No pipe of any kind shall be laid under any floor slab" could be simplified to: "Pipe shall not be laid under floor slab." Consider the following: "Should any trouble develop during this year because of defective material or faulty workmanship, this Contractor shall furnish all necessary material and labor to correct every trouble without any cost to the Owner." The following eliminates all indefinite words: "The Contractor, at no cost to the Owner, shall repair or replace defective material and faulty workmanship discovered during the guaranty period." "Apply a prime coat of zinc chromate to the back of all structural plates which rest on masonry" could be shortened to" "Back prime structural-steel plates resting on masonry with zinc chromate."

"either": "Either" is an indefinite word and should not be used in place of "both." "Install a block on either side of all beams at. . . ." Better wording would be: "Install solid blocking on both sides of beams at. . . ."

"same, said": Do not use "same" or "said" as a pronoun or adjective. "If the finish is damaged, the Contractor shall repair same." "Said damage shall be repaired by the Contractor." Instead use: "Repair damaged surfaces."

"similar, several, various, miscellaneous, ordinarily furnished, customarily used, normally required, usually furnished, when needed, as required": These indefinite words and phrases have no place in specifications. They can be subject to different interpretations by each person who reads them. These words and phrases are used as a tool by the specifications writer who does not know what will be required or who does not want to take the time to analyze exactly what is to be done.

"etc.": This abbreviation "etc." means "and others, and the rest, and so on and so forth." This should NEVER be used in specifications. Be specific.

"amount, quantity": The word "amount" is used as the sum total of several quantities, usually when speaking of money. If you are referring to volume, number of items, or number of gallons, use the word "quantity."

"intent": It is not necessary to explain our intentions, which should be obvious from the heading. Do not use the following in trade sections: "Plumbing—The intent of this section is to cover the complete installation of all plumbing."

SUMMARY

The various methods of specifying materials and processes, the possible advantages or disadvantages of the use of certain words or phrases, and other pertinent points in the writing of specifications have been discussed at some length. It must be realized that this is only a start. It would not be possible, within the limits of this book, to list all the many pitfalls that have appeared in the past or to anticipate all that will occur in the future. Each segment of the construction industry looks at specifications from a slightly different viewpoint. Even within a group of specifications writers there will be a divergence of views. While every effort has been taken to present views that express the convictions of many present-day specifications writers, there are those who feel that many of the points taken here are unimportant or wrong and who, for various reasons of their own, would disagree with what has been stated.

CONSTRUCTION SPECIFICATIONS INSTITUTE

The one point on which there is universal agreement is that the quality of most specifications and specifications writing can and should be improved. This is emphasized by the rapid growth of organizations such as the CSI. The purpose of this group is to foster and promote the interests of persons, firms, groups, associations, corporations, and others engaged in any phase of the business of writing, preparing, compiling, or in any way utilizing specifications in the construction and allied industries; to promote improved specifications practices in the construction and allied industries; and other aims. The growth of this organization to 4,940 members over a twelve-year period attests to the interest in its goal: "improved construction through better specifications." This organization can best be exemplified by its code of ethics:[2]

CODE OF ETHICS OF THE CONSTRUCTION SPECIFICATIONS INSTITUTE

1. Each member shall discharge his duties and responsibilities to his clients or employers in such a manner as to inspire respect and confidence.
2. Each member shall cooperate in extending the effectiveness of the profession and the Institute by the interchange of information and experience with his fellow members as the opportunity presents itself.
3. Each member shall endeavor to write specifications which will permit and encourage fair and equitable competition.
4. Each member shall endeavor to write specifications that are thorough, clear, and concise, and refrain from the use of loose, ambiguous, or unenforceable, unfair requirements.

[2]By permission of the Construction Specifications Institute, as published in the Construction Specifier, Spring, 1958.

5. Each member shall specify materials, equipment, services, and construction methods only on merit, without consideration for, or expectation of, personal gain or favors other than from his employers or his client.
6. Each member shall refrain from disclosing the interests or business affairs of any client or employer without his knowledge and consent.
7. Each member shall uphold the principle of appropriate and adequate compensation to those engaged in specifications writing and refuse to knowingly compete on basis of compensation.
8. Associate members shall pledge themselves never to misrepresent their fellow members in maintaining the high standards of service set forth in the Code of Ethics.

QUESTIONS

1. What dimensions should be included in the specifications?
2. Define the following: "the best quality," "workmanshiplike manner," "smooth," "roughened," "well-nailed,"
3. What is the imperative mood, and how can it be used in specifications?
4. Define a grandfather clause.
5. How can the use of punctuation change the meaning of a sentence? Give an example.

CHAPTER 13   Specifications for Governmental Agencies

The writing of specifications for agencies of the Federal government requires much of the same knowledge, abilities, and skills that would be required in the writing of specifications for privately financed construction projects. The specifications writer must understand construction processes and must have reference material at hand and be able to evaluate it. He must be able to assemble material and place it in a prescribed form for the final reproduced specification. The proper use of words and phrases is as necessary in work for the Federal government as it is in private practice. In fact, the precise use of language is of prime importance in government specifications work. The constant changes in, and increasing complexity of, large Federal projects and military construction and the exacting requirements of new missiles, missile-launching equipment, and related facilities make it necessary to have an extremely clear and concise word description of the actual construction of these devices and facilities.

The following excerpt from Engineering Manual 1110-345-720 of the Corps of Engineers, U. S. Army, points up this need for clear and concise thinking and writing when preparing government specifications: "The technical provisions will be in sufficient detail so that, when used with the applicable contract drawings, estimates and/or bids can be supplied by contractors, material suppliers, or manufacturers on a fair and competitive basis and construction can be completed without additional specifications except as necessary to deal with unforeseen conditions or to accomplish changes made during construction." It would be difficult to find a better description of a good set of specifications, whether written for the government or for a private practice.

In some instances, the materials and methods to be used are entirely new, and the specifications writer will not be able to use old sets of specifications and, simply by the "cut-and-paste" method, put together a new set of specifications. What he is called upon to describe may never have been built before. He must be able to analyze test results, and, from the reports of new materials and processes, describe a method of erection or assembly that will accomplish a given result. It may be necessary to call in laboratory technicians to determine methods of construction and establish new standards in order to accomplish the results desired.

MILITARY CONSTRUCTION PROGRAMS

A factor that further increases the complexity of specifications for military construction is the wide geographical distribution of the projects. Military construction is spread from Pakistan to Korea and from Iceland to Panama. Foundations must be designed to support installations weighing many tons on ground that must be refrigerated to keep the permafrost from melting. They must also be designed to support structures on what is seemingly a bottomless swamp in a tropical jungle. Many of the larger architects-engineers offices must maintain research and development staffs to work out previously unsolved problems that are continually being met. Much of this construction work is being done by native contractors and labor. The problems of language, trade names, and local construction techniques further complicate the work of the specifications writer. The following excerpt from a set of specifications being used for a seven-story building under construction near a large foreign military base illustrates a slight difference in standard construction techniques from those practiced in the United States:

Colour washing: Colour wash of approved tint shall be kept in solution for at least a week with a mixture similar to lime or white wash. A little amount of cow dung and washing soap mixed with the solution will give the colour washing a bigger span of life. Colour washing shall be applied in 2 coats over a coat of white wash. The solution shall be stirred constantly while putting it on to achieve an even unstreaky surface.

OPEN SPECIFICATIONS NECESSARY

It is seldom possible for the specifications writer, when preparing government specifications, to choose a well-known, specific product of a manufacturer and tie a specification down to the particular item that he knows will give satisfactory performance. A basic principle of government purchasing is to permit all known responsible suppliers to have an equal chance to compete for government contracts. This basic principle is enforced by insisting on completely open specifications. The use of trade names in government specifications must be avoided whenever possible. When it is necessary to specify materials or equipment not covered by an existing standard specification, minimum requirements must be stated in terms of physical characteristics, performance requirements, or any combination of these. Specifications for equipment of standard manufacture, in general, do not make reference to standard materials of the individual parts but are based upon acceptability of the equipment, capacity, or performance. Many government regulations require that where the specifications must include a catalog number or trade name, such use be qualified by the words "or equal." The difficulties that may be encountered by this "or equal" phrase have been discussed at length in previous chapters and would apply to specifications to be used on government projects as well as private projects. The question of who is to judge what is equal and the selection of criteria for judgment must be spelled out in some part of the specifications as it must also be done in private practice. In the Armed Services Procurement Regulations (ASPR), the following statement must be included:

Unless otherwise specifically provided in this contract, reference to any equipment, material, article, or patented process, by trade name, make, or catalog number, shall be regarded as establishing a standard of quality and shall not be construed as limiting competition, and the Contractor may, at his option, use any equipment, material, article, or process which, in the judgment of the Contracting Officer, is equal to that named.

In private practice, the specifications writer may specify exactly what he wants and can then expect that it will be furnished. In government work it is not that simple.

PATENTED EQUIPMENT IN PUBLIC WORK

Governmental agency regulations would seem to exclude patented or monopolized material, but these regulations have been variously interpreted from time to time. The general consensus has been that if a patented item is required to the exclusion of all others, the inclusion of this item with the specifications will be allowed if:
1. No Federal standard exists for the product
2. The words "or equal" follow the proprietary name
3. The owner of the patent makes it available to all bidders
4. There is no attempt to defraud or act in the restraint of trade
5. A note is included at some point in the contract documents that the use of proprietary names is intended to indicate the degree of excellence or performance that is required and that any equivalent that will produce the same result will be considered when submitted by the successful bidder as in substantial conformance with the specifications

In contracts for advanced space construction, many items are involved which are definitely critical for the safety of the construction and which must be based on patented processes. Generally, an architects-engineers firm must request the inclusion in the specifications of a certain item of equipment or material which can be specified only with a proprietary description. The authorization for the use of this material must come from the Department of Defense.

For further discussion of the government's position in regard to "brand name or equal," see Federal Procurement Regulations, chap. 1-1, 307-4 to 307-7 (41CFR 1-1, 307-4 to 307-7), which sets forth the procedures to be used.

UNPROVED METHODS AND MATERIALS

The use of unproved materials or unusual methods of construction on government projects is discouraged. However, if time allows, procedures have been set up whereby the product or method may be submitted for approval by governmental agencies. It is the responsibility of the manufacturer to prove the merit of the product he proposed to use in place of an accepted material. This testing must be done by a recognized independent testing laboratory. If a producer wishes to have his product evaluated, he must file GSA Form 1171 with the GSA. This form may be obtained at any GSA regional office. The GSA regional office will check on the identity and usefulness of the product and forward its recommendations and all papers to the central GSA office for final approval. Before approving a new product, the GSA central office will make tests of the product, at the expense of the prospective supplier, to verify that the product will measure up to the performance claimed.

LOCAL REGULATIONS AND FEDERAL PROJECTS

The specifications writer, when preparing specifications for a Federal project, must determine whether the municipal or state regulations, as well as the rules and regulations of the Federal agency, will apply to the public project that is being designed. If the land upon which the Federal project is to be placed is leased by the government, the local regulations will apply in most instances. In several cases in which the land was owned by the Federal government, regardless of whether it had been acquired by cessation or purchase, the courts found that local regulations did apply.[1] The jurisdiction may be qualified in accordance with agreements reached by the local and Federal governments. The rules in existence at the time of surrender of the property by the local government continue in effect until changed by Federal government regulations.

CONSOLIDATION OF GOVERNMENTAL AGENCIES

Many agencies exist in the Federal government, each of which controls, with some exceptions, construction policies and publishes rules and regulations to be followed in the preparation of specifications. Even though a continual effort is being made to consolidate these regulations, most agencies are still responsible for their own procurement. The

[1]H. A. Cohen, "Public Construction Contracts and the Law," McGraw-Hill Book Company, New York, 1961, pp. 249-253.

steady growth and complexity of government needs necessitate constant evaluation and changes in governmental agencies and their methods of procurement. One major consolidation of governmental procurement programs was made with the consolidation of purchasing under the GSA in 1949. This action consolidated the purchasing of many thousands of items by many governmental agencies into one administration.

No attempt will be made here to cite all the regulations and standards that must be considered. It is essential that the specifications writer become familiar with current policies of Federal agencies. New agencies are constantly being formed, and existing agencies are being consolidated. A brief description of governmental agencies and their divisions, policies, and jurisdictions will be covered here. Sources and types of information published by existing agencies and where and how this information may be obtained will be noted.

GOVERNMENT PROCUREMENT

Procurement is defined as the acquisition (and directly related matters), from non-Federal sources, of personal property and non-personal services (including construction) by such means as purchasing, renting, leasing, contracting, or bartering. Thus when we speak of procurement, we are referring to the instructions to be followed by the specifications writer in preparing specifications for governmental agencies. Government buying programs and contract regulations can be divided into three broad categories: (1) those of the military, (2) those of the GSA, and (3) those of other civil agencies. While each of these broad categories has certain individual requirements that must be familiar to the specifications writer, in many instances the regulations of one are accepted or required by others. Many agencies buy directly or contract for services on an individual basis for some projects, while they are dependent for certain types of services upon other agencies. The policies of all agencies are contained in the Federal Procurement Regulations (FPR), which prescribes the uniform policies and procedures of all Federal agencies. Those regulations are included in chap. 1, Title 41, of Public Contracts, which may be ordered in loose-leaf form from the Superintendent of Documents, U. S. Government Printing Office, Washington 25, D. C.

MILITARY PROCUREMENT

Each military service establishes the policies and procedures to be used in construction. The Department of Defense was created to coordinate and unify the policies and procedures under which the Army, Navy, and Air Force operate. Military procurement policies and procedures are contained in the Armed Services Procurement Regulations (ASPR). These regulations are implemented by the manuals, bulletins, and publications of each service. Two booklets are published by the Department of Defense which give detailed information about the procurement policies of the agencies within the Department of Defense. These are: How to Sell to Agencies within the Department of Defense and Selling to the Military. These booklets are available from the Superintendent of Documents, U.S. Government Printing Office, Washington 25, D.C. For further information on, or answers to specific questions about, military procurement or construction problems, a request may be made to the Central Procurement Information Office, Office of the Assistant Secretary for Installations and Logistics, Department of Defense, Washington 25, D.C.

Department of the Army. The primary responsibility for the procurement activities and policies of the Department of the Army rests with the Assistant Secretary of the Army (Logistics). The procurement activities of the Department of the Army are governed by the Army Procurement Procedure (APP). The Corps of Engineers under the Chief of Engineers supervises most engineering and construction for the Army and Air Force.

Engineering Manuals and Bulletins. The guide to be followed for military construction, published by the Corps of Engineers, is entitled Engineering Manual for Military Construction. This manual also includes chapters to be used for civil works. A second manual, entitled Engineering Manual for Civil Works, and portions of the Engineering Manual for Military Construction are used as guides for all civil works under the jurisdiction of the Corps of Engineers. Civil Works Engineers bulletins are issued from time to time by the Chief of Engineers as a medium for disseminating technical information and advice on design and construction of civil-works projects.

Army Technical Services. The procurement activities of the Army are divided into seven technical services:

Chemical Corps--Commanding Officer, Edgewood Arsenal, Army Chemical Center, Md. Attention: Requirements and Specifications Office.

Corps of Engineers--Chief of Engineers, Department of the Army, Washington 25, D.C. Attention: Administrative Services Division.

Quartermaster Corps--Commanding General, Philadelphia Quartermaster Center, 2800 South 20th Street, Philadelphia 45, Pa.

Ordnance Corps--Commanding Officer, U.S. Army Ordnance District Office, in the appropriate city: Birmingham, Ala.; Boston, Mass.; Chicago, Ill.; Cincinnati, Ohio; Cleveland, Ohio; Detroit, Mich.; Oakland, Calif.; Passadena, Calif.; Philadelphia, Pa.; Springfield, Mass; St. Louis, Mo.; New York, N.Y.

Although the Corps of Engineers supervises the construction for all departments of the Army, each department has certain regulations and instructions that must be followed when projects are being designed for its use.

Department of the Navy. The Department of the Navy is divided into three principle elements: (1) the Operating Forces, composed of the seagoing Navy and Fleet Marine Forces, (2) the Navy Department in Washington, D.C., which directs the Operating Forces, and (3) the Shore Establishment, which provides for the needs of the fleet. Each department is responsible for the procurement of needs of that particular bureau. The Department of the Navy handles major construction contracts through the Department of Yards and Docks. Procurement by the three bureaus is under the general supervision and guidance of the Assistant Secretary of the Navy (Materiel). Information may be obtained from the Commanding Officer, Naval Supply Depot, 5801 Tabor Avenue, Philadelphia 20, Pa.

Department of the Air Force. Major construction contracts and architectural and engineering services are controlled by the major Air Commands and are contracted for by the Department of the Army, Corps of Engineers; or the Department of the Navy, Bureau of Yards and Docks. In the missile and space programs, the Air Force has the design and preparation of contract documents. The Army and Navy are only the construction agencies. Any construction or design of facilities under the control of the Air Force, except for the missile program, must follow the Air Force Manual 88-15. The purchasing officer of each Air Force base may contract for, and control, a particular group of items, which include minor construction and local repairs. Further information on Air Force procurement regulations or contract information may be obtained from one of the following Air Force procurement offices:

Boston Air Procurement District
Boston Army Terminal
Boston 10, Mass.

Newark Air Procurement District
218 Market Street
Newark, N.J.

New York Air Procurement District
111 East 16th Street
New York 3, N.Y.

Philadelphia Air Procurement District
1411 Walnut Street
Philadelphia 2, Pa.

Rochester Air Procurement District
20 Symington Place
Box 1669
Rochester 3, N.Y.

Chicago Air Procurement District
5555 South Archer Avenue
Chicago 38, Ill.

Dallas Air Procurement District
912 South Ervay
Dallas 1, Texas

Cleveland Air Procurement District
1279 West Third Street
Cleveland 13, Ohio

Detroit Air Procurement District
6200 Concord Avenue
Detroit, Mich.

Indianapolis Air Procurement District
1112 North Penn
Indianapolis 2, Ind.

Arizona Air Procurement District
2875 Sky Harbor Blvd.
Phoenix, Ariz.

Los Angeles Air Procurement District
1206 South Maple Avenue
Los Angeles 15, Calif.

St. Louis Air Procurement District
1114 Market Street
St. Louis 1, Mo.

Milwaukee Air Procurement District
770 North Plankington Avenue
Milwaukee, Wisc.

Dayton Air Procurement District
Building 70
Area C
Wright-Patterson AFB, Ohio

San Diego Air Procurement District
3054 Rosecrans Place
Box 1548
San Diego 10, Calif.

Atlanta Air Procurement District
41 Exchange Place S.E.
Atlanta 3, Ga.

San Francisco Air Procurement District
Oakland Army Terminal
Building 1
West Grand and Maritime
Oakland 14, Calif.

GENERAL SERVICES ADMINISTRATION (GSA) FEDERAL SUPPLY SERVICE

This agency of the Federal government, in addition to other services, has several functions that are of interest to the architect, engineer, and the specifications writer. Under Section 206 of the Federal Property and Administrative Services Act of 1949, it is authorized to prescribe standard specifications for all governmental agencies. The GSA provides assistance to business concerns interested in doing business with the Federal government, and it provides information on Federal procurement of real property, bids and related documents, contract forms, quantities and prices of past contract awards, names of current prime contractors, and other pertinent topics. GSA business service centers store and disperse Federal specifications and indexes, standards, Federal regulations and procedures, standard contract forms, and related publications.

Public Buildings Service. Under the GSA, the Public Buildings Service, Central Office of Design and Construction, negotiates professional service contracts with architects and engineers for the majority of new Federal buildings including post offices, court houses, and Federal office buildings and research centers. Questionnaires are sent to architects in the area of the project who are registered in that state. If the project is primarily of an engineering character, an engineer will be selected. If an architect is selected, he is responsible for furnishing competent engineering service. The AIA publishes a pamphlet entitled Federal Agencies Contracting for Building Designs. This pamphlet lists those agencies which use private architects and names the official who should be contacted for information concerning architectural work.

GSA Regional Offices and Business Service Centers. The GSA maintains thirteen GSA business service centers throughout the United States, in each city where a GSA regional office is located. These GSA service centers provide a central source of information for all GSA activities and operations in each major geographical area in the United States. Business service centers display current bid invitations, give contract-award data, and distribute copies of specifications and indexes, Federal regulations and procedures, standard contract forms, and related forms and publications. In addition, GSA field representatives and area managers in many cities throughout the United States are available to render general information with respect to GSA procurement activities. This information may be obtained at the following locations:

Broadway & Main
New U.S. Courthouse
Portland, Ore.

49 Fourth Street
San Francisco 3, Calif.

U.S.P.O. and Courthouse Building
2 North Spring Street
Los Angeles 12, Calif.

Building 41
Federal Center
Denver 25, Colo.

Federal Center
300 West Vickery
Fort Worth 2, Texas

1114 Commerce Street
Dallas 2, Tex.

GSA Building
2306 East Bannister Road
Kansas City, Mo.

Peachtree—Seventh Building
50 Seventh Street N.E.
Atlanta 5, Ga.

U.S.P.O. and Courthouse Building
Boston 9, Mass.

250 Hudson Street
New York 13, N.Y.

GSA Regional Office Building
7th and D Streets S.W.
Washington 25, D.C.

OTHER CIVIL AGENCIES

The procedures, policies, and contract practices of civil agencies of the Federal government vary to a certain extent. Although all are governed by Federal procurement regulations, each agency may set up additional policies supplementing these regulations. Normal procurement is usually decentralized to permit regional or field offices to control the bulk of their contracts, but large purchases and construction contracts are usually handled by a central office. The Small Business Administration publishes a directory entitled U.S. Government Purchasing and Specifications Directory, which lists who buys what, and where, and gives sources of government specifications. It also publishes A Guide for Contracting of Construction and Related Architectural or Engineering Services, which discusses policies and types of contracts involved in construction for civil agencies. These pamphlets are on sale at field offices of the Department of Commerce or may be obtained from the Superintendent of Documents, U.S. Government Printing Office, Washington 25, D.C.

Atomic Energy Commission (AEC). The policies of the AEC vary from those of the usual governmental agency. Most of its expenditures represent cost-reimbursement agreements with certain private corporations who have the facilities to undertake large-scale projects. These projects are usually carried out with one of the ten operations offices. For complete information on the policies and procurement procedures, a pamphlet entitled Selling to the AEC is available from the Superintendent of Documents, U.S. Government Printing Office, Washington 25, D.C.

Department of Agriculture (USDA). The programs of the USDA are widely varied. The department has prepared a pamphlet entitled Selling to the USDA, which is available without charge, from the Procurement and Property Management Division, Office of Plants and Operations, U.S. Department of Agriculture, Washington 25, D.C. This pamphlet describes the programs of the USDA, its policies, and the procurement practices of each agency. It also includes a directory of USDA purchasing offices and their locations.

Department of Commerce. This department is composed of thirty-two bureaus, offices, or administrations, each of which controls most of its own procurement and originates its own construction contracts and procedures. Following is a list of the activities of the Department of Commerce, whose publications may be of interest to the specifications writer: The Maritime Commission, Bureau of Public Roads, Weather Bureau, Bureau of International Programs, Bureau of International Business Operations, Coast and Geodetic Survey, St. Lawrence Seaway Development Corporation, Great Lakes Pilotage Administration, Defense Air Transportation Administration, Office of Administrative Operations, Office of Investigations and Security, Offices of Emergency, Planning Coordinator and Appeals Board, Bureau of Standards, and Business and Defense Services Administration. The last two agencies are of particular interest to specifications writers. The Business and Defense Services Administration, Office of Technical Services, Commodity Standards Division, Washington 25, D.C., publishes commodity standards that are used on private work as well as government projects. This office acts as the government representative

in coordinating Federal government standards with the American Standards Association. The Bureau of Standards is primarily concerned with basic research; however, it reviews all commodity standards for technical accuracy. The Bureau of Standards performs such functions as evaluating radiation penetration and protection studies for the Office of Civil and Defense Mobilization and the Department of Defense. Information on the program of the Bureau of Standards may be obtained from the Procurement Section, National Bureau of Standards, Washington 25, D.C.

The U.S. Department of Commerce maintains thirty-four field offices which can supply information on the policies of the Department.

Department of Health, Education, and Welfare. The rulings and publications of this department are of special interest to those who design Federally financed schools, hospitals, rest homes, and similar buildings. Most of the procurement of the department is decentralized to its field offices. Inquiries regarding agency-wide contracts, that is, those which are applicable to overall agency supply operations, and requests for the addresses of local contracting or control offices may be sent to the Division of General Services, Department of Health, Education, and Welfare, Washington 25, D.C.

Department of the Interior. Agencies operating under the Department of the Interior include: Fish and Wildlife Service, Southwestern Power Administration, Bonneville Power Administration, Geological Society, Bureau of Reclamation, Bureau of Mines, Bureau of Indian Affairs, Bureau of Land Management, and the National Park Service. For information regarding the regulations of the various divisions of the Department of the Interior, contact the Division of Property Management, Department of the Interior, Washington 25, D.C.

Department of Justice. Each bureau and service under the Department of Justice handles its own procurement. The Bureau of Prisons, the Federal Prison Industries, and the Federal Bureau of Investigation purchase materials and contract for services. Construction of Federal prisons and maintenance are handled by the individual institutions. Federal Prisons Industries, Inc., buys raw material on a contract basis from local sources. The products manufactured by this corporation are sold to governmental agencies through the GSA. Information may be obtained from the Bureau of Prisons, Department of Justice, HOLC Building, Washington 25, D.C., or the Purchasing Division, Federal Prisons Industries, Inc., Department of Justice, Washington 25, D.C.

Post Office Department. Construction of post office facilities is handled by the GSA, Public Building Service. Items peculiar to the Post Office Department such as postage meters, stamp-dispensing machines, letter racks, and similar items are purchased through the central offices. Information on the needs and policies of the Post Office Department may be obtained from the Bureau of Facilities, U.S. Post Office Department, Washington 25, D.C. Attention: Chief of Procurement.

Treasury Department. The United States Coast Guard is the largest purchaser of supplies, equipment, and facilities under the Treasury Department. Since the Coast Guard is primarily an operation similar to the military, much use is made of military specifications. A considerable portion of its supplies and facilities is obtained through contracts made by the Department of the Navy. Inquiries may be addressed to the Commandant, U.S. Coast Guard, 1300 E Street, Washington 25, D.C.

Veterans Administration (VA). Architectural or engineering firms interested in being considered for design work on VA projects should request the VA to provide them with the Architect-Engineer Form, on which they must list their qualifications. There is no competitive bidding on architectural and design contracts, and the fee for the contract is negotiated on a strictly professional basis. This is true of all Federal agencies, not the VA alone. For information and application, contact the Veterans Administration, Washington 25, D.C. For information on standards and specifications developed by the VA, contact the Development and Standards Division, Department of Medicine and Surgery, Veterans Administration, Washington 25, D.C.

FEDERAL STANDARDS AND SPECIFICATIONS

In order to ensure that materials purchased by the Federal government are suitable for their intended use, standards and specifications have been established that describe en-gineering and technical limitations, methods of fabrication, design criteria, and testing methods to be used in order to ensure uniformity and quality of products. These standards can be grouped into three types: One type of standard has the objective of reducing the number of types, sizes, colors, and varieties of items to be used by the government. The second type of standard describes methods to be used in testing commodities or products. A third type sets up the engineering standards and design criteria to be used. Each standard is given a number and is listed in the Index of Federal Specifications, Standards, and Handbooks. If a modification of the standard is made, a suffix letter is added to the number to indicate this change. Standards are referenced in the body of a specification. When a Federal standard has been established, the Federal specification which will be used in the designation of a particular item will be based on type, size, color, and testing procedure as described by the Federal standard. Standards have been developed for hundreds of manufactured items, such as file cabinets, desks, chairs, batteries, and many more basic materials such as those shown below (Federal standards are numbered from 1 to 1,000):

48--Tolerances for steel and iron wrought products

48 change No. 1--Tolerances for steel and iron wrought products

The second item (48 change No. 1) indicates that an amendment has been made to this standard. If a reference was made to this standard, "item 48" and "48 change No. 1" would have to be used. If a standard is revised, a small letter is added after the number--38a, 39b, etc. If the number is preceded by "00," for example, 0098a (int.), this standard is an "interim standard" developed by one agency. The use of this interim standard is required of the agency that developed it but is optional for other agencies.

GOVERNMENT SPECIFICATIONS

A working knowledge of government specifications is essential to the specifications writer. The use of these specifications is required for all work done by the Federal government. In general, government specifications consist of written descriptions, drawings, commercial designations, industry standards, and other material describing a specific product or process. They describe the technical requirements for materials, products, or services. These government specifications have been developed after extensive research by experts in the government and in industry.

Development of Government Specifications. The GSA, under the authority of Section 206 of the Federal Property and Administrative Services Act of 1949 as amended, is authorized to prescribe standard purchase specifications for use by Federal agencies. To develop a new government specification or modify one that is in existence, the GSA coordinates the work of representatives of governmental agencies, trade associations, and suppliers in preparing a specification that will best serve its purpose. Whenever possible, the government specifications are based on standards established by industry. Standards developed by the ASTM, the ASA, and other associations are used whenever possible. In return, these associations use government specifications as references. Normally each government specification is reviewed every five years. However, they may be reviewed oftener if the need arises. The GSA welcomes suggestions from industry for improvements in government specifications. Recommendations should be submitted to the Standardization Division, Federal Supply Service, General Services Administration, Washington 25, D.C.

Types of Government Specifications. Specifications prepared for government use are public documents and, as such, may be used by private enterprises. These specifications are of several types. Each type of governmental specification can be recognized by a symbol printed in the upper right-hand corner of the first sheet of the specification. The specifications writer should become familiar with each type of specification and should know the uses and limitations of each. Government specifications may be divided into four types: Federal, interim Federal, military, and departmental.

FEDERAL SPECIFICATIONS

A Federal specification is of a permanent nature and is prepared for the use of two or more agencies, one of which is a civil agency. All agencies of the Federal government, including the Department of Defense, are required to use Federal specifications if applicable.

Federal specifications are identified first by a single, double, or triple letter which designates the group for procurement to which the specification relates. These groups are set forth in the Index of Federal Specifications, Standards, and Handbooks and consist of such items as:

L—Cellulose products and synthetic resins
DD—Glass and glassware
LLL—Wood products

The second part of the designation usually consists of the first letter of the item to be considered. Thus:

L-P—Cellulose or plastic—Plastic
DD-R—Glass—Rods
LLL-I—Wood products—Insulation

The last portion of the symbol consists of a serial number determined by the alphabetical location of the title. The entire symbol would appear as:

L-P-416—Cellulose or plastic—Polystyrene
L-P-504—Cellulose or plastic—Cellulose acetate

Amendments to Federal Specifications. If minor changes are made in a Federal specification, an amendment is issued. This amendment is printed on green paper and must be attached to the specification to which it refers. If one amendment has been issued the specification would be listed as GGG-S-58 (1). If second or third amendments are issued, the number (2) or (3) would be used. When a second, third, or fourth amendment is issued, it incorporates all changes that were included in previous amendments.

Revisions of Federal Specifications. When a specification is revised, a small letter is added after the specification serial number. This revision then supersedes entirely the previous edition including all amendments to the previous edition. A revised specification would then appear as H-B-222a, Z-V-401b, or GG-H-941c.

Interim Federal Specifications. If an agency has need of a specification for a product or a service that is peculiar to that agency, an

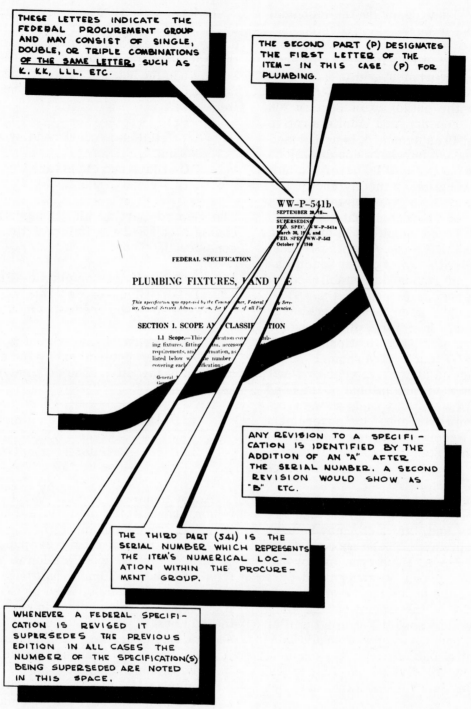

Fig. 13-1. A Federal specification. (By permission of the General Services Administration.)

interim Federal specification may be developed. The use of this specification will then be mandatory for that agency and optional for all other agencies. If more than one agency uses the item repetitively, the interim Federal specification may be changed to a Federal specification. Before this change can take place, the proposed specification is coordinated with industry and all other Federal agencies.

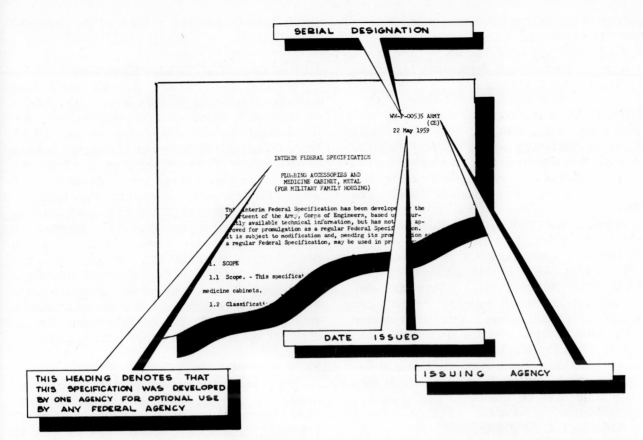

SERIAL DESIGNATION

WW-P-00535 ARMY
(CE)
22 May 1959

INTERIM FEDERAL SPECIFICATION

PLUMBING ACCESSORIES AND
MEDICINE CABINET, METAL
(FOR MILITARY FAMILY HOUSING)

This interim Federal Specification has been developed by the
Department of the Army, Corps of Engineers, based upon cur-
rently available technical information, but has not yet approved for promulgation as a regular Federal Specification.
It is subject to modification and, pending its promulgation as
a regular Federal Specification, may be used in pr...

1. SCOPE

1.1 Scope. - This specificat...

medicine cabinets.

1.2 Classificati...

DATE ISSUED

ISSUING AGENCY

THIS HEADING DENOTES THAT
THIS SPECIFICATION WAS DEVELOPED
BY ONE AGENCY FOR OPTIONAL USE
BY ANY FEDERAL AGENCY

Fig. 13-2. An interim Federal specification. (By permission of the General Services Administration.)

An interim Federal specification is identified by the "00" in front of the serial number and letters in parentheses, as in the following:

Ink, drawing, waterproof, colored—TT-I-00531a (1) (GPO)
Ink, duplicating machine stencil, paste—TT-I-00535 (GSA-FSS)

The first item would indicate that this is an interim specification developed for the Government Printing Office. The second item is also an interim specification which was developed for, and used by, the GSA, Federal Supply Service. Other agencies may use these interim specifications, but their use is mandatory for the agency designated.

How to Obtain Federal Specifications. Each year an Index of Federal Specifications, Standards and Handbooks is issued by the GSA. The Federal specifications are listed alphabetically and numerically, and the cost of each specification is included. The index may be purchased on a subscription basis by the year. This subscription includes a basic yearly index and a cumulative monthly or periodic supplement of all revisions, amendments, and cancellations. Notices listed in the index or supplement may be obtained at the price indicated, upon application, accompanied by a check, money order, or cash, to the General Services Administration, Region 3, Federal Supply Service, Buying Division, General Services Regional Office Building, Washington 25, D.C. These are also available from the Superintendent of Documents, United States Government Printing Office, Washington 25, D.C.

A complete set of all printed specifications, standards, supplements, revisions, amendments, cancellations, and notices may be purchased from the GSA. The current price is $175. Copies of individual Federal specifications, if needed for bidding purposes, may be obtained from any GSA business service center without charge. If desired for other than business purposes, or if more than two copies are needed, they may be purchased from the central GSA office. Complete copies of all Federal specifications are on file at

207

government depository libraries for reference. All additions and revisions made to Federal specifications are sent to these libraries. For a list of government depository libraries, see Appendix C.

MILITARY SPECIFICATIONS

For materials, products, or services used only or predominately by the military, a military specification (mil-spec) is used. Civil agencies may use a military specification when it covers a military-type item or service required in their operations. The military services may also use Federal specifications when no military specification exists.

A military specification may be identified by the prefix "Mil" or, in some instances, "JAN" (Joint Army-Navy). There are two types of military specifications, coordinated and limited coordination. The coordinated specification is approved for all bureaus and services, and the limited coordination specification was prepared for use by a single department. The limited coordination military specification may be identified by the letters in parentheses following the serial number:

Mil-E-4182 (1) (USAF)
Mil-C-12994 (CE)
Mil-T-1590

The first line of the above identifies an oblong rubber eraser used by the U.S. Air Force. The second line indicates a crane shovel used by the Corps of Engineers, U.S. Army. The third item is a folding utility table that can be used by all military services and civil agencies.

How to Obtain Military Specifications. Files of military specifications are available for reference at many points throughout the United States. Copies may be seen at government depository libraries, as listed under Federal specifications, at most military installations, GSA business service centers, and field offices of the Small Business Administration. The Department of Defense issues a Department of Defense Index of Specifications and Standards. This index is published annually with monthly supplements. The index and all military specifications may be purchased from the Commanding Officer, Naval Supply Depot, 5801 Tabor Avenue, Philadelphia 20, Pa., and the United States Government Printing Office (USGPO). Any bidder, prospective bidder, or prime contractor who requests a specification and refers to the applicable invitation for bids, contract, or mission

is entitled to receive a copy of the pertinent specification.

DEPARTMENTAL SPECIFICATIONS

In cases where an item is of interest to only one department and no Federal specification or interim Federal specification exists, a departmental specification may be developed. Certain agencies, because of a large volume of purchases of items peculiar to their own needs, may play a large role. Agencies such as the Federal Aviation Agency, Veterans Administration, Post Office Department, Atomic Energy Commission, National Bureau of Standards, and the Weather Bureau find it necessary to develop their own standards and specifications. These departmental specifications may be used by other agencies of the Federal government. Copies of departmental specifications may be obtained from the individual agencies where they are developed.

FEDERAL CONTRACT FORMS

The use of standard contract forms is optional for all agencies of the government. These forms were developed in 1921 and revised in 1953 and 1961 and are now used by all agencies. If the forms are used by an agency, no changes may be made in the body of the form; but, if they must be modified, the modification would appear on a continuation sheet or in the specifications. The standard Federal construction contract forms and their use are found in Title 41 of the Code of Federal Regulation (CFR) as revised on January 1, 1960. The forms may be inspected at any GSA regional office or obtained from the Superintendent of Documents, U.S. Government Printing Office, Washington 25, D.C.

The standard Federal forms of interest to the specifications writer are as follows:

19—Invitation, Bid, and Award (construction, alteration, or repair): to be used for construction contracts of less than $2,000.

19A—Labor Standards Provisions: applicable to contracts in excess of $2,000; can be used with Form 19 for contracts between $2,000 and $10,000.

20—Invitation for Bids (construction contract): to be used for contracts over $10,000.

21—Bid Form (construction contract): contains information on price and related matters; also statement that contractor will execute Standard Form 23 within a definite number of days.

22—Instruction to Bidders (construction contract): this is not a part of the contract documents.

23—Construction Contract: a short description of the work, a statement including Form 23A in the contract, and the signatures of the parties of the agreement.

23A—General Provisions (construction contract): takes the place of what would be classed as the general conditions in private practice.

24—Bid Bond: assures that the contractor will sign a construction contract.

25—Performance Bond: assures that the contractor will fulfill the contract and perform the work.

25A—Payment Bond: assures that the contractor will pay for all labor and materials used on the project.

27—Performance Bond: corporate cosurety form, similar to Form 25.

27A—Payment Bond: corporate cosurety form, similar to Form 27.

27B—Continuation Sheet: corporate cosurety form used as a continuation sheet for form 27 or 27A.

28—Affidavit of Individual Surety: to be used with individuals and not corporations.

FEDERAL GUIDE SPECIFICATIONS

In order to provide the maximum uniformity in specifications and construction throughout the United States, several agencies require the use of standard or guide specifications. The Bureau of Public Roads uses standard specifications for road and bridge construction, supplemented by special provisions to provide for deviations from the standard and for construction not covered in the standard. The Veterans Administration, the FHA, the U.S. Navy Bureau of Yards and Docks, and the U.S. Army Corps of Engineers prepare standard or guide specifications for some or all of their projects. These specifications state requirements for materials and methods of construction that will meet the general requirements of the agency. The guide specifications cover the general requirements of most projects and have blanks to be filled in as the requirements vary from project to project. They sometimes include words or phrases that may be added to modify the basic paragraphs. When a guide specification is applicable to the project at hand, the use of the guide specification is mandatory. Guide specifications are not available unless they are to be used for a specific project. They help to establish the grade and qualities of materials and workmanship that will be required by the various governmental agencies. As new methods of construction are introduced, new materials are developed, and field experience indicates a need for change, these guide specifications are modified to fit the new or improved techniques. The various agencies welcome suggestions for editorial or technical changes to establish guide specifications. While guide specifications are a tremendous help to the specifications writer, they should be used with extreme caution. They can be used only when the design of the project coincides exactly with the guide specification. Most guide specifications make extensive use of Federal specifications as references. Unfortunately, it is not possible to revise these guides as often as the Federal specifications which are used as references. The specifications writer must check each reference cited in a guide specification to be sure that current Federal specifications are used.

STANDARD SPECIFICATIONS FOR MATERIALS, TESTING, AND PRACTICES

A standard specification establishes the requirements for a specific material or process. Specifications for a project will make use of these standards by reference. The standard may be a Federal specification, an interim Federal specification, or a departmental specification. Governmental agencies must give precedence in the following order: If there is an applicable Federal specification, it must be used. An interim Federal specification would be the second choice. If neither of these exists for a given product or process, a departmental standard may be used. If no governmental specification exists that satisfies the requirement, an industry specification may be used. This might be a standard developed by the ASTM, or the ASA, or it might be a commercial standard or one developed by an association. Standard specifications may be up to date when a guide specification is written; however, the specifications writer must check each reference to make certain no revision has been made to the standard without a corresponding revision to the project specification. Standard specifications are provided by the U.S. Bureau of Public Roads for building a complete bridge or structure and by the

Corps of Engineers for a complete facility such as an armory.

The use of government and federal documents in the course of the work of a specifications writer, engineer, or architect has been covered briefly. References have been made to governmental agencies and publications. Much emphasis has been placed on where to find government and commercial documents, with only a limited description of these documents and how to use them. This chapter, and, for that matter, the entire book, is only the starting point of a fascinating, exacting, and rewarding career.

QUESTIONS

1. Discuss three factors that tend to complicate the writing of government specifications.
2. What special precautions must be taken into consideration when designing a project to be built in a foreign country?
3. What procedures must be followed when new or unused products are to be included in a government project?
4. Under what conditions do local building codes govern the construction of a Federal project?
5. May a lien be filed against the Federal government?
6. Who may obtain copies of agency guide specifications, and how are they used?
7. Which agency of the government distributes Federal specification standards?
8. Describe the differences between a Federal specification standard and an interim standard.
9. What does the following abbreviation refer to: "mil-spec"?
10. What is a departmental specification?
11. How can Federal specifications be used in private work?

APPENDIX A Specification Checklist

Checklists will vary in scope and content for many reasons. The checklist included below is a good example of one prepared and used in a particular section of the country for a limited range of commercial and industrial projects:

SPECIFICATION CHECKLIST[1]
by Alfred C. Kluge, Wisconsin Chapter, CSI
JOB _____ FILE NO. _____

Place check mark at all items that apply to project. Fill in blanks where information is required. Under "Remarks" fill in any additional information covering particular division, such as manufacturers' names, catalog page numbers, types, sizes, etc.

List any special materials, features, details, etc., which need attention in specifications.

CODE REQUIREMENTS   REMARKS
  State
  City
  Occupancy
  Type of construction
ZONING REQUIREMENTS
  District
  Set back
  Side yards
  Rear yards
SITE INFORMATION
  Test boring
  Plot and survey
  Utilities
    Sewer
    Water
    Gas
    Electric
    Telephone
EXCAVATING, GRADING, AND SITE WORK
  Subsurface soil data
    Test boring
    Water conditions

[1] A. C. Kluge, Specifications Methods, Construction Specifier, July, 1959.

Clearing site   REMARKS
  Removal of trees
  Removal of topsoil
  Rough grading
  Finish grading
  Subbeds
  Drain tile
  Temporary roads
  Paving
CONCRETE WORK
  Underpinning
  Forms and finishes
    Form lining
    Special textures
  Structural slabs
    Concrete-joist type
    Fireproofing of steel
  Topping
    Over steel joists
    Precast slabs
    Mesh
  Stairs and steps
    Cement finish
    Terrazzo or tile
    Metal pan fill
    Nosing
  Anchorage items
    Slots
    Wire inserts
    Pipe hangers
    Sleeper clips
  Special finishes
    Color
    Abrasive
    Hardener
  Cast in place
    Sills
    Copings
    Chimney caps
  Paving
    Walks
    Driveways
    Curbs
  Miscellaneous items
    Equipment foundation
  Expansion joints
    Premolded
    Poured

Joint compound   REMARKS

MASONRY WORK
  Face brick
    Type
    Price
  Back up
    Brick
    Block
    Tile
  Partitions
    Block
    Tile
    Gypsum
  Facing stone
    Type
  Structural glazed tile
    Ceramic glaze
    Salt glaze
    Size
    Shapes
  Precast concrete
    Sill
    Copings
  Furring
  Chimney
    Flue linings
    Fire brick
    Incinerator
    Fireplace
  Wall reinforcing
  Fireproofing of steel
  Glass blocks
  Dampproofing plaster
CUT STONE
  Type
  Copings
  Sills
  Chimney caps
  Window and door trim
  Cornerstone
  Carving
  Floors
DAMPPROOFING AND WATERPROOFING
  Membrane
    Floors on grade
    Radiant-heat slabs
    Under wood floors
    Tunnels
    Mopped
    Rigid
    Plastic
  Dampproofing
    Basement walls
STRUCTURAL STEEL
  Trusses

Rigid frames   REMARKS
Lintels
STEEL JOISTS
  Type
    Standard
    Long span
    Nailer
  Special fittings and bridging
  Centering
    Metal lath
    Corruform
ROOF DECK
  Type
    Composition
  Concrete
  Gypsum
  Metal
PRECAST FLOOR SLABS
  Type
MISCELLANEOUS METALS
  Access doors
  Area gratings
  Base angles
  Pit covers
  Trench
  Guards
    Wheel guards
    Corner guards
    Jamb guards
  Ladders
    Vertical
    Ship
  Pipe rails
    Roof
    Stairs
    Pits
    Docks
  Sidewalk doors
  Stairs
    Channel frame and steel pan
    Bent plate
    Grating
  Window guards
  Wire screens
    Partitions
    Windows
    Doors
  Building expansion joints
  Structural reinforcing at doors and
    windows
  Chimney irons
    Cleanout doors
    Ash dumps
    Fireplace dampers
    Joist hangers

212

Where?	REMARKS	Toilet	REMARKS

Where?   REMARKS   Toilet   REMARKS
Sleepers   Bathrooms
  Wood bucks   Dressing
Wall sheathing   Bookcases
  Rigid insulating board   Cupboards
  Wood   Wardrobes
  Plywood   Counter tops
Roof sheathing   Linoleum
  Board   Formica
  Plank   Metal
Flooring   Cabinet hardware
  Subfloors   Sliding door
  Softwood   Adjustable shelf rests
  Hardwood   Drawer extension
Cornice   Closet poles
  Soffit material   Garment hangers
Insulation   Racks
  Roof   Bottle
  Wall   Trunk
  Ceiling   Shoe
  Sound-deadening   Pamphlet
  Rigid   Bulletin Boards
  Fill   Built-in equipment
  Blanket   Vestment cases
  Reflective   Desks
Windows   Telephone shelf
  Frames   Organ grills
  Sash   Wood seats
  Prefab   Wood stairs
  Storm   Wood shelving
  Screens   Closets
  Weatherstrips   Special in room numbers
Exterior door frames   Wallboard
  Material   Material
  Transoms   CAULKING
  Sliding   Windows
Wood bumpers   Doors
Exterior wood finish   Special locations
Interior wood finish   Materials
Doors   LATHING AND PLASTERING
  Soundproof   Plaster
  Fireproof   Gypsum
  Sliding   Keene's cement
  Cabinet   Portland cement
Interior frames   Bonding
Interior sash and frames   Sound-absorbing
  Borrowed lights   Colored
  Ceiling lights   Textured
  Serving windows   Fireproofing
Wood base   Ornamental
Paneling   Lathing and furring
  Vertical boards   Gypsum lath
  Veneered panels   Metal lath
  Prefinished   Metal studs
Wood stalls   Furring

Suspended ceilings
Screeds
Base screeds
Expansion screeds
Plaster stops

CERAMIC TILE
Wall and wainscot
Ceramic glaze (size)
Mosaic
Trim
Floors
Quarry tile
Mosaic
Setting beds
Cement
Mastic
Greaseproof
Conductive
Accessories
Towel bars
Paper holders
Tumbler holders
Soap dishes
Grab bars

MARBLE WORK
Material
Wainscot
Stools
Panels
Altars
Communion railing
Credence shelves
Shrines
Stalls
Toilet
Shower
Bath
Floors
Stairs
Treads
Risers
Stringers
Slate
Floors
Standing

TERRAZZO
Floors
Base
Plinths
Stairs
Over concrete
Steel pan
Showers
Service sinks
Planters

COMPOSITION FLOOR
COVERINGS
Asphalt tile
Vinyl asbestos
Vinyl
Tile
Sheet
Linoleum
Cork
Rubber
Base
Rubber
Vinyl

WOOD FLOORING
Parquet
Block
Strip
In mastic
Nailed
Heavy-duty Block
Underlayment
Finish

GLASS AND GLAZING
Double glazing
Stained Glass
Allowance $
Storm glass
Obscure
Clear
Plate glass
Clear window glass
Obscure glass
Light diffusing
Heat-absorbing
Leaded
Mirrors
Molded glass
Fibered glass
Wire glass
Metal setting
Type

ACOUSTICAL TREATMENT
Tile
Fiber
Mineral
Metal
Pan
Corrugated
Installation
Cement
Metal suspension
Nail or screw

FINISH HARDWARE
Allowance $
Schedule

PAINTING AND DECORATING	REMARKS	MISCELLANEOUS EQUIPMENT	REMARKS
Exterior		Blackboards	
Woodwork		Book stacks	
Soffits		Bulletin boards	
Masonry		Cabinets	
Metalwork		Church furniture	
Interior		Floor mats	
Walls and ceilings		Folding doors	
Masonry		Key cabinets	
Floors		Kitchen equipment	
Woodwork		Lab equipment	
Paint		Library furniture	
Varnish		Laundry equipment	
Metalwork		Movable partitions	
Wallpaper		Overhead doors	
SPECIAL WALL FINISHES		Seating	
Vinyl-coated fabric		Stage equipment	
Baked enamel		Window cleaner's bolts	
		X-ray equipment	

Organizations in the Construction Industry

ACIDPROOF CEMENT MANUFACTURERS
ASSOCIATION
1015 Chestnut Street
Philadelphia, Pa.

ACOUSTICAL CONTRACTORS' ASSOCIATION
1632 K Street N.W.
Washington 6, D.C.

ACOUSTICAL MATERIALS ASSOCIATION
335 East 45th Street
New York 17, N.Y.

ACOUSTICAL SOCIETY OF AMERICA
335 East 45th Street
New York 17, N.Y.

AIR CONDITIONING & REFRIGERATION
INSTITUTE
1346 Connecticut Avenue N.W.
Washington 6, D.C.

AIR DISTRIBUTION INSTITUTE
2130 Keith Building
Cleveland 15, Ohio

AIR FILTER INSTITUTE
2753 Fourth Avenue South
Minneapolis 8, Minn.

AIR MOVING AND CONDITIONING
ASSOCIATION
2159 Guardian Building
Detroit 26, Mich.

ALLIED STONE INDUSTRIES
11732-56 South Halsted
Chicago, Ill.

ALUMINUM ASSOCIATION
420 Lexington Avenue
New York 17, N.Y.

ALUMINUM EXTRUDERS COUNCIL
1015 Chestnut Street
Philadelphia 7, Pa.

ALUMINUM SIDING ASSOCIATION
Tribune Tower
Chicago, Ill.

ALUMINUM WINDOW MANUFACTURERS
ASSOCIATION
630 Third Avenue
New York 17, N.Y.

AMERICAN ARBITRATION ASSOCIATION
477 Madison Avenue
New York 22, N.Y.

AMERICAN ASSOCIATION OF STATE
HIGHWAY OFFICIALS
917 National Press Building
Washington 4, D.C.

AMERICAN CERAMIC ASSOCIATION
4055 North High Street
Columbus, Ohio

AMERICAN CONCRETE INSTITUTE
7400 South Boulevard
Detroit, Mich.

AMERICAN CONCRETE PIPE ASSOCIATION
228 North LaSalle Street
Chicago 31, Ill.

AMERICAN COUNCIL OF INDEPENDENT
LABORATORIES, INC.
4302 East-West Highway
Washington 14, D.C.

AMERICAN FOREST PRODUCTS
INDUSTRIES, INC.
1816 North Street, N.W.
Washington 6, D.C.

AMERICAN FOUNDRY ASSOCIATION
Golf and Wolf Roads
Des Plaines, Ill.

AMERICAN GAS ASSOCIATION
420 Lexington Avenue
New York 17, N.Y.

AMERICAN HARDBOARD ASSOCIATION
205 West Wacker Drive
Chicago 6, Ill.

AMERICAN HARDWARE MANUFACTURERS
ASSOCIATION
342 Madison Avenue
New York 17, N.Y.

AMERICAN HOT DIP GALVANIZERS'
ASSOCIATION
3211 First National Bank Building
Pittsburgh 22, Pa.

AMERICAN INSTITUTE OF ARCHITECTS
1735 New York Avenue N.W.
Washington 6, D.C.

[1]This is a partial list of those organizations active in the construction industry.

AMERICAN INSTITUTE OF CHEMICAL
    ENGINEERS
25 West 44th Street
New York 19, N.Y.
AMERICAN INSTITUTE OF CONSULTING
    ENGINEERS
33 West 39th Street
New York 18, N.Y.
AMERICAN INSTITUTE OF DECORATORS
673 Fifth Avenue
New York 22, N.Y.
AMERICAN INSTITUTE OF ELECTRICAL
    ENGINEERS
39 West 39th Street
New York 18, N.Y.
AMERICAN INSTITUTE OF INDUSTRIAL
    ENGINEERS
145 North High Street
Columbus 15, Ohio
AMERICAN INSTITUTE OF MINING,
    METALLURGICAL AND PETROLEUM
    ENGINEERS, INC.
29 West 39th Street
New York 18, N.Y.
AMERICAN INSTITUTE OF PLANT
    ENGINEERS
Box 185
Barrington, Ill.
AMERICAN INSTITUTE OF STEEL
    CONSTRUCTION
101 Park Avenue
New York 17, N.Y.
AMERICAN INSTITUTE OF TIMBER
    CONSTRUCTION
1757 K Street N.W.
Washington 6, D.C.
AMERICAN IRON AND STEEL INSTITUTE
150 East 42nd Street
New York 17, N.Y.
AMERICAN SOCIETY FOR METALS
7301 Euclid Avenue
Cleveland 3, Ohio
AMERICAN SOCIETY FOR TESTING AND
    MATERIALS
1916 Race Street
Philadelphia 3, Pa.
AMERICAN SOCIETY OF ARCHITECTURAL
    HARDWARE CONSULTANTS
220 E Street
Santa Rosa, Calif.
AMERICAN SOCIETY OF CIVIL ENGINEERS
33 West 39th Street
New York 18, N.Y.

AMERICAN SOCIETY OF HEATING AND
    VENTILATING CONSULTANTS
62 Worth Street
New York 13, N.Y.
AMERICAN SOCIETY OF HEATING,
    REFRIGERATING AND AIR-
    CONDITIONING ENGINEERS, INC.
342 Fifth Avenue
New York 1, N.Y.
AMERICAN SOCIETY OF LANDSCAPE
    ARCHITECTS
9 Park Street
Boston 8, Mass.
AMERICAN SOCIETY OF MECHANICAL
    ENGINEERS
345 East 47th Street
New York 13, N.Y.
AMERICAN SOCIETY OF REFRIGERATION
    ENGINEERS
40 West 40th Street
New York, N.Y.
AMERICAN SOCIETY OF SANITARY
    ENGINEERS
228 Standard Building
Cleveland 13, Ohio
AMERICAN STANDARDS ASSOCIATION
10 East 40th Street
New York 16, N.Y.
AMERICAN WALNUT MANUFACTURERS
    ASSOCIATION
666 North Lake Shore Drive
Chicago 11, Ill.
AMERICAN WOOD PRESERVERS
    ASSOCIATION
1427 E Street N.W.
Washington, D.C.
AMERICAN WOOD PRESERVERS INSTITUTE
111 West Washington Street
Chicago 2, Ill.
AMERICAN ZINC INSTITUTE
292 Madison Avenue
New York 17, N.Y.
APPALACHIAN HARDWOOD
    MANUFACTURERS, INC.
1015 Mercantile Library Building
414 Walnut Street
Cincinnati 2, Ohio
ARCHITECTURAL TERRA COTTA
    INSTITUTE
1520 18th Street N.W.
Washington, D.C.
ARCHITECTURAL WOODWORK INSTITUTE,
    INC.
322 South Michigan
Chicago, Ill.

ARKANSAS SOFT PINE BUREAU
Boyle Building
Little Rock, Ark.
ASBESTOS-CEMENT PRODUCTS
    ASSOCIATION
509 Madison Avenue
New York 22, N.Y.
ASPHALT AND VINYL ASBESTOS TILE
    INSTITUTE
101 Park Avenue
New York 17, N.Y.
ASPHALT INSTITUTE
Asphalt Institute Building
University of Maryland
College Park, Md.
ASPHALT ROOFING INDUSTRY BUREAU
2 West 45th Street
New York 19, N.Y.
ASSOCIATED BRICK MANUFACTURERS OF
    SOUTHERN CALIFORNIA
553 South Western Avenue
Los Angeles 5, Calif.
ASSOCIATED FACTORY MUTUAL FIRE
    INSURANCE COMPANIES
1151 Boston Providence Turnpike
Norwood, Nebr.
ASSOCIATED GENERAL CONTRACTORS OF
    AMERICA, INC.
1918 E Street
Washington 6, D.C.
ASSOCIATED PLUMBING CONTRACTORS
1404 Humbolt Bank Building
785 Market Street
San Francisco 3, Calif.
ASSOCIATION FOR APPLIED SOLAR
    ENERGY
c/o Arizona State University
Tempe, Ariz.
ASSOCIATION OF IRON AND STEEL
    ENGINEERS
1010 Empire Building
Pittsburgh 22, Pa.
BETTER HEATING-COOLING COUNCIL
250 Park Avenue
New York 17, N.Y.
BUILDING OFFICIALS CONFERENCE OF
    AMERICA, INC.
1525 East 53rd Street
Chicago 15, Ill.
BUILDING RESEARCH INSTITUTE
2101 Constitution Avenue N.W.
Washington 25, D.C.
BUILDING STONE INSTITUTE
2115 Martindale Avenue
Indianapolis, Ind.

BUILDING TRADES EMPLOYER'S
    ASSOCIATION
711 Third Avenue
New York 17, N.Y.
CALIFORNIA REDWOOD ASSOCIATION
566 Sacramento Street
San Francisco 11, Calif.
CANVAS AWNING INSTITUTE, INC.
P.O. Box 1851
Memphis 1, Tenn.
CAST IRON SOIL PIPE INSTITUTE
1627 K Street N.W.
Washington 6, D.C.
CERAMIC SOCIETY OF THE SOUTHWEST
P.O. Box 935
Austin, Tex.
CERAMIC TILE INSTITUTE
3415 West 8th Street
Los Angeles 5, Calif.
CLAY BRICK AND TILE ASSOCIATION
55 New Montgomery Street
San Francisco 5, Calif.
CLAY FLUE LINING INSTITUTE
161 Ash Street
Akron 8, Ohio
CLAY PIPE INSTITUTE
315 West 9th Street
Los Angeles 15, Calif.
CLAY PRODUCTS ASSOCIATION OF THE
    SOUTHWEST
109 Perry-Brooks Building
Austin, Tex.
CLAY SEWER PIPE ASSOCIATION, INC.
Room 311
High-Long Building
5 East Long Street
Columbus 15, Ohio
COLD ROLL FORMED STRUCTURAL
    FRAMING INSTITUTE
38 South Dearborn Street
Chicago, Ill.
CONCRETE MASONRY ASSOCIATION
5205 Hollywood Boulevard
Los Angeles, Calif.
CONCRETE REINFORCING STEEL
    INSTITUTE
38 South Dearborn Street
Chicago 3, Ill.
CONSTRUCTION AND CIVIC DEVELOPMENT
    DEPARTMENT
Chamber of Commerce of the United States
1616 H Street N.W.
Washington 6, D.C.

CONSTRUCTION EMPLOYERS ASSOCIATION
2565 St. Marys Avenue
Omaha, Nebr.
CONSTRUCTION INDUSTRY
    MANUFACTURERS ASSOCIATION
135 South LaSalle Street
Chicago 3, Ill.
CONSTRUCTION SPECIFICATIONS
    INSTITUTE
632 DuPont Circle Building
Washington 6, D.C.
CONSTRUCTION SURVEYORS INSTITUTE
101 Park Avenue
New York 17, N.Y.
CONSULTING ENGINEERS COUNCIL
326 Reisch Building
Springfield, Ill.
COPPER INSTITUTE
50 Broadway
New York 4, N.Y.
CORK INSTITUTE OF AMERICA
342 Madison Avenue
New York 17, N.Y.
DIMENSION HARDWOOD MANUFACTURERS
    ASSOCIATION
3813 Hillsboro Road
Nashville 12, Tenn.
DISTRIBUTORS COUNCIL, INC.
3329 8th Street N.E.
Washington 17, D.C.
DOOR OPERATION AND REMOTE CONTROL
    ASSOCIATION
110 North Wacker Drive
Chicago, Ill.
DOUGLAS FIR PLYWOOD ASSOCIATION
1119 A Street
Tacoma 2, Washington
DRAPERY HARDWARE MANUFACTURERS
    ASSOCIATION
53 Park Place
New York 7, N.Y.
EDISON ELECTRIC INSTITUTE
750 Third Avenue
New York 17, N.Y.
ELECTRIC OVERHEAD CRANE INSTITUTE
2 Thomas Circle N.W.
Washington 5, D.C.
ELECTRICAL CONTRACTORS' ASSOCIATION
1200 18th Street N.W.
Washington 5, D.C.
ELECTRICAL MANUFACTURERS
    ASSOCIATION
155 East 144th Street
New York 17, N.Y.

ELEVATOR MANUFACTURING INDUSTRY
    ASSOCIATION
101 Park Avenue
New York 17, N.Y.
ENGINEERS JOINT COUNCIL
29 West 39th Street
New York 18, N.Y.
EXPANSION JOINT INSTITUTE
1460 East River Road
South Aurora, Ill.
FACING TILE INSTITUTE
1520 18th Street N.W.
Washington 6, D.C.
FELT ASSOCIATION
631 Third Avenue
New York 17, N.Y.
FINE HARDWOODS ASSOCIATION
666 Lake Shore Drive
Chicago 11, Ill.
FINISHING LIME ASSOCIATION OF OHIO
United Savings Building
Toledo, Ohio
FIR DOOR INSTITUTE
Tacoma Building
Tacoma, Wash.
FIRE EQUIPMENT MANUFACTURERS
    ASSOCIATION
759 One Gateway Center
Pittsburgh 22, Pa.
FIREPLACE EQUIPMENT MANUFACTURERS
    ASSOCIATION
332 South Michigan Avenue
Chicago 4, Ill.
FOREST PRODUCTS RESEARCH SOCIETY
P.O. Box 2010
University Station
Madison 5, Wis.
GAS APPLIANCE MANUFACTURERS
    ASSOCIATION
60 East 42nd Street
New York 17, N.Y.
GAS VENT INSTITUTE
332 South Michigan Avenue
Chicago 4, Ill.
GYMNASIUM SEATING COUNCIL
122 South Michigan Street
Chicago 4, Ill.
GYPSUM ASSOCIATION
201 North Wells Street
Chicago 6, Ill.
GYPSUM DRYWALL CONTRACTORS
    INTERNATIONAL
608 South Hill Street
Los Angeles, Calif.

HARDWOOD PLYWOOD INSTITUTE
2310 South Walter Reed Drive
Arlington, Va.
HEATING, PIPING AND AIR CONDITIONING
    CONTRACTORS NATIONAL
    ASSOCIATION
30 Rockefeller Plaza
New York 23, N.Y.
HOIST MANUFACTURERS ASSOCIATION
1 Thomas Circle N.W.
Washington 5, D.C.
HOME MANUFACTURERS ASSOCIATION
1117 Barr Building
910 17th Street N.W.
Washington 6, D.C.
ILLUMINATING ENGINEERING SOCIETY
1860 Broadway
New York 23, N.Y.
INDIANA LIMESTONE INSTITUTE
Box 757
Bloomington, Ind.
INDUSTRIAL FASTENERS INSTITUTE
1517 Terminal Tower
Cleveland 13, Ohio
INDUSTRIAL UNIT HEATER ASSOCIATION
2159 Guardian Building
Detroit, Mich.
INSECT WIRE SCREENING BUREAU
630 Third Avenue
New York 17, N.Y.
INSTITUTE OF BOILER AND RADIATOR
    MANUFACTURERS
60 East 42nd Street
New York, N.Y.
INSULATING SIDING ASSOCIATION
1201 Waukegan Road
Glenview, Ill.
INSULATION BOARD INSTITUTE
111 West Washington Street
Chicago 2, Ill.
INTERNATIONAL ASSOCIATION OF
    BLUEPRINTS AND ALLIED INDUSTRIES
33 East Congress Parkway
Chicago 5, Ill.
INTERNATIONAL CONFERENCE OF
    BUILDING OFFICIALS
610 South Broadway
Los Angeles 14, Calif.
INTERNATIONAL CUT STONE
    CONTRACTORS AND QUARRYMENS
    ASSOCIATION
40 East 56th Street
Indianapolis, Ind.

INTERNATIONAL FUEL OIL COUNCIL
424 Madison Avenue
New York 17, N.Y.
INTERNATIONAL STAINED GLASS
    ASSOCIATION
15 Prince Street
Paterson 1, N.J.
KRAFT PAPER ASSOCIATION, INC.
122 East 42nd Street
New York 17, N.Y.
LEAD INDUSTRIES ASSOCIATION
292 Madison Avenue
New York 17, N.Y.
LIQUEFIED PETROLEUM GAS ASSOCIATION
11 South LaSalle Street
Chicago 3, Ill.
MAHOGANY ASSOCIATION, INC.
666 Lake Shore Drive
Chicago 11, Ill.
MAPLE FLOORING MANUFACTURERS
    ASSOCIATION
35 East Wacker Drive
Chicago 1, Ill.
MARBLE INSTITUTE OF AMERICA, INC.
32 South 5th Avenue
Mount Vernon, N.Y.
MASONRY INSTITUTE
422A Washington Building
Washington, D.C.
MATERIAL HANDLING INSTITUTE, INC.
Suite 759
One Gateway Center
Pittsburgh 22, Pa.
MECHANICAL CONTRACTORS ASSOCIATION
    OF AMERICA, INC.
45 Rockefeller Plaza
New York 20, N.Y.
MEDICINE CABINET COUNCIL
1145 19th Street
Washington 6, D.C.
METAL COMPARTMENT MANUFACTURERS
    ASSOCIATION
405 Lexington Avenue
New York 17, N.Y.
METAL LATH MANUFACTURERS
    ASSOCIATION
636 Engineers Building
Cleveland 14, Ohio
METAL ROOF DECK TECHNICAL
    INSTITUTE
2250 East Grand Boulevard
Detroit, Mich.

METAL VENTILATOR INSTITUTE
22 West Monroe Street
Chicago 3, Ill.
MICHIGAN ARCHITECTURAL WOODWORK
ASSOCIATION
1119 Bank of Lansing Building
Lansing 16, Mich.
MIRROR MANUFACTURERS ASSOCIATION
2217 Tribune Tower
Chicago 11, Ill.
MODULAR BUILDING STANDARDS
ASSOCIATION
2029 K Street N.W.
Washington 6, D.C.
MO-SAI INSTITUTE, INC.
P.O. Box 606
New Haven, Conn.
NATIONAL ACOUSTICAL CONTRACTORS'
ASSOCIATION
1632 K Street N.W.
Washington 6, D.C.
NATIONAL AMERICAN WHOLESALE
LUMBER ASSOCIATION
3 East 44th Street
New York 17, N.Y.
NATIONAL ASSOCIATION OF
ARCHITECTURAL METAL
MANUFACTURERS
228 North LaSalle Street
Chicago 1, Ill.
NATIONAL ASSOCIATION OF COMMISSION
LUMBER SALESMEN, INC.
3903 Olive Street
St. Louis 8, Mo.
NATIONAL ASSOCIATION OF CORROSION
ENGINEERS
1061 M & M Building
Houston 2, Tex.
NATIONAL ASSOCIATION OF DISTRIBUTORS
AND DEALERS OF STRUCTURAL CLAY
PRODUCTS
1258 Donahue Avenue
St. Paul, Minn.
NATIONAL ASSOCIATION OF ELECTRICAL
DISTRIBUTORS
290 Madison Avenue
New York 17, N.Y.
NATIONAL ASSOCIATION OF FAN
MANUFACTURERS, INC.
2159 Guardian Building
Detroit, Mich.
NATIONAL ASSOCIATION OF FOOD
EQUIPMENT MANUFACTURERS
714 Pine Street
Roselle Park, N.J.

NATIONAL ASSOCIATION OF HOME
BUILDERS
1625 L Street N.W.
Washington 6, D.C.
NATIONAL ASSOCIATION OF ORNAMENTAL
METAL MANUFACTURERS
209 Cedar Avenue
Tacoma Park
Washington 12, D.C.
NATIONAL ASSOCIATION OF PLASTIC
MANUFACTURERS
812 Engineers Building
Cleveland 14, Ohio
NATIONAL ASSOCIATION OF PLUMBING
CONTRACTORS, INC.
1026 20th Street N.W.
Washington 6, D.C.
NATIONAL ASSOCIATION OF STORE
FIXTURES MANUFACTURERS
53 West Jackson Building
Chicago 4, Ill.
NATIONAL AUTOMATIC SPRINKLER AND
FIRE CONTROL ASSOCIATION
60 East 42nd Street
New York 17, N.Y.
NATIONAL BOARD OF FIRE UNDERWRITERS
85 John Street
New York 38, N.Y.
NATIONAL BUILDERS HARDWARE
ASSOCIATION
515 Madison Avenue
New York 22, N.Y.
NATIONAL BUILDING GRANITE QUARRIES
ASSOCIATION, INC.
114 East 40th Street
New York 16, N.Y.
NATIONAL BUILDING MATERIAL DEALERS
SERVICE CORPORATION
Suite 302
Ring Building
Washington 6, D.C.
NATIONAL CERTIFIED PIPE WELDING
BUREAU
Suite 570
45 Rockefeller Plaza
New York 20, N.Y.
NATIONAL CINDER CONCRETE PRODUCTS
ASSOCIATION
P.O. Box 67
Primos, Pa.
NATIONAL COAL ASSOCIATION
802 Southern Building
Washington 5, D.C.

NATIONAL CONCRETE MASONRY
ASSOCIATION
1015 Wisconsin Avenue N.W.
Washington 7, D.C.

NATIONAL CONTRACT HARDWARE
ASSOCIATION
420 Madison Avenue
New York 17, N.Y.

NATIONAL COUNCIL ON SCHOOLHOUSE
CONSTRUCTION
George Peabody College for Teachers
Nashville 4, Tenn.

NATIONAL CRUSHED STONE ASSOCIATION
1415 Eliot Place N.W.
Washington 7, D.C.

NATIONAL DOOR MANUFACTURERS
ASSOCIATION
332 South Michigan Avenue
Chicago 4, Ill.

NATIONAL ELECTRICAL MANUFACTURERS
ASSOCIATION
155 East 44th Street
New York 17, N.Y.

NATIONAL FIRE PROTECTION ASSOCIATION
60 Batterymarch Street
Boston 10, Mass.

NATIONAL FOUNDATION FOR LATHING AND
PLASTERING, INC.
173 West Madison Street
Chicago 2, Ill.

NATIONAL HARDWOOD LUMBER
ASSOCIATION
59 East Van Buren Street
Chicago 5, Ill.

NATIONAL INSULATION MANUFACTURERS
ASSOCIATION
441 Lexington Avenue
New York 17, N.Y.

NATIONAL LANDSCAPE NURSERYMANS
ASSOCIATION
8620 Crest Road
Minneapolis 20, Minn.

NATIONAL LUMBER MANUFACTURERS
ASSOCIATION
1619 Massachusetts Avenue N.W.
Washington 6, D.C.

NATIONAL METAL AWNING ASSOCIATION
Hotel Normandie
Philadelphia 4, Pa.

NATIONAL MINERAL WOOL INSULATION
ASSOCIATION
2916 Americas Building
Rockefeller Center
New York 20, N.Y.

NATIONAL OAK FLOORING
MANUFACTURERS ASSOCIATION
814 Sterick Building
Memphis 3, Tenn.

NATIONAL ORNAMENTAL IRON
MANUFACTURERS ASSOCIATION
211 Madison Avenue
Memphis, Tenn.

NATIONAL PAINT, VARNISH & LACQUER
ASSOCIATION
1500 Rhode Island Avenue N.W.
Washington 5, D.C.

NATIONAL PARTICLE BOARD ASSOCIATION
1145 19th Street N.W.
Washington 6, D.C.

NATIONAL READY MIXED CONCRETE
ASSOCIATION
Munsey Building
Washington 4, D.C.

NATIONAL RETAIL FLOOR COVERINGS
COUNCIL
Suite 810, Harrison Building
4 South 15th Street
Philadelphia 2, Pa.

NATIONAL ROOFING CONTRACTORS
ASSOCIATION
189 West Madison Avenue
Chicago 2, Ill.

NATIONAL SAFETY COUNCIL
425 North Michigan Avenue
Chicago 11, Ill.

NATIONAL SAND AND GRAVEL
ASSOCIATION
1411 K Street N.W.
Washington 6, D.C.

NATIONAL SANITARY SUPPLY ASSOCIATION
159 North Dearborn Street
Chicago, Ill.

NATIONAL SCHOOL SUPPLY AND
EQUIPMENT ASSOCIATION
27 East Monroe Street
Chicago 3, Ill.

NATIONAL SLAG ASSOCIATION
613 Perpetual Building
Washington 4, D.C.

NATIONAL SLATE ASSOCIATION
455 West 23rd Street
New York 11, N.Y.

NATIONAL SOCIETY OF PROFESSIONAL
ENGINEERS
2029 K Street N.W.
Washington 6, D.C.

NATIONAL SWIMMING POOL INSTITUTE
Harvard, Ill.

NATIONAL TERRAZZO & MOSAIC
  ASSOCIATION
Manufacturers Division
2000 K Street N.W.
Washington 6, D.C.
NATIONAL WARM AIR HEATING AND AIR
  CONDITIONING ASSOCIATION
145 Public
Cleveland 14, Ohio
NATIONAL WHOLESALE LUMBER
  DISTRIBUTING YARD ASSOCIATION, INC.
1144 North 11th Street
Omaha, Nebr.
NATIONAL WOODWORK MANUFACTURERS'
  ASSOCIATION
332 South Michigan Avenue
Chicago 4, Ill.
NON-FERROUS HOT WATER TANK
  MANUFACTURERS ASSOCIATION
75 Federal Street
Boston, Mass.
NORTHEASTERN LUMBER
  MANUFACTURERS' ASSOCIATION, INC.
271 Madison Avenue
New York 16, N.Y.
NORTHERN HEMLOCK AND HARDWOOD
  MANUFACTURERS ASSOCIATION
207 Norther Building
Green Bay, Wis.
NORTHERN PINE MANUFACTURERS
  ASSOCIATION
4329 Oakland Avenue
Minneapolis 7, Minn.
OXYCHLORIDE CEMENT ASSOCIATION
1832 M Street N.W.
Chicago 11, Ill.
PAINT RESEARCH INSTITUTE
P.O. Box 593
New Albany, Ind.
PAINTING AND DECORATING
  CONTRACTORS OF AMERICA
2625 West Peterson Avenue
Chicago 45, Ill.
PERLITE INSTITUTE
45 West 45th Street
New York 36, N.Y.
PHILIPPINE MAHOGANY ASSOCIATION
111 West 7th Street
Los Angeles, Calif.
PLUMBING AND DRAINAGE INSTITUTE
Room 814
20 Wacker Drive
Chicago 6, Ill.

PLUMBING BRASS INSTITUTE
Suite 759
One Gateway Center
Pittsburgh 22, Pa.
PLUMBING FIXTURE MANUFACTURERS
  ASSOCIATION
1145 19th Street N.W.
Washington 6, D.C.
PLUMBING-HEATING-COOLING
  INFORMATION BUREAU
35 East Wacker Drive
Chicago 6, Ill.
PLUMBING INDUSTRY PROGRESS AND
  EDUCATIONAL FUND
608 South Hill Street
Los Angeles, Calif.
PONDEROSA PINE WOODWORK
  ASSOCIATION
39 South LaSalle Street
Chicago 3, Ill.
PORCELAIN ENAMEL INSTITUTE, INC.
1145 19th Street N.W.
Washington 6, D.C.
PORTLAND CEMENT ASSOCIATION
33 West Grand Avenue
Chicago 10, Ill.
PORTLAND CEMENT ASSOCIATION
  RESEARCH AND DEVELOPMENT
  LABORATORIES
5420 Old Orchard Road
Skokie, Ill.
POWER ACTUATED TOOL
  MANUFACTURERS INSTITUTE
25 East 43rd Street
New York 17, N.Y.
PRESTRESSED CONCRETE INSTITUTE
205 West Wacker Drive
Chicago 6, Ill.
PRODUCERS COUNCIL, INC.
2029 K Street N.W.
Washington 6, D.C.
PROPELLER FAN MANUFACTURERS
2159 Guardian Building
Detroit, Mich.
RAIL STEEL BAR ASSOCIATION
38 South Dearborn Street
Chicago 3, Ill.
RED CEDAR SHINGLE BUREAU
5510 Burrard Street
Vancouver 1, B.C., Canada
REFRIGERATION AND AIR CONDITIONING
  CONTRACTORS ASSOCIATION
1028 Connecticut Avenue N.W.
Washington 6, D.C.

REFRIGERATION SERVICE ENGINEERS
    SOCIETY
435 North Waller Avenue
Chicago 44, Ill.
ROOFING AND SHEET METAL CRAFTS
    INSTITUTE
254 West 23rd Street
New York 17, N.Y.
RUBBER AND PLASTIC ADHESIVE &
    SEALANT MANUFACTURERS COUNCIL
759 North Dearborn Street
Chicago 1, Ill.
RUBBER MANUFACTURERS ASSOCIATION,
    INC.
444 Madison Avenue
New York 17, N.Y.
SCHOOL FACILITIES COUNCIL
26 Washington Place
New York 3, N.Y.
SCIENTIFIC APPARATUS MAKERS
    ASSOCIATION
20 North Wacker Drive
Chicago 6, Ill.
SCREEN MANUFACTURERS ASSOCIATION
110 North Wacker Drive
Chicago 6, Ill.
SHEET METAL CONTRACTOR'S NATIONAL
    ASSOCIATION, INC.
170 Division Street
Elgin, Ill.
SLIDING GLASS DOOR AND WINDOW
    INSTITUTE
6132 Whitter Boulevard
Suite B
Los Angeles 22, Calif.
SOCIETY OF PLASTICS ENGINEERS, INC.
65 Prospect Street
Stamford, Conn.
SOUTHEASTERN CONCRETE MASONRY
    ASSOCIATION
1025 Jefferson Avenue
Paducah, Ky.
SOUTHERN BRICK AND TILE
    MANUFACTURERS ASSOCIATION
230 Spring Street N.W.
Atlanta 3, Ga.
SOUTHERN BUILDING CODE CONGRESS
Brown-Marx Building
Birmington, Ala.
SOUTHERN CLAY PIPE INSTITUTE
1401 Peachtree Street N.E.
Atlanta, Ga.

SOUTHERN CYPRESS MANUFACTURERS
    ASSOCIATION
P.O. Box 5772
Jacksonville 7, Fla.
SOUTHERN HARDWOOD PRODUCTS, INC.
805 Sterick Building
Memphis 3, Tenn.
SOUTHERN PINE ASSOCIATION
P.O. Box 1170
New Orleans 4, La.
SOUTHERN PINE INSPECTION BUREAU
National Bank of Commerce Building
New Orleans 4, La.
SOUTHERN TILE CONTRACTORS
    ASSOCIATION
P.O. Box 8596
Battlefield Station
Jackson, Miss.
SOUTHERN WOODWORK ASSOCIATION
P.O. Box 1804
Knoxville, Tenn.
STAINED GLASS ASSOCIATION OF AMERICA
822 Wilmington Avenue
St. Louis 11, Mo.
STAINED SHINGLE AND SHALE ASSOCIATION
835 Central Building
Seattle 4, Wash.
STEAM HEATING EQUIPMENT
    MANUFACTURERS ASSOCIATION
Barnes & Jones, Inc.
Newtonville
Boston, Mass.
STEEL BOILER INSTITUTE
366 Madison Avenue
New York, N.Y.
STEEL DOOR INSTITUTE
2130 Keith Building
Cleveland 15, Ohio
STEEL JOIST INSTITUTE
DuPont Circle Building
Washington, D.C.
STEEL KITCHEN CABINET
    MANUFACTURERS ASSOCIATION
Cleveland 14, Ohio
STEEL LOCKER COUNCIL
737 Guardian Building
Cleveland 14, Ohio
STEEL STRUCTURES PAINTING COUNCIL
4400 5th Avenue
Memphis, Tenn.
STEEL WINDOW INSTITUTE
805 Rowland Avenue
Sheltenham, Pa.

STRUCTURAL CLAY PRODUCTS INSTITUTE
1520 18th Street N.W.
Washington 6, D.C.
STRUCTURAL WOOD FIBER PRODUCTS
    ASSOCIATION
535 East Broad Street
Columbus 15, Ohio
STUCCO MANUFACTURERS ASSOCIATION,
    INC.
347 North Central Avenue
Glendale 3, Calif.
SURETY ASSOCIATION OF AMERICA
60 John Street
New York, N.Y.
TEXAS CERAMIC TILE CONTRACTORS
    ASSOCIATION, INC.
1026 South Adams
Fort Worth 4, Texas
THERMAL INSULATION SOCIETY
c/o Industrial Insulators, Inc.
Houston, Texas.
TILE CONTRACTORS ASSOCIATION OF
    AMERICA
1420 New York Drive N.W.
Washington 5, D.C.
TILE COUNCIL OF AMERICA
800 Second Avenue
New York 17, N.Y.
TILE MANUFACTURERS ASSOCIATION, INC.
50 East 42nd Street
New York 17, N.Y.
TWISTED JUTE PACKING AND OAKUM
    INSTITUTE
19 West 44th Street
New York 36, N.Y.
UNDERWRITERS LABORATORIES, INC.
207 East Ohio Street
Chicago, Ill.
VERMICULITE INSTITUTE
208 South LaSalle Street
Chicago 4, Ill.
VINYL FABRICS INSTITUTE
65 East 55th Street
New York 22, N.Y.
VITREOUS CHINA PLUMBING FIXTURES
    ASSOCIATION
1709 M Street N.W.
Washington 6, D.C.
WALLPAPER INSTITUTE
509 Madison Avenue
New York 22, N.Y.
WATER AND SEWAGE WORKS
    MANUFACTURERS ASSOCIATION, INC.
165 Broadway
New York 6, N.Y.

WATER CONDITIONING FOUNDATION
Box 103
1201 Waukegan Road
Glenview, Ill.
WATERPROOF PAPER MANUFACTURERS
    ASSOCIATION
122 East 42nd Street
New York 17, N.Y.
WATERPROOFERS ASSOCIATION, INC.
Building 60
East 42nd Street
New York 17, N.Y
WEATHERSTRIP RESEARCH INSTITUTE
Box 128
Riverside, Ill.
WELDED STEEL TUBE INSTITUTE, INC.
1604 Hanna Building
Cleveland 15, Ohio
WEST COAST LUMBER INSPECTION BUREAU
1410 S.W. Morrison Street
Portland 5, Ore.
WEST COAST LUMBERMEN'S ASSOCIATION
1410 S.W. Morrison Street
Portland 5, Ore.
WESTERN LUMBER MANUFACTURERS
    ASSOCIATION, INC.
271 Madison Avenue
New York 16, N.Y.
WESTERN PINE ASSOCIATION
510 Yeon Building
Portland 4, Ore.
WESTERN RED AND NORTHERN WHITE
    CEDAR ASSOCIATION
500 Investors Building
Minneapolis 2, Minn.
WESTERN RED CEDAR LUMBER
    ASSOCIATION
4403 White-Henry-Stuart Building
Seattle 1, Wash.
WIRE ASSOCIATION
453 Main Street
Stamford, Conn.
WIRE REINFORCEMENT INSTITUTE, INC.
National Press Building
Washington 4, D.C.
WOOD FLOOR INSTITUTE OF AMERICA
201 North Wells Street
Chicago 6, Ill.
WOODWORK INSTITUTE OF CALIFORNIA
1833 Broadway
Fresno, Calif.
WOVEN WIRE PRODUCTS ASSOCIATION
1721 West School Street
Chicago 13, Ill.

APPENDIX C

Government Depository Libraries

The specifications writer may see copies of all Federal specifications at the following locations:

ALABAMA
    Library, Auburn University
    Auburn, Ala.

    Public Library
    Birmingham, Ala.

ARKANSAS
    Library, University of Arkansas
    Fayetteville, Ark.

CALIFORNIA
    General Library
    University of California
    Berkeley, Calif.

    Eureka Free Library
    Eureka, Calif.

    Public Library
    Long Beach, Calif.

    Los Angeles Public Library
    Los Angeles, Calif.

    Library, University of California at Los
       Angeles
    Los Angeles, Calif.

    Library, University of Southern California
    Los Angeles, Calif.

    Oakland Public Library
    Oakland, Calif.

    California State Library
    Sacramento, Calif.

    Public Library
    San Diego, Calif.

    San Francisco Public Library
    San Francisco, Calif.

    Library, University of California
    Santa Barbara, Calif.

    Library, Stanford University
    Palo Alto, Calif.

COLORADO
    Library, University of Colorado
    Boulder, Colo.

    Mary Reed Library
    University of Colorado
    Denver, Colo.

    Library, Colorado State University
    Fort Collins, Colo.

CONNECTICUT
    Bridgeport Public Library
    Bridgeport, Conn.

    Hartford Public Library
    Hartford, Conn.

    Connecticut State Library
    Hartford, Conn.

    Library, Yale University
    New Haven, Conn.

DELAWARE
    Library, University of Delaware
    Newark, Del.

DISTRICT OF COLUMBIA
    U.S. Department of Agriculture
    Washington, D.C.

    Central Library
    U.S. Department of the Interior
    Washington, D.C.

FLORIDA
    Library, University of Miami
    Coral Cables, Fla.

Library, University of Florida
Gainesville, Fla.

Miami Public Library
Miami, Fla.

GEORGIA
Public Library
Atlanta, Ga.

ILLINOIS
Library, University of Illinois
Chicago, Ill.

Chicago Public Library
Chicago, Ill.

Peoria Public Library
Peoria, Ill.

Public Library
Rockford, Ill.

Illinois State Library
Springfield, Ill.

Library, University of Illinois
Urbana, Ill.

INDIANA
Public Library
Fort Wayne, Ind.

Gary Public Library
Gary, Ind.

Indiana State Library
Indianapolis, Ind.

Library, Purdue University
Lafayette, Ind.

IOWA
Library, Iowa State University of Science
and Technology
Ames, Iowa

Public Library, State University of Iowa
Iowa City, Iowa

KANSAS
Library, Kansas State University
Manhattan, Kans.

Kansas State Library
Topeka, Kans.

KENTUCKY
Library, University of Kentucky
Lexington, Ky.

Louisville Free Public Library
Louisville, Ky.

LOUISIANA
Library, Louisiana State University
Baton Rouge, La.

New Orleans Public Library
New Orleans, La.

MAINE
Library, University of Maine
Orono, Maine

Portland Public Library
Portland, Maine

MARYLAND
Library, Johns Hopkins University
Baltimore, Md.

Enoch Pratt Free Library
Baltimore, Md.

Library, University of Maryland
College Park, Md.

MASSACHUSETTS
Public Library of the City of Boston
Boston, Mass.

Library, Massachusetts Institute of
Technology
Cambridge, Mass.

Library, Lowell Technological Institute
Lowell, Mass.

Free Public Library
Worcester, Mass.

MICHIGAN
General Library, University of Michigan
Ann Arbor, Mich.

Willard Library
Battle Creek, Mich.

Detroit Public Library
Detroit, Mich.

Library M, Michigan State University
East Lansing, Mich.

Grand Rapids Public Library
Grand Rapids, Mich.

Michigan College of Mining and Technology
    Library
Houghton, Mich.

Michigan State Library
Lansing, Mich.

MINNESOTA
    Duluth Public Library
    Duluth, Minn.

    Public Library
    Minneapolis, Minn.

    Library, University of Minnesota
    Minneapolis, Minn.

    St. Paul Public Library
    St. Paul, Minn.

MISSISSIPPI
    Library, University of Mississippi
    Oxford, Miss.

MISSOURI
    Library, University of Missouri
    Columbia, Mo.

    Kansas City Public Library
    Kansas City, Mo.

    Library, University of Kansas City
    Kansas City, Mo.

    St. Louis Public Library
    St. Louis, Mo.

NEBRASKA
    Library, University of Nebraska
    Lincoln, Nebr.

    Omaha Public Library
    Omaha, Nebr.

NEVADA
    Library, University of Nevada
    Reno, Nev.

NEW JERSEY
    Public Library
    Elizabeth, N. J.

    Library, Rutgers University
    New Brunswick, N. J.

    Public Library
    Newark, N.J.

    Free Public Library
    Trenton, N.J.

NEW YORK
    New York State Library
    Albany, N.Y.

    Brooklyn Public Library
    Brooklyn, N.Y.

    Library, Pratt Institute
    Brooklyn, N.Y.

    Buffalo & Erie County Public Library
    Buffalo, N.Y.

    Queens Borough Public Library
    Jamaica, N.Y.

    Library, Cornell University
    Ithaca, N. Y.

    Astor Branch, New York Public Library
    New York, N.Y.

    Lenox Branch, New York Public Library
    New York, N.Y.

    City College Library
    City University of New York
    New York, N.Y.

    Library, University of Rochester
    Rochester, N.Y.

NORTH CAROLINA
    Library, University of North Carolina
    Chapel Hill, N.C.

    D. H. Hill Library
    North Carolina State College
    Raleigh, N.C.

NORTH DAKOTA
    Library, North Dakota State University of
       Agriculture and Applied Sciences
    Fargo, N.D.

OHIO
    Akron Public Library
    Akron, Ohio

    Public Library
    Cincinnati, Ohio

    Cleveland Public Library
    Cleveland, Ohio

    Ohio State Library
    Columbus, Ohio

    Library, Ohio State University
    Columbus, Ohio

    Dayton & Montgomery County
       Public Library
    Dayton, Ohio

    Toledo Public Library
    Toledo, Ohio

    Youngstown Public Library
    Youngstown, Ohio

OKLAHOMA
    Library, Langston University
    Langston, Okla.

    Library, University of Oklahoma
    Norman, Okla.

    Oklahoma State Library
    Oklahoma City, Okla.

    Library, Oklahoma State University
    Stillwater, Okla.

OREGON
    Library, Oregon State University
    Corvallis, Ore.

    Library Association of Portland
    Portland, Ore.

    Oregon State Library
    Salem, Ore.

PENNSYLVANIA
    Pennsylvania State Library
    Harrisburg, Pa.

    Fackenthal Library
    Franklin & Marshall College
    Lancaster, Pa.

    Free Library of Philadelphia
    Philadelphia, Pa.

    Library, University of Pittsburgh
    Pittsburgh, Pa.

    Carnegie Library of Pittsburgh
    Pittsburgh, Pa.

    Reading Public Library
    Reading, Pa.

    Library, Pennsylvania State University
    University Park, Pa.

    King's College Library
    Wilkes-Barre, Pa.

PUERTO RICO
    General Library
    University of Puerto Rico
    Rio Piedras, Puerto Rico

RHODE ISLAND
    Providence Public Library
    Providence, R.I.

SOUTH CAROLINA
    Library, Clemson College
    Clemson, S.C.

TENNESSEE
    Chattanooga Public Library
    Chattanooga, Tenn.

    Library, University of Tennessee
    Knoxville, Tenn.

    Cossitt Reference Library
    Memphis, Tenn.

    Joint University Libraries
    Nashville, Tenn.

TEXAS
    Library, University of Texas
    Austin, Tex.

Dallas Public Library
Dallas, Tex.

Fondren Library
Southern Methodist University
Dallas, Tex.

Fort Worth Public Library
Fort Worth, Tex.

Houston Public Library
Houston, Tex.

San Antonio Public Library
San Antonio, Tex.

UTAH
Library, University of Utah
Salt Lake City, Utah

VIRGINIA
Library, Virginia Polytechnic Institute
Blacksburg, Va.

Virginia State Library
Richmond, Va.

Library, University of Virginia
University, Va.

WASHINGTON
Washington State Library
Olympia, Wash.

Library, Washington State University
Pullman, Wash.

Library, University of Washington
Seattle, Wash.

Seattle Public Library
Seattle, Wash.

Spokane Public Library
Spokane, Wash.

Tacoma Public Library
Tacoma, Wash.

WEST VIRGINIA
Library, West Virginia University
Morgantown, W. Va.

WISCONSIN
Library, University of Wisconsin
Madison, Wisc.

Milwaukee Public Library
Milwaukee, Wisc.

WYOMING
Library, University of Wyoming
Laramie, Wyo.

APPENDIX
D Sample Specification

The sample specification included as Appendix D was prepared for, and used during, the construction of a $140,000 wood-frame and concrete-masonry motel alteration and addition in Los Angeles. While this project was not of a large size or dollar value, many elements were present that would also appear in one that was much larger. Many elements are similar to those found in residential construction.

A full-time architect's superintendent was not to be employed on this project, and consequently many instructions that would have been included in a large project were deleted. Testing, checking, and inspection were limited to those items that would normally be checked by the architect in periodic visits to the job site. The list of contractors asked to bid was carefully selected from well-known, responsible contractors who had conscientiously striven to produce quality projects.

The set of specifications presented here is a sample of specifications written under certain conditions, for a particular project, on a given date, for a building to be constructed under the codes and ordinances of one city. It is presented only as a sample of a rather brief specification illustrating the use of a standard format and a method of arranging the material to be presented in each trade section.

These specifications, as used during construction, consisted of twenty-six individual trade sections. The material, as presented, has been rearranged to conform to the CSI Format for Building Specifications.

Specifications

For the

Addition to

And

Alteration of

The Victor Motel

420 Eaton Drive

Hollywood, California

Job 106-62

Owner:

James L. Cain

92 Laurel Avenue

Pasadena, California

Date: August 3, 1962

Architect

Don A. Watson A.I.A.

1624 Hyland Avenue   Arcadia, California

ELgin 5-6706

INDEX TO SPECIFICATIONS

Job 106-62   INDEX TO SPECIFICATIONS   1

DIVISION 1   GENERAL REQUIREMENTS

Section 1A   General Contractors Work

1. **GENERAL**

The "General Conditions" and the "Supplementary General Conditions" form a part of the contract and all subcontracts and shall govern the work performed under each section of these specifications.

2. **CHECKING FEES**

All fees covering the checking of drawings and specifications by the controlling building authority prior to the closing of bids will be paid by the Owner.

3. **BUILDING PERMITS**

The building permit required for the operations under this contract and all other permits and inspections required shall be obtained and paid for by the contractor.

4. **SURVEY OF EXISTING CONDITIONS**

Before the work is begun, the Contractor and the Architect shall make a thorough survey of the working area and approaches, listing existing defects. This survey shall be approved and signed by the Contractor and the Architect.

5. **LAYING OUT WORK**

Contractor shall, immediately upon entering project site for purpose of beginning work, locate all general reference points and take action as is necessary to prevent their destruction; lay out his own work and be responsible for all lines, elevations and measurements of buildings, grading, paving, utilities and other work executed by him under the Contract. He must exercise proper precautions to verify figures shown on the drawings before laying out work and will be held responsible for any error resulting from his failure to exercise such precaution.

6. **WORKING AREA**

A portion of the site will be allotted the Contractor for the prosecution of his work and he shall build a barricade around the area, to confine his operations, of a type which deters trespassing and complies with the Local Building Code.

7. **PROGRESS SCHEDULE**

Within seven (7) days after award of Contract, Contractor shall prepare and submit to Architect for approval, a feasible schedule covering starting and completion dates for salient features and principal construction operations involved in its performance.

8. **CONSTRUCTION FORCE**

The Contractor shall provide and maintain, in full operation at all times during the performance of the contract, a sufficient crew of laborers, mechanics and foremen to prosecute the work with dispatch. The Contractor shall provide a full time superintendent who shall be on the job during all working periods.

234

1. GENERAL

All provisions of the "General Conditions" and "Supplementary General Conditions" form a part of this section.

2. SCOPE

This section covers the furnishing of all appliances, labor, materials, tools, transportation and services required to perform and complete all preliminary work and temporary construction required for the building and site as indicated on the drawings and as specified.

3. WATER

All water used on the work will be furnished by the Owner. The Contractor shall furnish the necessary temporary piping or hose, from the distribution point to the points on the site where water is necessary.

4. TEMPORARY ELECTRIC SERVICE

Electric service required in the performance of the contract shall be furnished and paid for by the Contractor who shall furnish, install, and maintain all temporary poles and overhead construction, transformers, meters, drops, and other wiring and fittings for both light and power at locations required in the work, and shall bear the cost of making the service connections.

5. TOILET FACILITIES

The Contractor shall provide, install and maintain, for the duration of the work, temporary outside toilet facilities for the use of workmen. The toilet facilities shall be adequate, housed in a weather-tight and elevated floored structure and located advantageously. The toilet shall be kept in a clean and sanitary condition until the completion of the work, then shall be removed from the site, and the portion of the site occupied by same properly cleaned up, graded and left in acceptable condition.

Facilities shall comply with all applicable building and sanitation ordinances, laws and codes.

6. BARRICADES

a. The Contractor shall erect temporary barricades as indicated on the plot plan, or as required to safely conduct the work.

b. Barricades shall be substantially built of posts not to exceed eight feet apart and not less than two 1" x 6" rails. The top rail shall not be less than thirty-six inches from the ground, and the open spaces approximately twelve inches. Where barricades join to or are within four feet of any parts of a building which is to be reconstructed, they shall be of sufficient height and be sheathed solidly with one inch boards, to provide the necessary protection.

---

9. PUMPING AND DRAINAGE

Surface or subsurface water or other fluid shall not be permitted to accumulate in excavations nor under structures. Should such conditions develop or be encountered, the water or other fluid shall be controlled and suitably disposed of by means of temporary pumps, piping, drainage lines and ditches, dams, or other methods as approved by the Architect.

10. DUST PALLIATION

Throughout the entire contract period, the Contractor shall effectively dust-palliate the working area, roads used in the operations, and involved portions of the site with such frequency as will satisfactorily allay the dust during all hours that work is being performed.

11. CLEANING

The Contractor shall from time to time remove all dirt and rubbish caused by the work, from the building and the site. At completion of the work, the Contractor shall thoroughly clean the interior and exterior of the building, including hardware, floors, roofs, sills, ledges, glass or other surfaces where debris, plaster, paint spots and dirt may have collected. All glass shall be washed clean at completion.

* * * * *

DIVISION 2   SITE WORK

Section 2A Demolition

1. GENERAL

a. All provisions of the "General Conditions" and the "Supplementary General Conditions" form a part of this section.

b. Complete demolition work as indicated on the drawings, as specified, or both.

c. All work performed under this section shall be done prior to filling and grading as specified under Section 2B, Earthwork.

d. Secure and pay for the necessary permits for all demolition work.

2. EXAMINATION OF SITE

The Contractor shall visit the site of the work and examine the premises so as to fully understand all of the existing conditions relative to the work. No increase in cost or extension of performance time will be considered for failure to know its condition.

3. DEMOLITION

Demolition work in general shall consist of the following:

a. Remove all standpipes and existing irrigation lines which cross the site at locations indicated on sheet A-1 of the drawings.

b. Cap existing irrigation lines at the property line which extend from adjacent property.

c. Remove existing concrete slab as indicated on sheet A-2 of the drawings.

d. Demolish and remove from the site the wood framed building, porches, and garage as indicated on sheet A-2 of the drawings.

e. Remove walls, doors, windows, cabinets, plumbing, electrical appliances, and pertinent services from building "A" as indicated on sheets A-8, and A-9 of the drawings.

4. PROTECTION OF STRUCTURES AND PROPERTY

a. Execute demolition work in such a manner as to insure adjacent property, shrubs, trees, and lawns against damage which might occur from falling debris or other cause.

b. Repair damage done to property of any person or persons, on or off the premises, by reason of required work.

5. DISPOSAL OF MATERIALS

All surplus materials to be removed shall become the property of the Contractor and shall be removed from the premises.

Job 106-62   DEMOLITION   2A-1

c. Parts of work in place that are subject to injury, because of operations being carried on adjacent thereto, shall be covered, boarded up, or substantially enclosed with adequate protection. Permanent openings used as thoroughfares for the introduction of work and materials to structure shall have heads, jambs and sills well blocked and boarded. All forms of protection shall be such as will be deemed safe and sufficient by Architect; intention of contract being that, upon completion, entire work will be delivered to Owner in proper, whole and unblemished condition.

7. SCAFFOLD AND RUNWAYS

The Contractor shall furnish, erect, and maintain for duration of work as required all scaffold, runways, guard rails, platforms, and similar temporary construction as may be necessary for the performance of the contract. Such facilities shall be of type and arrangement as required for their specific use; shall be substantially constructed throughout, strongly supported, and well secured; and shall comply with all applicable rules and regulations of the Industrial Accident Commission of the State of California.

8. ARCHITECT'S SIGN

a. The Architect will deliver a 20" x 30" sign to the Contractor for erection on the site as directed. The sign shall be maintained in good condition during construction and be returned to the Architect's office upon notice or at completion of the work.

b. No other signs or advertisements will be permitted on the building enclosures, or on the premises, unless prior written approval is obtained from the Architect.

9. REMOVAL OF TEMPORARY CONSTRUCTION

Temporary office facilities, toilets, barricades, storage sheds, utilities and other construction of temporary nature shall be removed from the site as soon as the progress of the work will permit in the opinion of the Architect and the portions of the site so occupied shall be properly reconditioned and restored to a condition acceptable to the Owner and the Architect.

* * * * *

Job 106-62   TEMPORARY FACILITIES   1B-2

1. GENERAL

All provisions of the "General Conditions" and "Supplementary General Conditions" form a part of this section.

2. WORK INCLUDED IN THIS SECTION

   a. Excavations for building.

   b. Providing suitable fill for sub-grade under structure.

   c. Compaction of earth under building slabs.

   d. Back fill and compaction.

   e. All grading including areas where paving has been removed.

   f. Fill of basement area where building has been removed.

3. WORK NOT INCLUDED IN THIS SECTION

   a. Excavation and backfill for underground utilities.

   b. Fine grading and rolling of subgrade under asphaltic paving.

   c. Excavation for swimming pool.

4. VERIFICATION OF EXISTING CONDITIONS

   It shall be the responsibility of the Contractor to examine the site of the work and, after investigation, to decide for himself the character of materials to be encountered and all other existing conditions affecting the work.

5. EXCAVATIONS

   a. Excavations shall be made to the dimensions and elevations indicated on the drawings, or required for the buildings. Should unsuitable bearing be encountered at the elevations indicated, excavation shall be carried to such greater depths as will be directed by the Architect, and the contract price will be adjusted accordingly. Excavations shall extend a sufficient distance from walls and footings to allow for forms, installation of services, and for inspection.

   b. Should excavations through error he carried to a greater depth or size than indicated or required, such additional depth or size shall be filled with concrete as specified under "Concrete" section at the Contractor's expense.

   c. Bottoms of excavations shall be level, free from loose material, and brought to the indicated or required levels in undisturbed earth or compacted fill.

---

6. DEBRIS

   a. Remove, as it accumulates, debris resulting from demolition operations. Do not store or permit debris to accumulate on the site.

   b. Wood and other debris resulting from demolition operations may not be burned on the site.

7. CLEANING

   a. Upon completion of the work, remove all barricades, tools, materials, plant, apparatus, and debris.

   b. Leave the premises clean, neat and orderly.

                    * * * * *

7. FILL

All existing earth within building lines that has been disturbed, shall be compacted to the same density as specified for fills. Construct all fills under building as necessary to bring the site to the required elevations as indicated on the drawings. Fill material shall be obtained from sources off the site, shall be free of deleterious matter, and shall be placed in 6" layers and compacted to 95% of maximum density.

8. BACKFILL

After completion of foundations, footings and other construction below the elevation of final grades and all forms removed, the excavations shall be cleaned of all debris prior to backfilling. Material for backfilling shall be free of any deleterious matter. Backfilling shall be brought to a suitable elevation above grade to provide for all anticipated settlement and shrinkage, and shall be deposited in layers and compacted as specified for fill.

9. GRADING

The areas to be graded shall include all areas where changes of grade are indicated on the drawings by contours, elevations, or dimensions. All earth supplied shall be clean, free from deleterious materials, and shall be of such nature to form a firm and stable subgrade.

10. PREPARATION OF SUBGRADE

Wherever concrete slabs or walks are laid directly on ground, the rough excavation shall be left sufficiently high to permit the removal of all loose earth.

11. CLEAN-UP

Upon completion of the work, the Contractor shall remove from the site all debris resulting from the operations, and shall leave the entire site in a neat, clean, and acceptable condition.

12. DISPOSAL OF EXCAVATED MATERIAL

All surplus material resulting from the site excavating and grading operations shall be removed from the site and disposed of in a legal manner.

* * * * * *

DIVISION 2 SITE WORK

Section 2C Asphaltic Concrete Paving

1. GENERAL

All provisions of the "General Conditions" and "Supplementary General Conditions" section form a part of this section.

2. WORK INCLUDED IN THIS SECTION

a. All new asphaltic concrete paving as indicated on the drawings.

b. Redwood headers at property lines and where indicated.

3. WORK NOT INCLUDED IN THIS SECTION

a. Rough grading

b. Concrete aprons and approach

4. MATERIALS

a. Asphaltic concrete shall be full two (2) inches minimum finished thickness above finish subgrade, and compacted to indicated finish grades. It shall be mixed in proper proportions of sand, crushed stone and gravel, limestone or Portland cement filler and asphaltic cement heated to a temperature between 275 and 350 F., all as established in the standards of "Topeka" mix.

b. After the asphaltic concrete surfacing has been completed, the Contractor shall provide a seal by spraying the surface with Asphaltic Emulsion MD-2 at a rate of 1/10 gallons per square yard. Avoid sticky or tacky areas. Block off the area for at least 24 hours to avoid damage to the surface from human or vehicle traffic.

5. PREPARATION OF SUBGRADE

a. The subgrade shall be cultivated to a minimum depth of 4" below the required finish elevation of the sub-grade and alternately watered and cultivated until it will properly compact.

6. GUARANTY

The Contractor shall furnish a written guaranty to repair or restore any portion of the asphaltic concrete paving in which defects due to improper placing or defective material has become apparent within one (1) year from date of completion. This guaranty shall include the extermination of vegetation which grows through paving within a period of one (1) year.

7. CLEANING

The Contractor shall remove from the site surplus materials and debris resulting from this work.

* * * * *

DIVISION 2 SITE WORK

Section 2D Chain Link Fencing

1. GENERAL

All provisions of the "General Conditions" and "Supplementary General Conditions" form a part of this section.

2. WORK INCLUDED IN THIS SECTION

Chain link fencing work, as indicated on the drawings.

3. WORK NOT INCLUDED IN THIS SECTION

Wood fencing and aluminum screens.

4. MATERIALS

a. Galvanizing: All materials shall be galvanized by the hot-dip proces.

b. Fabric: Fence fabric shall be No. 9 guage steel wire woven in 2" mesh. Top and bottom finish knuckled.

c. Posts: 2½" o.d. zinc-coated steel pipe, spaced not to exceed 10 feet on centers.

d. Post tops: Heavy malleable iron of the type for use with top rail with a base apron to fit around the outside of the posts.

e. Top rail: 1-5/8" o.d. galvanized steel pipe. Top rail shall pass through line post tops and form a continuous brace from end to end of each stretch of fence.

f. Fittings: Galvanized, cast iron.

g. Fabric bands: Fasten fabric to line posts with fabric bands on 14" centers and to top rail with tie wires on 24" centers.

h. Gates: Gate frames 2" o.d. galvanized pipe. Frames shall be properly braced and trussed. Gate fittings shall include offset hinges for 180 swing, latch catch, device for padlock and keeper which automatically engages the frame when swung into the open position. If the frame is welded, the welds shall be ground smooth and the entire frame shall be galvanized after fabrication.

i. Concrete and footings:

(1) Concrete for post footings shall be as specified under "Concrete Work".

(2) Footing sizes shall be as follows:
   End posts - 10" diameter x 36" deep post embedment
   Line posts - 8" diameter x 36" deep post embedment

(3) Tops of footings shall be troweled smooth and beveled to drain moisture away from posts. Lower edge of bevel shall meet established finished grade.

5. FENCE ERECTION AND WORKMANSHIP

a. Fencing shall be erected in a rigid manner, plumb and true to line without buckles or kinks.

b. Embed posts in concrete footings to depths as specified and locate accurately as to alignment and grade.

c. Fence fabric shall be erected so that the bottom of the fabric shall be in full contact with the ground or paving.

*****

DIVISION 3 CONCRETE

Section 3A Concrete & Cement Finish

1. GENERAL

All provisions of the "General Conditions" and the "Supplementary General Conditions" form a part of this section.

2. WORK INCLUDED IN THIS SECTION

a. Footings, foundations, slabs, curbs, walks, and steps. "poured-in-place" concrete steps.

b. The furnishing and placing of steel reinforcement in concrete.

c. The furnishing, and installation of dowels, bolts, sleeves, and anchors embedded in concrete.

d. Construction and removal of all forms for concrete.

e. Concrete driveway approaches.

f. Concrete splash blocks.

3. WORK NOT INCLUDED IN THIS SECTION

a. Pre-cast concrete steps.

b. Footings for pre-cast step stringers.

c. Reinforcing for concrete masonry except dowels in concrete.

4. MATERIALS

Materials to be incorporated in the concrete work shall comply with the following requirements:

a. Cement: A standard brand of domestic Portland Cement, conforming to ASTM C-150, Type I or II.

b. Concrete aggregates shall conform to ASTM C33.

(1) Aggregate shall not contain opaline, chert, feldspar, siliceous magnesium limestone, or other deleterious substances.

(2) Fine aggregate shall consist of washed natural sand having hard, strong, durable particles and which does not contain more than 1% by weight of deleterious substances such as clay lumps, shale, mica, schist, alkalai, coated grains, or soft and flaky particles.

c. Reinforcing bars shall be intermediate grade conforming to ASTM A15.

d. Mesh shall conform to ASTM A185.

e. Water required will be furnished by Owner.

f. Integral Waterproofing: Concrete in slabs on earth shall be integrally water-proofed, in strict accordance with manufacturer's directions, with "Red Label" Suconem, at the rate of one (1) pint per sack of cement. Maximum of four (4) inch slump shall be maintained for floors.

g. Curing Compound shall be "Hunt's Process Clear" or "Hunt's Process Black".

5. CONCRETE

Concrete shall develop a compressive strength at the age of twenty-eight (28) days, of 2000 psi.

a. Concrete shall be a workable, non-segregating mixture with maximum slumps as designated in the General Structural Notes on the drawings.

b. The Contractor shall use Ready Mixed Concrete.

c. The manufacturer of the ready-mixed concrete shall deliver to the Architect a certificate with each mixer truck stating the quantity of cement, water, fine and coarse aggregate, and admixture, if any, contained in the load.

6. FORMS FOR CONCRETE

Forms shall be substantial, unyielding, true to line and level, sufficiently tight to prevent leakage of mortar, and shall conform exactly to the dimensions of the finished concrete.

7. PLACING CONCRETE REINFORCEMENT STEEL

a. Reinforcement steel, bars, and wire fabric shall be thoroughly cleaned before placing and again before the concrete is placed; shall be accurately positioned and secured in place. Metal spacers shall be used to secure the proper bracing of the steel. Stirrups shall be accurately and securely wired to bars at both top and bottom. No brick or porous materials may be used to support steel off the ground.

b. Steel shall be wired together at points where bars cross and shall be lapped thirty (30)diameters at splices. Splices in horizontal bars shall be staggered so that adjacent splices will be four (4) feet apart. Horizontal bars shall extend around corners not less than thirty (30) diameters.

c. Proper clearance shall be maintained between parallel bars and from the forms. Lapped splices shall be made wherever possible in such a manner to provide at least one (1) inch clearance between the spliced bars. Lapped splices shall, in general, be staggered. Dowels and bars extending through construction joints shall be secured in position against displacement before concrete is placed and shall be cleaned of concrete before subsequent pouring.

8. CONVEYING AND PLACING CONCRETE

a. Cleaning of Forms: Before the placing of any concrete, forms shall be cleaned, washed and made tight.

b. Time of Placing: Concrete shall not be placed until all reinforcement steel, and other embedded materials are securely fastened in their proper places and positions, and unless the reinforcement steel and forms have been inspected and approved by the Architect.

c. Before new concrete is deposited upon concrete that has hardened, all incrustations shall be removed from the forms and reinforcement steel, all laitance removed from the concrete, and the concrete surfaces and the forms thoroughly cleaned and washed with water. The concrete surface shall be covered with concrete mixed as specified but with one-half (½) the coarse aggregate omitted. The thickness of this mixture shall not be less than five (5) inches.

d. Concrete shall be delivered to the point of pouring directly from spouts or troughs of trucks or by carts, and shall not be spouted or dumped into carts, with a fall of more than six (6) feet.

e. Concrete shall be so deposited that the surface shall be kept level throughout.

f. The fresh poured concrete shall be tamped into place with steel rammer and slicing tools until the concrete is thoroughly compact and without voids. Mechanical vibrators operated by experienced personnel shall be used in conjunction with hand tamping.

9. CURING OF SLABS

Contractor shall cure floor slabs, paving, walks, steps and other flat cement finish by wetting down twice daily and keeping wet for seven (7) days; or, with approved liquid compound. Curing compounds shall be as specified. Use "Clear" on exposed flatwork only. "Black" shall be used on floors scheduled to receive asphalt or vinyl asbestos flooring. No curing compound may be used where ceramic or glass tile, cement fill, or terrazzo is scheduled for installation.

10. REMOVING FORMS

Forms shall not be disturbed or removed until the concrete has sufficiently hardened to permit their removal with safety. Walls shall not be stripped in less than five (5) days; floor slabs in not less than seven (7) days.

11. CONCRETE SLABS, WALKS AND PAVING

All slabs, walks and paving shall be screeded to true planes, lines and grades indicated on the drawings, and finished to uniform surfaces. Interior slabs shall be finished as specified below. Exterior slabs, walks, and paving shall be four (4) inches thick.

12. DEFECTIVE CONCRETE

a. IF ANY CONCRETE WORK IS NOT FORMED AS INDICATED; has voids or honeycomb that has been filled, unless under the direction of the Architect; or has any debris embedded in it; shall be deemed to be defective materials or faulty workmanship, and the Contractor shall remove defective work from the site.

b. When directed, defective concrete will be cut by the Contractor and refilled under the supervision of the Architect.

13. CEMENT FINISH

a. Mixture: Cement finish mixture shall be proportioned by volume of one-part Portland cement, one-part fine aggregate and one-part coarse aggregate for cement finish.

b. Mixing: The materials shall be mixed in an approved batch mixer for five (5) minutes, with the minimum proportion of water which will permit good workability with no excess of surface water.

c. Defective Work: Cement finish which is not true to line and place; which varies more than one-eighth inch from the required finish grades or levels; which taps hollow, which scuffs or has any roughed top surface; which is cracked; and which does not connect properly to adjoining work, shall be removed by the Contractor and be replaced by him with cement finish complying with the requirements of the specifications.

d. Floating and Troweling: When concrete has hardened sufficiently it shall be floated to a compact and smooth surface. The top surfaces shall then be steel-troweled to an even, hard surface, free from low and high spots.

e. Machine Troweling: Machine troweling will be permitted instead of hand troweling. After the leveling and compacting, the surface shall be thoroughly troweled and hardened by machine troweling with a motor driven rotary trowel. The final troweling shall be for the purpose of burnishing and shall be performed sufficiently late so that it will show a sheen on the surface. The machine compacting, hand and machine troweling operations, shall leave a smooth, hard, impervious even finish.

f. Markings: The cement finish of paving and walks shall be marked off as indicated. The marking shall be made with a V marking tool. The marks shall have rounded edges free from burrs and obstructions and shall have true, straight, clean cut angles.

14. DRIVEWAY APPROACH

Construct new concrete driveway approaches in locations shown on drawings and in accordance with the Los Angeles City Standard Plan D-6879, and Los Angeles City Standard Specifications.

15. PUBLIC WALKS

New public walks, shall conform to all local ordinances. Existing walks which are damaged during the construction period shall be replaced with new work as directed by the Architect. New work shall match existing finish on adjacent similar existing work.

16. CONCRETE SPLASH BLOCKS AND PANS

Provide precast concrete splash blocks and pans of size and type shown on drawings. (C.D. Wailes #2). Place where downspouts spill on earth as indicated on drawings. Roof pans shall be eighteen (18) inches square by one and one-half (1½) inches thick.

17. CLEAN-UP

During construction keep the area as clean and clear as possible. Do not dispose of waste materials on the site. Promptly remove all waste materials.

* * * * *

DIVISION 3 CONCRETE

Section 3B   Precast Concrete Steps & Railing

1. GENERAL

All provisions of the "General Conditions" and the "Supplementary General Conditions" section form a part of this section.

2. WORK INCLUDED IN THIS SECTION

   a. Precast concrete treads.

   b. Steel stair stringers with end plates and necessary connections.

   c. Stair and balcony rails and balustrades and necessary connections.

   d. Steel angle at balcony edge.

   e. Prime coat all steel.

   f. Foundations for steel stringers.

   g. Anchor bolts in footings for steel stringers.

3. WORK NOT INCLUDED IN THIS SECTION

   a. Finish painting

   b. Poured-in-place concrete steps

4. MATERIALS

   a. Precast treads: shall be "Best" concrete steps, exposed aggregate, grey, as manufactured by Badger Blocks, 10261 Glenoaks, Pacoima, California, Empire 9-5414.

   b. Steel Stringers: steel stringers and end plates shall be as specified for structural steel in "Structural Steel" section.

   c. Welding: shall conform to the quality as specified under welding in the "Structural Steel" section.

   d. Hand rails and balustrades shall be standard grade mild steel.

   e. 4" x 8" plates on balustrades shall be eighteen (18) guage galvanized iron.

5. SAMPLES

The Contractor shall submit samples of exposed aggregate steps to the Architect for approval. Finished steps must match approved sample.

6. SHOP DRAWINGS

The Contractor shall submit to the Architect for approval, four (4) sets of shop drawings. The shop drawings shall show elevations and plans of each stairway and balcony; sections showing sizes, materials, connections and details of construction; a setting plan for the use of the Contractor. No fabrication or installation of stairways or balcony rails shall commence until written approval has been obtained from the Architect and the Structural Engineer.

7. INSTALLATION

Stairways and balcony rails shall conform to details shown on Sheet #A-7 and on the structural drawings.

8. PRIMING

All steel or iron shall be prime coated as specified in the "Structural Steel" section.

* * * * *

242

DIVISION 4 MASONRY

Section 4A Concrete Masonry

1. GENERAL

All provisions of the "General Conditions" and the "Supplementary General Conditions" section form a part of this section.

2. WORK INCLUDED IN THIS SECTION

a. Concrete block walls, partitions, columns, beams and lintels.

b. Reinforcing steel for concrete block construction.

c. Provisions for other trades: Chases, openings, and "spring-lock reglets" shall be installed as shown or as required for other work. Anchors, bolts, hangers and connections, furnished under other sections of the specifications, shall be installed in masonry walls where shown on the drawings or as required for the work of other trades. All metal to be imbedded in masonry walls shall be completely encased in grout with not less than two (2) inches coverage allaround.

3. WORK NOT INCLUDED IN THIS SECTION

a. Dowel bar anchors for attaching reinforced masonry to concrete.

b. Furnishing of spring-lock reglets and cap flashing.

4. MATERIALS

a. Concrete block shall be Grade A, sand and gravel, load bearing masonry units conforming to ASTM Des. C-90.

b. Units shall be manufactured in accordance with the requirements of the Concrete Masonry Association Specifications.

c. Reinforcing bars shall be as specified in "Concrete".

5. MORTAR

Type A: Shall be proportioned by volume as follows: One (1) Portland cement, three and one-half (3½) damp loose sand, one-fourth (¼) lime putty for interior walls. Add four-fifths (4/5) quart of water-proofing admixture per sack of cement for mortar in exterior walls.

6. GROUT

Grout for filling cells in masonry units shall be: One(1) Portland Cement, three (3) sand, two (2) pea gravel, one-tenth (1/10) lime putty. Grout for all other masonry shall consist of one part Portland Cement to not more than thre (3) part sand. Sufficient water shall be added to grout to cause it to flow without segregation into all joints of the masonry. Add admixture as specified above for mortar or grout in exterior walls only.

7. SCAFFOLDING AND PROTECTION

Provide and install all scaffold and forms of protection necessary for execution of the work.

8. LAYING

Concrete surfaces to receive block shall be cleaned and thoroughly wetted prior to laying the masonry units. All masonry units shall be clean and all dust or dirt removed from the surface before laying. Concrete block shall be laid dry. Fractional parts of units will not be permitted where whole units can be used. Chinking will not be permitted. All voids shall be filled with mortar. Vertical head joints shall be buttered well for a thickness equal to the face shell of the block and these joints shall be shoved tightly so that the mortar bonds well to both blocks.

9. CLEAN OUTS

Clean out openings shall be provided at the bottoms of all cells to be filled at each lift or pour of grout where such lift or pour of grout is in excess of four feet in height. Any overhanging mortar or other obstruction or debris shall be removed from the insides of such cell walls. The clean outs shall be sealed before grouting, after inspection.

10. JOINTS

Units shall be laid with full shoved bed and head joints. Joints shall be three-eighth (3/8) inch thick, with full mortar coverage on the face shells and on the webs surrounding the cells to be filled. Joints shall be as uniform as possible. All exposed joints shall be raked three-eighth (3/8) inches deep and tooled firmly to produce a smooth tight surface.

11. GROUTING

Clearance between units and reinforcing shall be not less than one-fourth (¼) inch. The grout shall be puddled immediately to cause it to flow into all the interstices between the units. All cells shall be filled where reinforcing occurs.

12. BOND

Stacked bond, all vertical joints plumb and all horizontal joints level.

13. WORK RELATED TO MASONRY

The Contractor shall coordinate placing of all items imbedded in masonry, and be responsible for changes in position.

* * * * *

243

DIVISION 5 METALS: STRUCTURAL & MISC.

Section 5A   Structural Steel

1. GENERAL

All provisions of the "General Conditions" and "Supplementary General Conditions" section form a part of this section.

2. WORK INCLUDED IN THIS SECTION

a. Structural steel shapes, pipe, tubing

b. Steel studs

c. Steel deck

d. Metal plates and fastenings, one-eighth (1/8) inch thick or greater

e. Priming of ferrous metal

3. WORK NOT INCLUDED IN THIS SECTION

a. Chain link fencing

b. Sheet metal

c. Metal plates and fastenings less than one-eighth (1/8) inch thick or fasteners to connect wood to wood.

d. Steel stringers, hand rails, balustrades, fastenings for precast concrete steps.

4. SPECIAL REQUIREMENTS

The current rules and practices set forth in the Code of Standard Practice for Steel Buildings and Bridges, and the Specification for the Design, Fabrication and Erection of Structural Steel for Buildings of the American Institute of Steel Construction shall govern this work, except as otherwise noted on the drawings or as otherwise specified. Welding shall be in accordance with the Standard Code for Arc and Gas Welding in Building Construction of the American Welding Society.

5. SHOP DRAWINGS

Before commencing this work, submit four (4) copies of shop drawings.

6. MATERIALS

a. Structural steel shall conform to ASTM Des. A7.

b. Structural Pipe. Grade B Steel Pipe conforming to ASTM Designation A53.

c. Structural Tube shall conform to AISI C-1015 for hot rolled welded tubing.

d. Steel deck shall be twenty-four (24) ga "Penmetal" Galvanized "Steeldek".

e. Steel studs shall be "Penmetal", 362DS18 Pun.

f. Steel Primer shall be as specified under Painting.

7. WELDING

a. All welding shall be by a certified welder and each welder shall stamp his work.

b. Continuous inspection requirements for shop welding may be waived for fabricators whose shops are licensed by the City of Los Angeles, and if all welding is by certified welders. Fabricators to submit for approval license number prior to commencing work.

8. PRIMING

Remove all rust, scale and other foreign matter before leaving the fabricator's plant. Apply one coat of primer in accordance with the manufacturer's published recommendations to all exposed steel. After erection, touch up all burned or abraded areas.

* * * * *

244

Section 5B Aluminum Sun Screen

1. **GENERAL**

   All provisions of the "General Conditions" and "Supplementary General Conditions" section form a part of this section.

2. **WORK INCLUDED IN THIS SECTION**

   a. Decorative aluminum sun screen on south side of Building "A".

   b. Extruded aluminum mullions and framing members.

   c. All connections to existing building.

3. **WORK NOT INCLUDED IN THIS SECTION**

   New structural steel beams in existing building.

4. **MATERIALS**

   Sun screen shall be "Martina", pierced metal screens as manufactured by Almaco, Inc., 2526 N. Chico Ave., El Monte, California; Gilbert 3-4762. Pierced metal screen shall be of such thickness to withstand static wind pressures as required by the Los Angeles City Code. Fasteners shall be made of aluminum, stainless steel or other material that impedes corrosion.

5. **FINISH**

   Finish of pierced metal screen, mullions, perimeter framing members and all visible fasteners shall be given two coats of acrylic baked enamel to a thickness of 1.5 mils. Color samples shall be submitted to the Architect for approval. Finished installation shall match approved color samples.

6. **INSTALLATION**

   Panels shall be erected and installed in accordance with approved plans and shop drawings. Manufacturer shall furnish and install all accessories necessary to attach to supporting structure. All work shall be erected and installed under direct supervision of Almaco, Inc.

7. **GUARANTY**

   A written guaranty shall be furnished the Owner by Almaco, Inc. to repair or replace all members which may peel, crack or show signs of fading within a period of two (2) years from the date of installation.

   * * * * *

Section 6A Rough Carpentry

1. **GENERAL**

   All provisions of the "General Conditions" and "Supplementary General Conditions" section form a part of this section.

2. **WORK INCLUDED IN THIS SECTION**

   a. Provide all materials and equipment and perform all operations required to complete rough carpentry, as indicated on the drawings.

   b. Include in the work, plates and straps under one-eighth (1/8) inch in thickness, joist hangers, rough hardware, and all fasteners for connecting wood to wood.

   c. Install such miscellaneous iron and steel items furnished under other sections of the specifications and which are pertinent to carpentry work.

   d. Complete all alterations, modifications and new wood framing as indicated in Building "A" on sheets A-4, A-5, A-8, A-9, S-5, and Schedule 4A of sheet A-2.

   e. Openings, cutting, and patching for air conditioning ducts and equipment.

3. **WORK NOT INCLUDED IN THIS SECTION**

   a. Finish carpentry and millwork.

   b. Wood stripping for acoustical tile work.

   c. Priming and back priming

   d. Wood forms for concrete

4. **MATERIALS AND GRADES**

   a. Framing lumber, unless otherwise noted, shall be Douglas Fir of grades as specified.

   b. All lumber shall be surfaced four sides and dressed to mill sizes.

   c. All structural lumber which is exposed shall be graded for appearance.

   d. Paragraph numbers following refer to Standard Grading and Dressing Rules No. 15 of the West Coast Lumberman's Assn.

   (1) General:

   (a) Studding, Rafters, Fascias, Ridges, Blocking, Ceiling Joists, Struts, Posts, Headers, and Ledgers, 2" to 4" thick, 6" and Wider: "Construction"-- Joists and Planks, 1500f, paragraph No. 123-b.

   (b) Posts, 5" x 5" and Larger: "Construction" - Post and Timbers, 1200c, paragraph No. 125-b

(c) Solid Timbers Over 5" in Least Dimension: "Construction" - Beams and Stringers, 1500f, paragraph No. 124-b.

(d) Stripping, Furring, Grounds: "Standard and Better" - Boards, paragraph No. 120-c.

(e) Studding, Blocking, Small Posts, Ceiling Joists, and Stripping, 2" to 4" thick, 4" and Under in Width: "Construction" - Light Framing, paragraph No. 122-b.

(2) Roof Framing:

(a) Beams 2" to 4" Thick, 6" and Wider: "Select Structural" - Joists and Planks, 1900f, paragraph No. 123-a.

(b) Beams Over 5" in Least Dimension: "Select Structural" - Beams and Stringers, 1900f, paragraph No. 124-a.

(c) Rafters 2" to 4" Thick, 4" Wider: "1500f Industrial" - Light Framing, paragraph No. 153-b.

e. Sills: Foundation Grade Redwood or pressure-treated Construction Grade D.F. for wood sills which rest on concrete walls and are six (6) feet or less above grade.

f. Plywood Roof Sheathing: "Plyscord", Grade C-D, ext.

g. Fasteners and Universal Anchors: Sheet metal, fully galvanized. Fully nail all connectors.

5. MOISTURE CONTENT IN LUMBER

Only reasonably dry, well seasoned boards and dimension framing lumber will be accepted. All lumber and timber used for permanent structural purposes shall be air-seasoned for at least sixty (60) days in Los Angeles County, in dry weather. Lumber shall be stacked, off the ground, using spacers between rows of members so that free circulation of air is provided around all members in a stack.

6. WOOD PRESERVATIVE TREATMENT

a. All Douglas Fir sills and bearing blocks resting on concrete shall be pressure-impregnated with "Wolman Salts" (Tanalith) to a penetration depth of one-fourth (¼) inch.

b. Treat all ends of wood studs, blocking, and stripping, which are 2'-0" or less above finished exterior grade, by dipping material in "Woodlife" before erection.

c. Treat all ends and edges, sawed or cut after treatment, with a heavy brush application of same preservative.

7. COOPERATION

Cooperate with all trades and provide all grounds, blocking, wood backing and framing, and perform all necessary cutting and patching of rough carpentry work as required.

8. WORKMANSHIP

a. Framing: Common wire nails and spikes shall be used. Spikes and nails shall penetrate one-half (½) their length into member receiving point, except that 16d nails may be used to connect 2" material to 2" material. Nails shall not be driven closer together than one-half (½) their length.

b. Place wood sills and plates on concrete walls and secure as detailed. Set level and true and drypack.

c. Set walls and partitions plumb and true.

d. Where wood is bolted to steel plates or shapes, drill holes in wood one-sixteenth (1/16) inch larger than bolt size, using the steel for a template.

e. Provide fire stops in exterior and interior walls at ceiling and roof levels, including furred spaces. Fire-stop all other locations which could afford a passage for flames. Limit concealed air space to 8'-0" vertically and horizontally.

f. Cutting, notching, and boring of structural framing members for passage of pipes or conduits will not be permitted without approval of the Architect.

9. BLOCKING AND GROUNDS

a. Install blocking to properly support all woodwork, base, and trim, and for plumbing, heating, electrical fixtures and appliances.

b. Permanent and temporary wood grounds required for plastering shall be of sufficient length and depth for securing work and to insure anchoring of required materials by nailing or screwing into grounds.

c. Provide preservative-treated nailing strips where such are required. Strips shall be of indicated sizes and shapes, or as required to permit proper nailing.

* * * * *

246

DIVISION 6 CARPENTRY

Section 6B Finish Carpentry and Millwork

1. **GENERAL**

   All provisions of the "General Conditions" and "Supplementary General Conditions" section form a part of this section.

2. **WORK INCLUDED IN THIS SECTION**

   a. Finish carpentry as scheduled and indicated.

   b. Plastic paneling in lobby and restaurant.

   c. Wall insulation where indicated in interior portions.

   d. All case and cabinet work in existing and new construction

   e. Installation of finish hardware.

   f. Redwood fence

3. **WORK NOT INCLUDED IN THIS SECTION**

   a. Rough carpentry work.

   b. Doors, metal windows, door frames.

   c. Wood stripping for acoustic tile.

   d. Skylights and roof scuttles.

   e. Furnishing of finish hardware.

   f. Priming and back priming.

   g. Glass, glazine and mirrors.

4. **SAMPLES**

   Submit samples of all hardwoods, plywood, and laminated plastics in accordance with the "Supplementary General Conditions" section.

5. **STANDARDS**

   Grading Rules: Each piece of lumber shall be grade-marked, classified, sized, and measured according to the following codes and grade requirements:

   a. Douglas Fir: Standard Grading and Dressing Rules No. 15, latest revision as published by the West Coast Lumbermen's Association.

   b. Redwood: Standard Grading Rules for California Redwood, latest revision, as published by the California Redwood Association.

   c. Ponderosa Pine: Grading Rules of Western Pine Association.

   d. Plywood: U. S. Commercial Standard CS45. Each sheet shall be grade-marked with the symbol of the Association under which the material was graded.

6. **MATERIALS**

   a. Exterior Woodwork:

      (1) Exterior Trim: "B and Better", V.G.D.F.

      (2) Fascia: Redwood, Clear, All Heart.

      (3) Fence: Members 2" and thicker shall be "Construction Grade" Heart Redwood; members less than 2" in thickness shall be Grade "A" V.G. Redwood. Posts shall be Heart Structural Grade, 1300f.

   b. Interior Woodwork:

      (1) Interior trim (D.F.) "B and Better", V.G.D.F.

      (2) Shelving: Clear Ponderosa Pine.

      (3) Interior Trim (Hardwood): "Lauan" Mahogany first quality selected for color suitable for natural finish.

      (4) Handrails: Grade "A" Quarter sawn, white oak.

7. **MATERIALS OTHER THAN LUMBER**

   a. Laminated Plastic Counter Tops and Vanity shelves (Indicated on drawings as Plastic).

      (1) 1/16" thick, standard grade, high-pressure laminated plastic surfacing material conforming to NEMA standards, color and pattern as selected by the Architect. Color and pattern range shall be Formica's "Skylark", "Decorator", or "Nassau" patterns and solid colors.

      (2) Bond laminated plastic with phenol resorcinol water-proof adhesive to exterior grade plywood counter tops and splash, as detailed, in accordance with manufacturer's standards. Form integral top and splash with kiln-dried pine moulding, glued and screwed to plywood.

      (3) Seal plywood edges at sink cutout with mastic approved for this purpose by material manufacturer.

      (4) Counter edges: Self-edged, laminated plastic, as indicated on the drawings.

   b. Paneling: Wall and check-in desk paneling in lobby shall be "Marlite Random Plank". Soffit paneling in restaurant shall be "Marlite Woodpanel", as distributed by Marsh Wall Products, Inc., 3050 Leonis Blvd., Los Angeles 58, California. Color and finish to be as selected by the Owner.

   c. Division wall insulation: Furnish and install ½" Celotex insulating sheathing in all division walls as shown in the drawings. Nail lightly to one side only of staggered 2" x 4" stud walls.

8. WORKMANSHIP

All wood finish, millwork, and cabinet work shall be true to details, clean, and sharply defined. Panels shall be set to allow for free movement in case of swelling or shrinkage. Means of fastening various parts together shall be concealed.

9. EXTERIOR FINISH

a. Mill exterior finish from specified materials and erect in accordance with details. Set joints of assembled members in white lead paste. Sand exposed surfaces of finish woodwork ready to receive paint or other finish. Blind-nail where possible. Where face nailing is used, set face nails for putty stopping.

b. Door, window trim, and mouldings shall be in single lengths. Other exterior trim shall be in long lengths with joints staggered, concealed, or placed in inconspicuous locations. Joints shall be properly fitted and watertight. Corners shall be mitered.

c. Wood fascias shall be of sizes as detailed and shall be well primed on all sides and ends, as specified in the "Painting" section, before installing. Fascias shall be blind-nailed with galvanized nails. Exposed angles of fascias shall be mitered.

10. INTERIOR FINISH

a. Mill, fabricate, and erect interior finish as indicated. Machine-sand at the mill and hand-sand smooth at the job when necessary.

b. Interior trim set against plaster or wood shall be run with hollow backs. Make joints tight and in a manner to conceal shrinkage. Secure trim with fine finishing nails, screws, or glue where required. Set nails for putty stopping. Window and door trim shall be single lengths; base in long lengths. Miter mouldings at corners; cope at angles.

11. FIXED GLASS IN WOOD FRAMES

Where fixed glass is set in wood frames, thoroughly prime rabbets and wood stops. Fit stops and secure in place loosely with chrome-plated oval-head screws.

12. HANDRAILS

Handrails shall be two (2) inches in diameter, made of wood as specified above; handrail brackets will be furnished under the "Finish Hardware" section. Each run of handrail shall have two (2) brackets.

13. REMOVABLE DECK

The Contractor shall construct movable deck sections of 3/4" x 2-5/8" redwood slats spaced at 3" O.C. as a temporary walking deck to cover top of roof of Building D. These sections shall be of such a size and weight that they can be removed for roof repairs. Submit shop drawings indicating placement on the roof and construction details.

14. VANITY SHELVES

The Contractor shall furnish and install self-edged Formica topped vanity shelves where indicated on the drawings. Submit shop drawings.

5. CABINET WORK

a. Fabrication of all cabinet work shall be as indicated on the drawings; detailing in accordance with minimum standards adopted by the Woodwork Institute of California for Premium Grade work. All cabinets and casework shall bear the stamp "W.I.C." for Premium Casework.

b. Materials used for cabinet work shall conform to the following requirements:

(1) Hardwood: Exposed surfaces of cabinet work shall be close-grained, sound, clear, kiln-dried, "Lauan" Mahogany, free from checks, pitch pockets, or sap, and selected for light color matching veneered plywood.

(2) Cabinet Framing: Cabinet framing shall be "B and Better" Douglas Fir.

(3) Softwood Plywood: Douglas Fir, conforming to CS45-48 of U.S. Bureau of Standards, rotary cut faces. Type, grade int. A-D.

(4) Hardwood Plywood: "Lauan" Mahogany, first quality, good one side, sound back, light color selected to match solid hardwood.

(5) "Novocore" Cabinet Doors: "Novocore" Cabinet door stock, face veneer clear "Lauan" Mahogany matching solid hardwood face frames, as distributed by U. S. Plywood Corporation.

(a) Doors up to 4'-0" in height shall be 3/4" stock; doors over 4'-0" and up to 6'-6" in height shall be 1-3/8" stock.

(b) Band all edges with specified hardwood.

(6) Shelves: Shelves shall be dadoed into uprights, or set on wood cleats.

16. STORAGE AND PROTECTION

a. Protect millwork against dampness during and after delivery.

b. Do not bring interior finish, including doors, into building until plaster is thoroughly dry.

c. All measurements for millwork shall be checked and verified at the site prior to fabrication.

17. HARDWARE INSTALLATION

a. Accurately fit and install all finish hardware items furnished under the "Finish Hardware" section.

b. If surface-applied hardware is fitted and applied before painting, remove all such items, except butts, and reinstall after painting work is completed.

c. Properly label and deliver all keys to Owner.

18. FINISH

All interior wood finish and cabinet work shall be dressed, sanded, and cleaned before priming. All material showing machinery, sandpaper, or other defacing marks will be rejected.

19. PRIMING AND BACKPAINTING

All millwork shall be thoroughly primed and backpainted before installation. Priming and backpainting as specified in the "Painting" section, immediately following delivery to the site.

20. CLEAN-UP

Upon completion of the work all surplus and waste materials resulting from the operation shall be removed from the premises, and the entire structure and involved portions of the site shall be left in a neat, clean and acceptable condition.

* * * * *

DIVISION 6 CARPENTRY

Section 6C Floor Insulation

1. GENERAL

All provisions of the "General Conditions" and "Supplementary General Conditions" section form a part of this section.

2. WORK INCLUDED IN THIS SECTION

Furnish and install sound insulation troweled fill where indicated.

3. WORK NOT INCLUDED IN THIS SECTION

Plywood subfloor.

4. MATERIALS

Floor Insulation shall be "Elastizell" as distributed by Concretes of California, 2524 North San Gabriel Blvd., South San Gabriel, California.

5. INSTALLATION

a. Sound insulating fill shall be 1-5/8" thick, screeded and darbied to flat surface. All areas shall be hand troweled to a smooth hard finish.

b. Elastizell Sound Insulating Cellular Concrete shall be furnished and installed by Elastizell Concretes of California, or its authorized agents, in accordance with the Manufacturer's Specifications.

c. Self furring 4 x 4 x 14-14 welded mesh, developed by Elastizell, shall be used where reinforcement is required. The self furring reinforcement shall be positioned at the bottom 1/3 of the slab.

6. FINAL CLEANING

Immediately preceeding completion of the building, the Contractor shall thoroughly clean all surfaces free from protecting coatings and foreign matter, shall fill open joints, and repair or replace with new work all defective pieces. All surfaces shall be left in a neat, clean and acceptable condition.

* * * * *

DIVISION 7 MOISTURE PROTECTION

Section 7A Built-up Roofing

1. GENERAL

   All provisions of the "General Conditions" and "Supplementary General Conditions" section form a part of this section.

2. WORK INCLUDED IN THIS SECTION

   All built-up composition roofing where indicated on the plans. Make repairs and tie in to existing roofs which are faulty or have been damaged by new construction. Furnish and install cant strips at skylights, roof scuttles, and parapets.

3. WORK NOT INCLUDED IN THIS SECTION

   a. Metal gravel stops, edgings, metal flashings, counterflashings, and metal reglets.

   b. Roof drains, scuppers, gutters and conductor pipe.

   c. Furnishing of skylights, and scuttles.

4. MATERIALS

   Roofing shall be Johns-Mansville Flexstone "Standard" built-up Roof applied in accordance with the manufacturer's specification #103 (15 year type). Work shall be done by a roofing contractor approved by the manufacturer.

5. ROOF DECK PREPARATION

   Sheathing shall be dry, smooth and well nailed. Large cracks or knotholes shall be metal covered. Roof shall be swept broom clean. All metal fittings shall be in place ready for Roofing Contractor to attach his work.

6. MANUFACTURER'S INSPECTION SERVICE

   a. All surfaces over which built-up roofing is to be applied, including repairs to existing roofing, shall be subject to inspection by the roofing materials manufacturer.

   b. Furnish an affidavit to the owner, signed by a representative of the manufacturer, that all materials and work complies with the printed installation procedures as designated by this specification.

7. GUARANTY

   The Contractor shall issue a written guaranty to the Owner to maintain the entire roof, flashings and counterflashings in a watertight condition for a period of two (2) years.

* * * * *

DIVISION 7 MOISTURE PROTECTION

Section 7B Sheet Metal Work

1. GENERAL

   All provisions of the "General Conditions" and "Supplementary General Conditions" section form a part of this section.

2. WORK INCLUDED IN THIS SECTION

   a. G.I. leader heads and downspouts.

   b. Reglets, flashing and gravel stops.

   c. Sheet metal coping of parapet walls.

3. WORK NOT INCLUDED IN THIS SECTION

   a. Roof exhaust system for kitchen equipment.

   b. Hoods and ducts for kitchen equipment.

   c. Air conditioning ducts.

4. MATERIALS

   Materials to be incorporated in the work of this section shall conform to the requirements of the following: Sheet steel or iron shall be a standard brand of galvanized iron sheets, furnished in 24 guage thickness unless otherwise indicated on the drawings, or specified. Galvanized sheets shall have a zinc coating applied by the hot dip process of all surfaces.

5. PREPARATION OF SURFACES

   Check surfaces to which flashings and other sheet metal is to be applied, to ascertain that such surfaces are smooth, properly prepared and have adequate provisions for fastening metal into position. Sheets of different material, subject to electrolysis, shall be thoroughly insulated in an approved manner.

6. DOWNSPOUTS

   The Contractor shall provide and install all exposed sheet metal downspouts of size and location as indicated on the drawings. These shall be constructed of 26 guage galvanized iron, with longitudinal seams lock-lapped and soldered and cross joints lapped with the flow lines and riveted and soldered. Downspouts shall be strongly secured to their structural backings with #10 gauge galvanized wall brackets and #10 gauge metal straps, galvanized lag screws and expansion shields. At each downspout, the leader head shall be fitted with a balloon strainer of ¼" mesh galvanized iron wire securely soldered to the leader head.

Section 7C   Skylights and Scuttles

1. GENERAL

All provisions of the "General Conditions" and "Supplementary General Conditions" section form a part of this section.

2. WORK INCLUDED IN THIS SECTION

   a. Plastic Dome Skylights

   b. Metal Roof Scuttles

   c. Counter flashing

3. WORK NOT INCLUDED IN THIS SECTION

   a. Flashing

   b. Cants

   c. Wood frames

4. MATERIALS

   a. Skylights shall be model C3636, 36"x36" square "Callaway Plastic-Domes" with clear colorless plexiglas 11. as manufactured by the Callaway Co., 1049 Venice Blvd., Los Angeles, California.

   b. Roof scuttles shall be model N-10, 2'x6" x 4'-6" steel, Prime painted, "Bilco" Roof Scuttles, as distributed by Daniel Dunner, 20400 Ruston Rd., Woodland Hills, California.

5. INSTALLATION

   a. Roof Scuttle: Shall be of a size as indicated on drawings. Fabricate of galvanized steel, 14 gauge for curb and cores, 22 gauge for cover liner, with 1 inch thick glass fibre insulation. Curb shall be 12 inches high formed with 3-½ inch flange for securing to roof deck and equipped with integral metal cap flashing full welded and ground at corners. Exterior of curb shall be insulated with 1 inch rigid fiberboard. Scuttle shall be furnished complete with manufacturing standard hardware, draft seal, padlocking provisions and automatic hold-open arm.

   b. Skylight: Each skylight shall be supplied complete including the removable roof counterflashing. It shall be ready for attachment to a 1-5/8" curb.

   c. Roof scuttles and skylights will be set in place and counterflashed at the completion of the roofing operations.

6. CLEANING

At completion of work, all sheet metal and glass shall be thoroughly cleaned of flux and other foreign matter. Galvanized metal shall be washed with clear water and left clean and ready for painting.

---

7. SPRING-LOCK FLASHING

Furnish and install where indicated on the drawings Brick spring-lock reglet and snap-in positive lock counterflashing of 24 gauge galvanized iron as manufactured by Metcoe Metal Flashing Products Co., Webster 6-1154. Reglets to be furnished to the mason for installation.

8. COPING

Furnish and install type G-8 extruded aluminum coping, as manufactured by the Aluminum Company of America, on top of all concrete masonry parapets.

9. GRAVEL STOPS, EDGINGS

26 gauge galvanized iron to be built into layers of roofing and shall be installed as specified in "Roofing" section.

10. PAINTING

All surfaces of all galvanized sheet metal work shall be cleaned of all flux and shop painted as specified under "Painting".

11. CLEAN-UP

Upon completion of the work, the Contractor shall remove all disused implements of service, rubbish and debris resulting therefrom, and shall leave the entire building and premises in a clean and acceptable condition.

* * * * *

DIVISION 7 MOISTURE PROTECTION

Section 7D Caulking

1. GENERAL

All provisions in the "General Conditions" and "Supplementary General Conditions" section form a part of this section.

2. WORK INCLUDED IN THIS SECTION

a. Joints around wood and metal frames attached to wood, plaster, or masonry finished exterior walls.

b. Joints at exterior door sills and metal thresholds.

c. All caulking, not specifically excluded, necessary to obtain complete weathertight construction.

3. WORK NOT INCLUDED IN THIS SECTION

a. Joints in concrete floor slabs.

b. Joints between members of metal window or door frames.

c. Caulking at roofing and sheet metal.

d. Caulking at pipe and vent flashing.

4. MATERIALS

a. Caulking compound shall be a two compound synthetic rubber sealant based on thiokol liquid polysulfide polymer LP-32 as manufactured by A. C. Horn Companies, Los Angeles, California.

b. Primer shall be as recommended by the manufacturer.

c. Oakum: Hand-picked, dry spun, free from tar, oil or other deleterious materials.

5. APPLICATION

a. Priming: Porous surfaces, as designated by the manufacturer, shall be primed before caulking is applied. All caulking shall be complete before final coats of paint are applied.

b. Mixing and Application: Mixing and application of caulking compound shall be in accordance with the manufacturer's printed directions.

c. Molds, not an integral part of door or window frames, shall be removed and caulked. Caulk solid between frames and abutting construction.

d. Joints and spaces deeper than 3/4" shall be filled solidly with oakum to within 3/4" of surface before caulking.

e. Caulk solidly around entire perimeter of openings using a nozzle of proper size to fit joints.

f. Set sills and thresholds in a full bed of caulking compound. Remove excess compound, after sill or threshold is set, and point.

g. Finish all caulked joints with the proper tool and remove caulking compound from all adjacent surfaces. Exposed caulking shall be free from wrinkles.

* * * * *

Section 8A Wood Doors and Frames

1. GENERAL

All provisions of the "General Conditions" and "Supplementary General Conditions" section form a part of this section.

2. WORK INCLUDED IN THIS SECTION

a. Wood door frames

b. Wood doors

c. Installation of finish hardware

3. WORK NOT INCLUDED IN THIS SECTION

a. Metal doors

b. Furnishing of finish hardware

4. MATERIALS

a. Exterior and Interior Wood Doors: "Weldwood" as manufactured by U. S. Plywood Corp., or "Roddiscraft" as manufactured by Roddis Plywood Corp. Doors shall be solid or hollow core, as noted on the drawings.

b. All doors shall be flush type, of sizes and thicknesses as shown and scheduled. Exterior doors shall be paint grade, Grade 2 Birch. Interior doors shall have face veneers of rotary cut Philipine "Lauan" Mahogany selected for light color, suitable for natural finish.

5. WOOD DOOR FRAMES

Frames shall be dadoed together at the head, and all joints set in white lead. All frames shall be accurately set, plumb, level and true, and with space between frame solidly shimmed back of all butts, and shall be securely nailed to the nailing blocks provided. Exterior door frames shall be vertical grain Ponderosa or White Pine. Stops shall be integral with the frames.

6. FITTING AND HANGING DOORS

Each door shall be accurately cut, trimmed and fitted to its frame and hardware, with allowance for painter's finish and possible swelling or shrinkage. The clearance at the lock and hanging stiles and at the top shall not exceed 1/8", at bottom shall not exceed 1/4". All arrises shall be rounded to a 1/6" radius, and lock rail edges shall be slightly beveled. The screws for hardware shall not be driven, merely started, by driving, and screwed home. All doors shall operate freely, but not loosely without sticking or binding, and with all hardware properly adjusted and functioning.

* * * * *

Section 8B Aluminum Doors & Glazed Framing Tubes

1. GENERAL

All provisions of the "General Conditions" and "Supplementary General Conditions" section form a part of this section.

2. WORK INCLUDED IN THIS SECTION

a. Aluminum 2-3/4" x 7-1/2" flush glazed framing tubes in panels above entrance.

b. Aluminum 2-3/4" x 7-1/2" flush glazed framing tubes in window panels of Building "D" and new lobby of Building "A".

c. Aluminum entrance doors to restaurant.

3. WORK NOT INCLUDED IN THIS SECTION

a. Glass and glazing

b. Sliding aluminum doors and windows

c. Steel framing tubes

4. MATERIALS

a. Aluminum doors, door frames and trim shall be as manufactured by Acme Metal Molding Co., Los Angeles, California.

b. Frame sections shall be extruded from 6063-T5 aluminum alloy not less than .125" in thickness. Glazing moldings shall not be less than .050" thick.

c. Frame, side light mullions and flush head glazing bead shall have vinyl glazing both sides. No metal to glass contact will be permitted.

5. DOOR FRAMES

Extruded aluminum frames, jambs, and posts, in connection with entrance doors shall be provided under this section. Submit shop drawings. Jambs enclosing structural members shall be formed in two sections with flush, tight joints and oval screws.

6. ALUMINUM NARROW STILE ENTRANCE DOORS

Frames, transoms, trim mouldings and other related items shall be as manufactured by Acme Metal Products Co. Sections will be extruded from 6063-T5 aluminum alloy, ASTM Designation B 235.

7. HARDWARE

The following hardware for entrance doors shall be furnished and factory applied. Hardware shall be furnished in polished alumilite.

a. Floor checks: Rixson #30 for entrance doors.

b. Lock: 77-1160 including cylinders #32-070.

c. Threshold: #2 x 700 AL for Rixson Floor check.

d. Push and Pulls: #32-220 Black.

8. FINISH

All aluminum shall be alumilited by the manufacturer using "ALCOA" Process 204-C1.

9. ERECTION

The doors, frames and trim, shall be erected plumb, square and true in their respective openings, complete with all bolts, reinforcements, anchors, sleeves and clips necessary for the proper fastening and supporting of units in place. All glazing beads and bars shall be tap-screw set and left loose. All items of hardware shall be adjusted for proper functioning.

10. PROTECTION

Before shipment from the factory, the aluminum work shall be completely covered with a plastic covering, Scotch Tape, or masked with paper to protect the finish surfaces from mortar, plaster, finger-prints or other stains. All aluminum surfaces in contact with plaster, steel bucks or other dissimilar metal parts, shall be given a heavy coat of suitable alkali-resistant bituminous paint. Aluminum shall have a hard, smooth satin finish and shall receive a coating of methacrylite lacquer as an additional protection.

11. INSPECTION

Before completing the work, carefully examine and clean all aluminum surfaces and test all framing and hardware. Make all repairs and adjustment to the work, leaving it in a satisfactory condition.

*****

DIVISION 8 DOORS, WINDOWS AND GLASS

Section 8C Sliding Aluminum Doors

1. GENERAL

All provisions in the "General Conditions" and "Supplementary General Conditions" section form a part of this section.

2. WORK INCLUDED IN THIS SECTION

a. Sliding aluminum doors, frames, and screens.

b. Hardware for sliding doors.

3. WORK NOT INCLUDED IN THIS SECTION

a. Glass and glazing

b. Caulking

4. MATERIALS

a. Aluminum sliding doors for single glazing shall be similar and equal to Miller Series #187, as manufactured by Miller Sliding Glass Door Company, 3216 Valhalla Drive, Burbank, California. Doors shall be bottom rolling on nylon sheaves with permanently lubricated and sealed ball bearings. Doors shall be completely weatherstripped with continuous wool pile at head, sill, stile and interlockers. All doors shall be equipped with standard Pulls and positive jam-proof, up-acting cam night latches. Glass mould shall be snap-on type, mounted with spring lock clips.

b. Door Screens: Sliding door screens shall be bottom rolling on adjustable nylon rollers housed in the bottom rail. Top of screen shall be equipped with nylon guide washers.

(1) Frames shall be wired with 14 x 18 mesh fiberglass cloth.

(2) Neoprene closure strip shall be secured to rear stile of screen.

5. FINISH

All aluminum parts of the door, screens, and frames shall have a satin finish Alumilite coating according to Aluminum Company of America Specification 204-R1.

6. ERECTION

All doors and frames shall be installed at locations ad indicated on the drawings, in accordance with the written instructions of the manufacturer.

*****

DIVISION 8 DOORS, WINDOWS, AND GLASS

Section 8D Metal Doors and Frames

1. GENERAL

All provisions of the "General Conditions" and "Supplementary General Conditions" section form a part of this section.

2. WORK INCLUDED IN THIS SECTION

a. Hollow metal doors and metal frames as scheduled.

b. Installation of hardware.

3. WORK NOT INCLUDED IN THIS SECTION

a. Furnishing of hardware

b. Wood doors and entrance doors

c. Metal sliding doors

4. MATERIALS

a. Door frames shall be pressed of 16 gauge cold rolled, pickled and annealed steel. Frames shall have all welded joints with welds ground smooth. Reinforcement for mortise hardware and for hinges shall be with inserts spotwelded in place. Hinge plates shall be 10 gauge or heavier, plates for lock and closers shall be at least 12 gauge. There shall be three (3) anchors at each jamb and two (2) at the head for anchoring to the structure. Frames shall be provided with temporary spreaders at bottom to preserve proper shape during transportation and erection. Door stops shall be not less than 5/8" x 1-5/8" in size.

b. Hollow Metal Doors shall be flush type, welded, 1-3/4" thick, of 18 gauge stretcher leveled steel with surfaces spaced and reinforced with steel channels or zee sections not over 8" o.c. vertically.

c. Finish: After fabrication, all welds and joints shall be ground smooth and filled flush with mineral filler so as to conceal all seams. All surfaces of the frames shall receive one shop coat of air dried, zinc chromate, rust inhibitive primer before shipment. Doors shall receive two (2) coats of a zinc chromate, rust inhibitive primer, baked on.

5. SHOP DRAWINGS AND DATA

The Contractor shall submit shop drawings of fabricated items. Shop drawings shall clearly show the sizes of all members and methods of joining and anchoring.

6. UNDERWRITERS LABEL

Labeled doors and frames as scheduled shall be constructed to conform to the regulations of the Board of Fire Underwriters, and shall bear proper "label" for the type of opening in which they occur.

7. HARDWARE

All metal doors and frames shall be mortised, reinforced, drilled and tapped for mortise hardware in accordance with templates or hardware furnished under "Finish Hardware".

8 INSTALLATION

a. All frames shall be erected plumb, square, and true to line and level, with secure fastening to structures and anchors. Formed steel stiffeners and reinforcement shall be installed within frames at all points where tap screw fastenings are used in connection with embedded strap anchorages.

b. Doors shall be installed by authorized representatives of the manufacturer, but not before all plastering is completed.

* * * * *

DIVISION 8 DOORS, WINDOWS AND GLASS

Section 8E Metal Windows

1. GENERAL

All provisions in the "General Conditions" and "Supplementary General Conditions" section form a part of this section.

2. WORK INCLUDED IN THIS SECTION

a. All horizontal sliding sash, and aluminum screens

b. All louver windows, and aluminum screens

c. Operating hardware, bolts, anchors, screws.

3. WORK NOT INCLUDED IN THIS SECTION

a. Glass and glazing

b. Sliding glass doors

c. Caulking around windows

4. MATERIALS

a. On drawings where aluminum horizontal sliding windows are indicated they shall be "E-Z Set" rolling windows as manufactured by "E-Z Set" Windows, Inc., National City, California.

b. On drawings where louver windows are indicated they shall be "Visualite" Louver Windows Series #900 as manufactured by Acker and Acker Mfg. Co., 5725 South Main St., Los Angeles, California.

5. ERECTION

All metal windows shall be installed by the manufacturer or his authorized representative, and shall be set plumb, square, level, and true within their respective openings. Frames shall be set and securely anchored to wood framing. Ventilators shall be aligned and adjusted prior to glazing to insure continuous contact against frames.

6. FINAL ADJUSTMENT

After the work of glazing and painting has been completed, all movable parts of the window installation shall be adjusted to insure proper fitting and functioning.

7. CLEAN-UP

Upon completion of the work, the Contractor shall remove all surplus materials and debris resulting from these operations.

* * * * *

DIVISION 8 DOORS, WINDOWS AND GLASS

Section 8F Glass, Glazing, and Mirrors

1. GENERAL

All provisions of the "General Conditions" and the "Supplementary General Conditions" section form a part of this section.

2. WORK INCLUDED IN THIS SECTION

a. Glass and glazing except as specifically excluded

b. Mirrors, mirror trim and backing

c. Setting of metal glazing beads

3. WORK NOT INCLUDED IN THIS SECTION

a. Furnishing of wood stops

b. Fire extinguisher glass

c. Furnishing of metal glazing beads

d. Final cleaning of glass

e. Glass or plastic in shower and tub enclosures.

4. MATERIALS

a. All glass and mirrors shall bear labels, and labels shall not be removed until glass and mirrors have been inspected and approved.

b. All door and window glass in lobby and restaurant shall be $\frac{1}{4}$" thick, polished plate glass, Parallel-O-Grey with 44% light transmission, as manufactured by Libbey-Owens-Ford Glass Company.

c. Fixed glass and glass in sliding doors in units 18 and 26 shall be glazing quality, plate glass, $\frac{1}{4}$ inch in thickness, Parallel-O-Plate, as manufactured by Libbey-Owens-Ford Glass Company.

d. Glass in horizontal sliding aluminum windows shall be 1/8" thick, double strength, clear "B" grade.

e. Glass in louver windows shall be 3/16" thick, flat drawn, heavy sheet glass, "B" quality, with ground edges.

f. Mirrors and Frames: "Registered Safety Mirrors", complete with back and frame, as manufactured by Tyre Brothers, Los Angeles, California. Polished plate glass shall be $\frac{1}{4}$" thick, silvering quality. Mirror backs shall be hermetically sealed by a uniform coating of copper, electroplated over a heavy film of silver. Mirror shall be laminated to $\frac{1}{4}$" plywood back with nonstaining adhesive. Provide corrosion-resistant, protective metal backing, not less than 24 gauge. Set mirror and backing in chrome-plated channel frame. Corners shall be rounded. Metal hangers shall be manufacturer's standard. Provide one mirror in each new living unit.

g. Glazing Compound: "DAP 1012" glazing compound, as manufactured by Armstrong Co., Richmond, California.

5. SETTING

a. Accurately cut and fit all glass; set without springing or forcing. Run glazing compound neatly, cleanly, and even with inside of glazing rabbet.

b. Glass in metal frames shall be set in a full and complete bed of glazing compound on all four sides. Entire installation shall be in strict accordance with aluminum window manufacturer's recommendations.

6. ACCEPTANCE

Improperly set glass, broken glass, or glass which does not fully meet the requirements of its grade, will not be accepted. Replace such glass without extra cost to the Owner.

7. CLEANING

After glazing compound has set, remove all glazing compound and other stains, resulting from work performed under this section, from glass and adjoining work and leave in a neat and clean condition. Final cleaning of glass is specified in the Section 1A.

* * * * *

DIVISION 9 FINISHES

Section 9A Lathing and Plastering

1. GENERAL

All applicable provisions in the "General Conditions" and "Supplementary General Conditions" section form a part of this section.

2. WORK INCLUDED IN THIS SECTION

a. Gypsum lath

b. Metal lath, wire fabric, lath, wire lath, metal grounds, clips.

c. Metal screeds at terrazzo or masonry

d. Corner reinforcements

e. Paper backing

f. Hangers, runners, furring channels for hung ceilings.

g. All plastering, gypsum and cement

h. Scratch coats behind ceramic tile, glass mosaic or terrazzo.

i. Patching in existing and new construction

3. WORK NOT INCLUDED IN THIS SECTION

a. Wood grounds

b. Metal door frames

c. Plaster rings for electrical fixtures

d. Metal studs

4. MATERIALS

a. Metal Lath: 3.4 lb. copper-bearing steel, 3/8" diamond mesh, galvanized, or coated with rust inhibiting paint after fabrication.

b. Tie Wire: No. 18 W & M gauge, galvanized, annealed tie wire.

c. Runner Channels: Cold rolled steel, size 1½", weighing not less than 475 pounds per 1,000 feet.

d. Furring Channels: Cold rolled steel, size 3/4", weighing not less than 300 pounds per 1,000 feet. All channels shall be given a coat of rust-inhibiting paint or shall be galvanized.

e. Hangers supporting runner channels shall be soft steel wire, 8 gauge, zinc-coated.

f. Expanded Corner Bead: No. 1 "Milcor", 26 gauge, galvanized.

g. Casing Beads or Plaster Stops: No. 66 "Milcor", 24 gauge, galvanized.

h. Gypsum Lath shall be 3/8" gypsum lath perforated with 3/4" holes.

i. Waterproof Building Paper shall be Orange Label, "Sisalkraft", as manufactured by American Sisalkraft Corp., San Francisco, California.

j. Terrazzo Strips shall be zinc, standard 1/8" heavy top, flush type.

k. Gypsum Plaster: Standard brand, ASTM Designation C28-57.

l. Sand: ASTM C 35, except, when used with Portland cement for scratch coat plastering, the amount of sand retained on a No. 8 sieve shall not be less than 10% nor more than 30%.

m. Water: Clean, free from oils, acids, alkalies, organic and other matter injurious to plaster.

n. Portland Cement: ASTM C 150, Type I.

o. Hydrated Lime: ASTM C 206-49, plus the added requirement limiting unhydrated oxides to 8% maximum.

5. INSPECTION OF SURFACES

The Contractor shall inspect all areas or surfaces adjacent to, covered by, or affecting his work. He shall ascertain from the proper authorities that all work which will be concealed behind, or incorporated in lath or plaster, is complete, and that all required inspections have been made. All unsatisfactory conditions shall be reported to the Architect in writing. No materials in this section shall be applied until such defects or conditions have been corrected.

6. LATHING APPLICATION

a. The application of metal lath, gypsum lath, and exterior plaster reinforcement shall conform to the processes outlined in "Reference Specifications, Lathing, Furring and Plastering in California", 1958 edition; or as specified.

b. Masonry and Concrete Walls: Where metal or gypsum lath abuts an exposed concrete or masonry wall, install metal plaster stop.

c. Apply gypsum lath to all interior ceilings and stud walls indicated to receive plaster.

d. Gypsum lath at sound-insulated division walls between living units shall be fastened to studs with resilient clips. Clips shall be used on both sides of wall. Lath shall have a minimum clearance of ½" from the studs.

e. Cornerite and Stripite

(1) Continuously reinforce all interior vertical and horizontal angles of gypsum lath with cornerite.

(2) Apply stripite at corners of all door and window openings of wood stud partitions.

f. Corner Beads: Install at all external corners of interior plastered walls.

g. Base Screeds and Terrazzo Strips: Install level and true at base and other locations shown. Supply fittings for in and out corners to fit base screeds.

h. Metal Casings: Apply as detailed or required.

6. SUSPENDED CEILINGS

a. Hanger wires shall be spaced not more than 48 inches on center in either direction.

b. Runner channels shall be spaced not more than 4 feet on centers.

c. Furring channels shall be spaced not more than 16 inches on centers for diamond mesh lath, and 24 inches on centers for rib lath.

7. PLASTER APPLICATION

The application of plastering materials shall conform to the processes outlined in the 1958 edition, "Reference Specifications for Lathing, Furring and Plastering in California", as published by the California Lathing and Plastering Contractor's Association; or as specified.

8. PLASTER BASE FOR CERAMIC TILE, GLASS MOSAIC WORK OR TERRAZZO

Apply where shown and as specified under lathing application, and Portland cement plaster, mixing, proportioning, and application, respectively. Provide specified waterproof building paper backing over wood studs, metal base screeds, and terrazzo strips at top and edge of terrazzo wainscot.

9. CURING

Keep each coat of plaster damp for at least 48 hours after application. Apply only as much water as will be readily absorbed. Protect plaster from uneven and excessive evaporation during hot, dry weather.

10. PATCHING

After installation of other work has been completed, do all such patching and pointing up of plaster as may be necessary to leave finished work free from cracks, stains, and other defects.

11. WORKMANSHIP

All surfaces shall be straight, plumb, with true angles, and free from trowel marks, checks, and other blemishes. Plane surfaces shall contact 10-foot straightedge with not over 1/8" variation either way. Plaster with cracks, blisters, pits, checks, or discoloration will not be accepted.

12. PROTECTION OF OTHER WORK

Protect work of other trades with tarpaulins and drop cloths. Remove excess material forced into openings. Provide protection under mixing boxes and wherever plastering materials are piled on floor.

13. CLEANING

At completion of the work, remove all tools, equipment, surplus materials, and debris resulting from lathing and plastering operations. Leave premises neat and broom-clean.

14. GUARANTY

The Contractor shall guarantee in writing that any defect in his work due to faulty workmanship or materials, discovered and made known to him within two (2) years from date of final acceptance of his work, shall be made good by him without additional expense to the Owner.

* * * * *

DIVISION 9   FINISHED

Section 9B   Tile Work

1. GENERAL

All provisions of the "General Conditions" and "Supplementary General Conditions" section form a part of this section.

2. WORK INCLUDED IN THIS SECTION

a. Ceramic Tile

b. Glass Mosaic

c. Repair or replacement of existing tile showers as indicated in Schedule 4A, of sheet A-2 of the drawings.

3. WORK NOT INCLUDED IN THIS SECTION

a. Wire reinforcing

b. Scratch coat

4. MATERIALS

a. Glass Mosaic Tile: Glass shall be "Standard Medley" "Quamagra", as distributed by Quality Marble and Granite Co., 4100 Lankershim Blvd., North Hollywood, California. Tile shall be as perfect as it is possible to manufacture. The colors and shades shall be reasonably uniform. The exposed face of the tile shall be a smooth, even surface uniform in texture without chips. Color shall be as selected by the Owner from the manufacturer's standard colors.

b. Ceramic Tile: Glazed interior tile with a "satinmatt" finish, square edged, as manufactured by Gladding, McBean and Co. Size shall be 4¼" x 4¼", including coves, bases, liners, trim, corners indicated or required. Colors and patterns shall be as selected by the Owner from the manufacturer's standard catalog.

c. Setting Materials:

(1) Portland Cement shall conform to ASTM designation C-150-56, Type I.

(2) Hydrated Lime shall conform to ASTM designation C-207-49, Type S, plus the added requirement limiting the unhydrated oxides to 8% maximum.

(3) Sand shall comply with "Specifications for Aggregate for Masonry Mortar", ASTM designation C-144-52T.

(4) Water shall be free from any impurity that is injurious to the construction.

(5) Grout and Buttering Mix shall be a waterproof grout mix with up to one part sand added to each two parts of Portland cement. Sand shall have no fine under 80 grit and no coarse over 30 grit. Color shall be white.

(6) Pure coat shall be pure Portland cement mixed with water into a trowelable wet slurry.

(7) Mortar setting bed shall be mixed in the proportions of one part Portland cement, one part hydrated lime, six parts of clean sharp sand.

ADJOINING WORK

5. Examine adjoining work before starting work. Report to Architect in writing work incorrectly located, or so located as to not give best results. Inspect surfaces to be covered. Grounds, bucks, outlet and receptacle boxes, rough plumbing, and other fixtures and fittings must be in place. Starting the work will be considered as an acceptance of the work of others.

SETTING GLASS MOSAIC

6. Glass mosaic tile shall be set by Journeymen tile setters experienced in setting tile of this type under similar conditions.

a. At no time shall the mortar setting bed be over ½" thick. Apply a plumb scratch coat where necessary to establish this.

b. Float the mortar setting bed to a uniform plumb and level surface, allowing room for glass mosaic, to bring finished surface to required plane. Thickness of mortar shall be from ¼" to ½" as required, cut through the setting bed horizontally and vertically every 24 inches.

c. Mosaic sheets shall be placed in position on the pure coat freshly combed into the mortar setting bed with notched trowel. All combing must be done in a horizontal direction. Sheets shall be tamped firmly into place, true and even with the finished surface line or plane.

d. Expansion joints or control joints at 20' o.c. must be continued through the mortar bed and glass mosaic and kept free of mortar and grout. These shall be filled with an approved thickol based caulking compound, as close as possible to the color of the grout.

e. Interior corners shall be butt. External corners shall have the glass mosaic fitted together with a close quick miter. Where external corners are subject to pedestrian traffic, they shall be carefully smoothed with a fine carborundum stone to remove sharp edges.

f. Grout all joints, after removal of the paper, leaving them completely and uniformly filled. At no time shall sand or any abrasive be used that will damage the natural sheen of the glass mosaic tile.

g. All excess grout and glue shall be removed from the face of the tile leaving the finished surface clean.

SETTING CERAMIC TILE

7. a. Layout: Layout work in accordance with Architect's drawings. Verify measurements at building and cooperate with other trades whose work adjoins or connects with work. Lay out work about center lines of areas to eliminate use of less than half tiles. Work out wall tile heights to within ½ course above or below indicated heights to eliminate cutting.

b. Cutting, Drilling and Patching: Cut, fill, drill, repair and patch as necessary for work of other trades. Clean and leave in perfect condition at completion.

c. Thoroughly soak tile in clean water for at least one hour prior to setting. Apply to setting beds within five minutes after soaking.

d. Set and tamp into full mortar beds with flush, well filled joints, finished in true planes, plumb, square, graded or level. Cut and fit to closely connect with abutting work. Set cut edges against fixtures with at least 1/16" joint

EXISTING TILE SHOWERS

8. The Contractor shall inspect existing tile showers that are to be replaced as indicated on the drawings. No tile work shall be commenced until repairs have been made and surfaces are in a satisfactory condition to receive tile.

PROTECTION

9. Contractor shall provide and install barriers or other forms of protection and coverings required to prevent damage.

CLEANING

10. Thoroughly clean after grouting and pointing has sufficiently set. Remove all traces of cement or foreign matter. Cover exposed hardware and plumbing trim, liable to injury, with vaseline. Following cleaning, remove vaseline and clean and polish metal work.

* * * * *

DIVISION 9 FINISHES
Section 9C Terrazzo

1. GENERAL

   All provisions in the "General Conditions" and "Supplementary General Conditions" section form a part of this section.

2. WORK INCLUDED IN THIS SECTION

   a. Terrazzo floor and 6" flush base throughout Building "D" and in lobby of Building "A"

   b. Divider strips

3. WORK NOT INCLUDED IN THIS SECTION

   a. Base slab

   b. Scratch coat

   c. Plaster grounds

4. MATERIALS

   a. Gray or white cement shall conform to ASTM designation C-150, Type I or II.

   b. Sand shall consist of washed natural sand containing less than 1% deleterous material such as clay lumps, shale, mica, schist, alkali, coated grains, or soft and flaky particles.

   c. Marble granules: Granules shall be chips selected from best quality domestic marble. Color and design will be as selected by the Owner. The granules shall be of sizes No. 1, 2 and 3.

   d. Divider strips shall be 1¼" x 1/8" white metal alloy. Divider strips shall be placed 3'x0" O.C. as indicated on plans.

5. WORKMANSHIP

   All terrazzo work shall be bonded to the structural slab and installed in accordance with the "Standard Terrazzo Specifications", 1958 edition, as published by the National Terrazzo & Mosaic Association, Inc.

* * * * *

Job 106-62   TERRAZZO   9C-1

DIVISION 9 FINISHES
Section 9D Oxychloride Flooring

1. GENERAL

   All provisions in the "General Conditions" and "Supplementary General Conditions" section form a part of this section.

2. WORK INCLUDED IN THIS SECTION

   a. Oxychloride balconies, base, and stairs of existing and new construction where indicated.

   b. Felt membrane

   c. Mesh reinforcing

   d. Sealing of finish floor

3. WORK NOT INCLUDED IN THIS SECTION

   a. Subfloor

   b. Wood blocking

   c. Plaster screeds (Parting bead)

   d. Precast concrete stairs

4. MATERIALS

   a. Oxychloride flooring shall be magnesium oxychloride cement material as manufactured by the Diato Co., and shall conform to the published standards of the Oxychloride Cement Association. Color shall be as selected by the Architect from full color range.

   b. Reinforcing for base shall be 3.4 metal lath.

   c. Sealer shall be a clear acrylic sealer.

5. INSTALLATION

   a. Installation shall be by licensed applicators, and in strict conformance with manufacturer's requirements.

   b. Wood balcony and stairs shall be clean and in acceptable condition to receive flooring materials. Plaster screeds shall be in place, and plastering shall be completed before commencement of this work.

   c. Apply one layer of 15# felt over wood subfloors and stairs. Lay mesh reinforcing over felt, nailing or stapling to subfloor every 6" and turning up at walls. Apply metal lath to walls for reinforcing of base.

   d. Oxychloride cement shall be applied to a minimum thickness of ½" and shall be screeded level and steel troweled for a dense hard finish. Base shall be coved and as detailed.

Job 106-62   OXYCHLORIDE FLOORING   9D-1

6. SEALING

After oxychloride has set, apply a clear acrylic sealer over all areas.

7. PROTECTION

Finish floors and stairs shall be temporarily covered with heavy building paper or other means to protect from damage until completion of the building.

* * * * *

DIVISION 9 FINISHES

Section 9E   Resilient Floor Covering

1. GENERAL

All applicable provisions of the "General Conditions" and "Supplementary General Conditions" section form a part of this section.

2. WORK INCLUDED IN THIS SECTION

a. Vinyl tile floor covering and cove base as indicated on the drawings.

b. Metal edge stripe

3. WORK NOT INCLUDED IN THIS SECTION

a. Terrazzo, tile, or oxychloride floors

b. Waxing of finished floor

4. MATERIALS

a. Tile shall be 1/8" thick, all vinyl tile as manufactured by the following:

Armstrong Cork Co.   "Custom Corlon" or "Burl"

Kentile Inc.   Solid Vinyl "Terrazzo" or "Marbleized"

b. Cove shall be formed integrally of matching sheet material.

c. Adhesives: As recommended by the manufacturer.

d. Leveling compound and Crack filler: As manufactured by Aetna Manufacturing Co. for concrete floors.

e. Concrete Primer: Coat all concrete floors on earth grade with primer as recommended by the manufacturer.

f. Metal Edging: Chromedge Type 114-A as manufactured by B & T Metals Company, distributed by William Volker & Co., Los Angeles, California.

5. SAMPLES

Submit a complete range of colors and types for the Owner's selection. One of each color or type selected shall be retained by the Owner. All material placed in the building shall match such samples.

6. INSTALLATION

a. Floors which are to receive resilient covering shall be thoroughly inspected and a report made to the Architect in writing of all areas which are unsatisfactory for receiving flooring materials. No flooring shall be applied over unsatisfactory areas until corrections or defects in workmanship or materials of other trades have been made.

DIVISION 9 FINISHES

Section 9F Acoustical Tile

1. GENERAL

All provisions in the "General Conditions" and "Supplementary General Conditions" section form a part of this section.

2. WORK INCLUDED IN THIS SECTION

a. The furnishing and installation of wood stripping of all wood ceiling joists which are to receive acoustical tile.

b. The furnishing and application of all acoustical tile to ceilings in accordance with the Finish Schedule.

c. Hung ceiling support system and acoustical tile in kitchen and restaurant.

3. WORK NOT INCLUDED IN THIS SECTION

a. Wood furring and wood sheathing.

b. Fixtures and grilles in acoustical ceilings.

4. MATERIALS

a. Acoustical tile in lobby and living units shall be 12"x12"x½", Butt edge, full Random "Cushiontone" as manufactured by the Armstrong Cork Co.

b. Acoustical tile in restaurant and kitchen shall be Armstrong Full Random, "Acoustical Fire Guard" suspended on Armstrong TDR System.

c. Wood stripping shall be 1" x 3" Douglas Fir

5. SAMPLES

Samples of the acoustical tile shall be submitted to the Architect for his approval before proceeding with the work.

6. PATTERN AND DESIGN

All acoustical tile shall be laid in regular pattern without border, and with joints parallel to walls.

7. WOOD STRIPPING

In areas indicated on the drawings or specified, apply wood stripping at centers as indicated on the drawings and secure to each support with 8d common nails. Install stripping so as to provide a level and true mounting for the tile ceiling.

---

b. Clean all undersurfaces and make them suitable for the installation of the resilient flooring materials. Correct irregularities in floor with leveling compound if they are correctable with this procedure.

c. Cement surfaces shall have cracks filled with leveling compound and crack filler as specified.

d. Primer: Coat all concrete floors on grade with primer.

e. All materials shall be installed with joints tight, floor true, level and even. Cut to, and around all permanent fixtures. Roll coverings with a 150 lb. roller and remove all irregularities. Remove all surplus adhesive ready for waxing.

f. Laying of tile shall be done symmetrically about the centers of rooms. Cutting of tile shall be done by methods which produce square and true edges.

g. Metal strips and edgings shall be installed in minimum lengths of 12'-0" except when total length of edge or piece is less than 12'-0".

7. SERVICE GUARANTY

Within one (1) year following date of completion of the work, all floors which show edges of undue wear, have become loose, are cracked or otherwise defective, shall be removed and replaced with new floor at the expense of the Contractor.

8. PROTECTION

It is the Contractor's responsibility to protect all resilient work as specified until final acceptance of the buildings by the Owner.

* * * * *

8. INSTALLATION

a. Tiles shall be spaced symmetrically about the center lines of the room or space. Joints shall be tight and aligned with walls. Tiles shall be cut to fit snugly around pipes and fixtures.

b. Tiles shall be secured at each corner with rust-resistive nails or screws concealed in the perforations or through tongues as recommended by the tile manufacturer. Sizes and types of nails or screws shall be as recommended by the manufacturer.

c. A 20 gauge steel edge mold shall be installed at exposed edges of tile. Tile shall be neatly scribed to wall where tile intersect or abut a wall surface.

9. PAINTING

The tiles including the bevel edges shall be factory painted two coats before installation. All edges that have been cut and all abrasions shall be touched up after installation.

10. COOPERATION WITH OTHER TRADES

Full cooperation and timely instruction shall be furnished all other trades in establishing fixtures and inserts, to the end that the completed work will finish in true alignment and precise position, with proper support at all points and connections, and with a minimum amount of cutting and fitting.

11. CLEANING AND TOUCHING UP

After installation of acoustical material has been completed, the Contractor shall clean the entire surfaces removing any discolorations or foreign matter. Touch up all abraded spots and edges with the same paint as was used in the factory applied finish.

12. GUARANTY

Upon completion of the work, the Contractor shall furnish the Owner a written guaranty covering the satisfactory repair and replacement free of charge of all workmanship and material that prove defective within a period of five (5) years from date of completion.

* * * * *

DIVISION 9 FINISHES

Section 9G Painting

1. GENERAL

All provisions in the "General Conditions" and "Supplementary General Conditions" section form a part of this section.

2. WORK INCLUDED IN THIS SECTION

a. All exterior surfaces of plaster, wood, metal not specifically excluded.

b. All interior surfaces as scheduled.

3. MATERIALS

All materials shall be pure, unadulterated, delivered to the building in the original unbroken packages bearing the maker's name, brand number, and the batch number, thereby completely identifying the contents. Materials shall be as manufactured by the Dunn Edwards Corporation of a type as listed below:

Exterior-Concrete Bock and Stucco
- 1st coat — 2 parts D-E Evershield 100% Acrylic Base Masonry paint - 1 part D-E Evershield Sealer, W-701-30
- 2nd coat — D-E Evershield 100% Acrylic Base Masonry paint, W-701

Exterior Doors Clear Water Repellant
- D-E Hydro-lox, clear silicone water repellant V-191 - Application in accordance with label directions

Exterior-Wood Painted
- 1st coat — D-E Apex Exterior Wood Primer, 42-9
- 2nd coat — D-E Permanent House and Trim
- 3rd coat — 40 series, (dark colors) or Rancho house and trim, 60 series (light colors)

Exterior-Metal Ferrous
- 1st coat — D-E Ferroprime Q.D. red lead Primer 43-2
- 2nd coat — D-E Loc Kote Exterior Synthetic Body Coat 42-23
- 3rd coat — D-E Enduratec Exterior Synthetic Enamel 42-8

Exterior-Metal Galvanized
- Pretreatment: Clean and apply a coat of Vinyl Wash Pretreatment. (Apply zinc Chromate Primer within four (4) hours, or, clean and etch with acid Component of Vinyl Wash Pretreatment then clean by water rinsing all surfaces then apply:
- 1st coat — D-E Zinc Chromate Primer 42-6
- 2nd coat — D-E Loc Kote Exterior Synthetic Body Coat 42-23
- 3rd coat — D-E Enduratec Exterior Synthetic Enamel 42-8

Exterior-Metal Aluminum
- 1st coat — D-E Duracrete Pórtland cement Paint 42-20 (flat finish)
- 2nd coat — D-E Duracrete Portland Cement Paint 42-20 (flat finish)

Interior-Wood Enamel
Finish (Synthetic)

1st coat	D-E Master Flat Undercoater 31-1 (Reduced for priming)
2nd coat	D-E Proflat Split Coat Type Undercoater 42-5
3rd coat	D-E Practical Synthetic Gloss Enamel 1-1 or D-E Practical Synthetic Eggshell enamel 1-1

Interior-Wood Doors
Light or Blonde
Clear Varnish Finish

1st coat	D-E Synseal Brushing Sanding Sealer V-106
2nd coat	D-E Syngloss pale synthetic gloss varnish V-197
3rd coat	D-E Synsatin Pale interior satin finish varnish V-199 or Syngloss V-197

Interior - Plaster

No finish in lobby or living quarters

Interior - Metal

1st coat	Prime coat same as exterior metal
2nd coat	Finish same as adjoining areas

Interior - Concrete
Bock (flat)

1st coat	D-E Alkyseal Synthetic Pigmented sealer 28-1X
2nd coat	D-E Alkyseal. Pigmented Sealer 28-1X (tint near finish color)
3rd coat	D-E Walltone 21-1

Interior - Plaster and
Concrete Block
(Kitchens only)

1st coat	D-E Alkyseal synthetic Pigmented wall sealer 28-1X
2nd coat	D-E Master flat undercoater 31-1 and finish coat mixed equal parts
3rd coat	D-E Practical synthetic gloss enamel 1-1 or Practical synthetic Eggshell enamel 1-1X

4. PAINTED LINES ON ASPHALT PAVING

Paint lines for automobile parking stalls where indicated on sheet A-1. Paint shall conform to the applicable specifications of the California State Highway Department.

5. WORKMANSHIP

All surfaces which are to be treated shall be in proper condition to receive the finish specified. The Contractor shall notify the Architect of any surface which is not in proper condition to be finished.

6. PROTECTION

Protect this work and work of other subcontractors. Furnish and place sufficient drop cloths to fully protect all parts of work during execution of this contract. The Contractor shall be held fully responsible for paint droppings on cement floor and base. Paint droppings shall be entirely removed, and damaged surfaces shall be repaired in a manner satisfactory to the Architect.

7. RIGHT OF REJECTION

No exterior painting or interior finishing to be done under conditions which would jeopardize appearance of work in any way. No work will be accepted which shows laps, stains, flat or glossy spots or imperfections in surface over which paint or other finish is applied.

8. WOODWORK

All woodwork shall be thoroughly hand-sandpapered and dusted. All nail holes, cracks, or defects in all work shall be puttied after the first coat. The putty shall match the color of the stain or paint. The woodwork on the interior shall be sandpapered smooth after each coat of material, except the last coat; and all surfaces of both interior and exterior work shall be free from dust, dirt, or other imperfections.

9. SAMPLES

No painting shall be done in the building until samples are approved. All finished work shall conform to the approved samples.

10. CLEANING

a. All rubbish, waste, or surplus material shall be removed from time to time, and all woodwork, hardware, floors, or other adjacent work shall be cleaned.

b. All glass throughout the buildings shall have all paint or varnish spots and brush marks removed, and upon completion of the painting work, all glass that is scratched or damaged by the Painter's work, or while cleaning off the paint from the glass shall be replaced at the Contractor's expense. Hardware and other unpainted metal surface shall be cleaned.

* * * * *

DIVISION 10 SPECIALTIES

Section 10A Finish Hardware

1. GENERAL

   All provisions of the "General Conditions" and "Supplementary General Conditions" section form a part of this section.

2. ALLOWANCE FOR FINISH HARDWARE

   The Contractor shall provide in his bid the sum of One thousand ($1,000.00) dollars for finish hardware not including the cost of installation. The Owner will select the finish hardware at a source of his choice. The Contractor shall receive, be responsible for, and store this material until it is installed. This amount includes sales tax but does not include Contractor's overhead, profit, or commission. Should the cost of finish hardware exceed the allowance, the net excess cost will be added to the contract sum. If the cost of hardware is less than the allowance, the difference shall be deducted from the contract sum.

3. HARDWARE INCLUDED IN THIS SECTION

   a. Finish hardware for hinged wood doors including butts.

   b. Pulls, knobs, catches for wardrobes, cabinets, doors and drawers.

   c. Metal thresholds and weatherstripping for exterior doors to living units.

   d. Metal hand rail brackets.

   e. Hardware for metal doors and frames.

4. WORK NOT INCLUDED IN THIS SECTION

   a. Installation of finish hardware

   b. Hardware for toilet compartments

   c. Hardware for aluminum entrance and sliding doors

   d. Hardware for fire extinguisher cabinets

   e. Operators and hardware for aluminum windows

5. TEMPLATES

   Hardware to be applied to metal frames or metal doors shall be made to template and furnished with machine screws of proper size and finish. Templates shall be supplied to the manufacturer of doors and frames.

* * * * *

DIVISION 10 SPECIALTIES

Section 10B Bath and Toilet Accessories

1. GENERAL

   All provisions of the "General Conditions" and "Supplementary General Conditions" section form a part of this section.

2. WORK INCLUDED IN THIS SECTION

   a. Bathroom mirrors

   b. Toilet tissue cabinets

   c. Lather dispensers

   d. Towel dispensers

   e. Sanitary napkin dispensers

   f. Metal toilet partitions

   g. Shower enclosures

   h. Shower doors

   i. Tub enclosures

3. WORK NOT INCLUDED IN THIS SECTION

   a. Items embedded in tile

   b. Plumbing fixtures and trim

4. MATERIALS

   a. Bathroom Mirror and Shelf: Install in toilet rooms of Building "D" Model #53020 mirror frame and stainless steel shelf, as manufactured by the Charles Parker Co., distributed by Lee G. Wirth, 714 W. Olympic Blvd., Los Angeles, California, Richmond 9-4053.

   b. Toilet Tissue Cabinets: One toilet tissue cabinet Model #0700 as manufactured by Charles Parker Co., at each water closet installed in Buildings "B", "C", "D".

   c. Lather Dispensers: One lather dispenser Model #B47CP as manufactured by the Charles Parker Co., in each toilet room in Building "D".

   d. Towel Dispensers: One towel dispenser Model #T500 as manufactured by the Charles Parker Co., in each toilet room in Building "D".

   e. Sanitary Napkin Dispenser: shall be Model #R-22 as manufactured by West Chemical Products, Inc. Install one dispenser in Women's Rest Room, Building "D".

f. Metal Toilet Partitions: Install in toilet rooms Building "D", "Academy" flush finish, as manufactured by Sanymetal Products Co., Inc. as distributed by Cunningham and Goin, Los Angeles, California. See drawings for locations.

g. Shower Enclosures: Corner shower enclosures shall be Model #101, two panel as shown on the drawings, glazed with "Safetylite" plastic as manufactured by the American Shower Door Co., Inc., 936 No. Cahuenga Blvd., Hollywood, California

h. Shower Doors: shall be "American Maid", #250 door, with "Safetylite" plastic glazing as manufactured by the American Shower Door Co., Inc. Replace glass in existing shower doors of building "A" with "Safetylite" plastic.

i. Tub Enclosures: shall be "Shower Maid" tub enclosures glazed with "Safetylite" plastic, as manufactured by the American Shower Door Co., Inc.

5. INSTALLATION

Furnish and install bath and toilet accessories where indicated on the drawings or as specified.

* * * * *

DIVISION 10 SPECIALTIES

Section 10C Miscellaneous Specialties

1. GENERAL

All provisions of the "General Conditions" and "Supplementary General Conditions" section form a part of this section.

2. WORK INCLUDED IN THIS SECTION

a. Wardrobe doors

b. Fire extinguishers and cabinets

c. Street numbers

d. Unit numbers

e. Plastic signs

f. Kitchenette units and metal cabinets

3. WORK NOT INCLUDED IN THIS SECTION

a. Electrical service to plastic signs

b. Electrical and plumbing services to kitchenette units

4. MATERIALS

a. Wardrobe doors: "Woodmaster Modernfold" mahogany finish doors equipped with all necessary hardware and track, as manufactured by the New Castle Products, Inc., New Castle, Indiana shall be installed at wardrobes in all new living units of Buildings "B" and "C".

b. Plastic Signs: Furnish and install two 8'-0" x 14'-0" plastic signs. The body of the sign shall be of white translucent plastic conforming to the Los Angeles Building Code. Raised colored plastic letters shall be mounted on the plastic base. Each sign shall have the following words in script mounted upon it. "ANNA CAPRI", as indicated on the drawings. The Contractor shall submit samples of all material to the Architect. Submit shop drawings showing construction details including the method of attachment to the existing tower. No work shall commence without written approval of the Architect.

c. Street Numbers: Provide and install two sets of street numbers containing four (4) digits as designated and located by the Architect. Numbers shall be 4" high of "Narrow Face Modern" cast aluminum, as manufactured by the A. J. Bayer Co., Los Angeles, California. Face of numbers shall be straight line buffed to a fine even satin finish with sharp edges. Sides shall be fine sandblasted to a uniform contrasting finish, after which entire number shall be given two coats of methacrylate lacquer. Numbers shall be installed free standing.

d. Unit numerals: Provide and install 3" metal numbers as specified for "Street Numbers" to be mounted flush on the door of each living unit from 1 to 40.

e. Fire Extinguishers and Cabinets: Furnish and install six (6) fire extinguisher cabinets where shown on the drawings. Model #480-AL, aluminum, 2 piece trim, single cabinet complete with 2½ gallon soda acid fire extinguisher, as manufactured by the "Fyr-Fyter" Co., Dayton, Ohio.

f. Kitchenette Unit, Metal Cabinets Above:

a. Provide and install as shown in Unit #12 a kitchenette, "General Chef" model #LK-2E-520, as manufactured by the General Air Conditioning Corp., Los Angeles, California.

b. Provide above Kitchenette Unit, as shown on the drawings, two (2) metal wall cabinets model #E2430 as manufactured by the St. Charles Manufacturing Co., Los Angeles, California. Provide fillers as required and necessary for proper installation. Finish of cabinets shall be manufacturer's standard baked enamel, white in color.

* * * * *

DIVISION 11 EQUIPMENT

Section 11A Kitchen Equipment

1. GENERAL

All provisions in the "General Conditions" and "Supplementary General Conditions" section form a part of this section.

2. WORK INCLUDED IN THIS SECTION

a. All kitchen equipment not specifically excluded

b. Hoods and kitchen ventilating ducts

3. WORK NOT INCLUDED IN THIS SECTION

a. Plumbing and electrical services to all equipment

b. Ventilating fan for range and dishwasher hoods

c. Plumbing fittings for sinks

d. Furnishing and installation of dishwasher and disposers

e. Furnishing of restaurant counter, stools and furnishings

f. Furnishing of equipment designated N.I.C.

g. Wood shelving

4. MATERIALS

All materials shall be new and of quality and gauge specified.

a. Galvanized sheet metal: Standard brands, stretcher-leveled, Federal Specification QQ-I-716, gauges as noted.

b. Galvanized Steel Shapes: ASTM A 7, latest edition

c. Galvanizing: ASTM A 93, latest edition

d. Stainless Steel: Type 302, 18-8, No. 4 finish

e. Brackets, Screws, Bolts, Fittings: Chrome plated brass.

5. SHOP DRAWINGS AND CATALOG CUTS

Submit shop drawings of all work specified to the Architect. Submit manufacturer's catalogs showing cuts of contemplated equipment.

(1) Fabricate of 20 gauge galvanized sheet steel with 1½" x 1½" x 1/8" standard galvanized angle iron frame. Construction shall be hipped seam type with 6" apron and 1½" x 6" grease gutter. Provide 1" round drain spout and bucket hanger at wall line. Fabricate with 4" duct from hood to fan.

(2) Filters: Farr Air Filter, Grease Type, Model #44HG- "Far-Air", set in sized 18 gauge galvanized frames as detailed on the drawings.

e. Symbol No. 6 - Soiled Dish Table: Table top, splash and ends, 14 gauge stainless steel, 10" in height, with all exposed corners rounded. Interior edge of table top shall have a 1-5/8" wide rounded edge which will be continuous from end splashes to dishwashing unit. Pitch table top to garbage disposal unit.

f. Symbol No. 7 - Clean Dish Table: Fabricate as specified for soiled dish table. Omit cut out and pitch top toward dishwasher.

g. Symbol No. 8 - Hood for Dishwasher: Fabricate of same materials and of the same construction as specified for range hood. Omit grease filters and filter frames.

10. OPERATION AND MAINTENANCE INSTRUCTIONS

Furnish a control chart showing complete kitchen layout of general system, including all piping, valves, wiring, and control mechanisms. Properly tag all shutoff valves. Furnish such special wrenches and other special tools as are necessary for the proper repair and maintenance of the equipment.

11. GUARANTY

The Contractor shall guarantee in writing that any defect in the work, discovered and made known to him within one (1) year of the filing of notice of completion, will be made good by him without additional expense to the Owner.

* * * * *

6. FABRICATION

a. Exposed and working surfaces shall be stainless steel. Exposed surfaces not specifically indicated as stainless steel shall be galvanized iron.

b. All framing and unexposed surfaces shall be galvanized iron or steel.

c. Sinks, drainboards, shelving, serving counters, and tables shall be round-cornered and of all-metal construction. Bottoms of sinks shall slope to drains.

d. Counters shall be of channel-type construction, with all joints fully electrically arc-welded, ground smooth, and polished. Visible joints shall not show in finished work. Provide openings in tops where indicated.

e. Metal Legs and Leveling Feet: 1½" standard, galvanized pipe legs with utility type, pear-shaped, cast brass, cadmium-plated, adjustable leveling feet.

f. Reinforce tables and counter tops with 14 gauge galvanized iron channel stiffeners. Provide silencing pads to lessen metallic sound.

g. Allow a 2" clearance between finish wall line and back of all kitchen units. Returns on splashes shall be integral and finish at wall line.

h. Verify measurements at the job site for fabricated items requiring job fitting.

7. HEALTH REGULATIONS

Construction and installation shall conform with all State, County, and City Health Department Regulations and Ordinances.

8. CLEANING

Debris or unused construction materials shall be removed from the site. At completion of job, clean all metal surfaces and leave entire installation in condition ready for use.

9. EQUIPMENT

a. Symbol No. 1 - Vegetable Sink: "Hepco" Model #1703 modified, double drainboards and 10" splash of 14 gauge 18-8 stainless steel all-welded construction. Provide stand pipe overflow drain and perforated metal strainer for each sink.

b. Symbol No. 2 - Scullery Sink: "Hepco" Model #1703 modified, three compartment sink with double drainboards and 10" splash of 14 gauge 18-8 stainless steel all-welded construction. Provide cast brass corner drains with overflow pipe and perforated metal strainers.

c. Symbols Nos. 3 and 4 - Work Counters: Fabricate with 14 gauge stainless steel and 10" splash with 2" sall return. Bottom, shelves, and facing shall be 18 gauge G.I., all riveted to 1½" x 1½" x 1/8" galvanized angle iron frame. Top and shelves, 2" turn down with bottom edges hemmed ¼" minimum.

d. Symbol No. 5 - Hood for Ranges:

DIVISION 12 FURNISHING

Section 12A Venetian Blinds

1. GENERAL

All provisions of the "General Conditions" and "Supplementary General Conditions" section form a part of this section.

2. WORK INCLUDED IN THIS SECTION

a. All windows of living units 1-40.

b. South windows of restaurant and lobby.

3. WORK NOT INCLUDED IN THIS SECTION

a. Wood valance boxes at heads

b. Blinds in bathrooms of living units 1-40.

4. MATERIALS

The Venetian blind shall be the "Levolor" Orange Line Blind, as manufactured by Levolor Lorentzen, Inc. The metal head and bottom rail shall be Orange Line. The head channel bottom rail shall be coated with high baked plastic coating. The bottom rail, shall have plastic Spiral design with caps or metal end pieces inserted into each end. All hardware shall be "Levolor" brand Orange Line. The slats shall be 2" wide aluminum with vinyl plastic ladder tapes and cords. The tilt cord shall be equipped with spiral design tassels. Standard colors will be selected by the Owner from manufacturer's standard colors.

5. INSTALLATION

All workmanship and procedure shall be in accordance with the standards set forth in the "Architects Manual for Venetian Blinds," Sixth Edition, by Levolor Lorentzen, Inc., dated 1962.

* * * * *

DIVISION 13 SPECIAL CONSTRUCTION

Section 13A Swimming Pool

1. GENERAL

All provisions of the "General Conditions" and "Supplementary General Conditions" section form a part of this section.

2. WORK INCLUDED IN THIS SECTION

a. Swimming pool, coping, filter system with necessary piping, and all earthwork in connection with the swimming pool.

b. Underwater light, chrome ladder, hooks, nylon rope and floats at shallow end.

c. Provision for filling, emptying and back washing pool.

d. Disposal of excess excavated material off of site.

3. WORK NOT INCLUDED IN THIS SECTION

a. Electrical and gas services and hook-up of pool equipment.

b. Water supply, drains to sewer and hook-up.

4. MATERIALS

The Contractor shall submit to the Architect complete shop drawings indicating construction details and the location and type of all equipment to be used.

5. PERMITS

The Contractor shall apply and pay for all permits necessary for his work.

6. GUARANTY

The Contractor shall guarantee in writing to repair any defects that appear in the pool or any pool equipment for a period of one (1) year after installation.

7. CLEAN-UP

Upon completion of the work, the Contractor shall remove from the site all excess earth and debris resulting from the operations and shall leave the site in a clean and acceptable condition.

* * * * *

270

DIVISION 15 MECHANICAL

Section 15A Plumbing

1. GENERAL

   All provisions of the "General Conditions" and "Supplementary General Conditions" section form a part of this section.

2. WORK INCLUDED IN THIS SECTION

   a. Soil, waste, vents, and connections to sewer.

   b. Replacement and removal of services and plumbing fixtures in Building "A" as indicated on the drawings.

   c. Hot, cold water, and gas piping. Hot water heaters and controls.

   d. Trim, valves, traps, drains, cleanouts, access plates, and hose bibbs.

   e. Roof flashing for vent piping.

   f. Water supply for swimming pool and hookup.

   g. Galvanized pipe downspouts, drains, and connections to the street.

   h. Floor sinks and drains from Air Conditioning condensate drain lines.

   i. Service and connection to Air Conditioning equipment.

   j. Service, wastes and connections for Restaurant equipment.

   k. Dishwasher and garbage disposers in kitchen.

   l. Pre-cast Shower Receptors.

   m. Cutting, excavation and backfill for plumbing lines.

2. WORK NOT INCLUDED IN THIS SECTION

   a. Sheet metal leaders and downspouts.

   b. Kitchen equipment, except as noted.

   c. Heating and Air Conditioning equipment

3. PERMITS, LICENSES AND INSPECTIONS

   The Contractor shall pay for all plumbing and sewer permits. All work shall conform to the Plumbing Code of the City of Los Angeles

DIVISION 14 CONVEYER SYSTEMS

(None in this project)

4. DRAWINGS

In general, drawings for the work are diagramatic and show the location, type and size of piping, plumbing fixtures and accessory equipment. The Contractor shall furnish all fittings necessary for the proper installation of the work. The Contractor shall verify all necessary dimensions before installing any of the work, and shall check his layouts to allow clearance required for other work as shown on the drawings.

5. SURVEY OF SITE

The Contractor shall be familiar with the plans and specifications and shall have examined the premises and understood the conditions under which he will be obliged to operate in performing the contract. No allowance shall be made subsequently in this connection, for any error through negligence on his part.

6. EXCAVATION, BACKFILL, CUTTING

a. Excavate trenches for underground pipes to required depths. After pipe lines have been tested and approved, backfill trenches to grade with approved material; tamped compactly in place as specified under "Earthwork" section. No puddling will be permitted.

b. When possible, place sleeves for pipes through foundation ahead of concrete pouring. Failing in this, the plumber shall do the necessary cutting, and seal thereafter in a satisfactory manner.

c. The Carpenter will do all cutting and heading in wood framing for pipes over 2" in size. Boring for pipes under 2" shall be done by the plumber. No structural member shall be cut, notched or drilled without written permission of the Architect.

7. WATER SUPPLY

a. All water piping shall be new galvanized steel.

b. Provide all connections to risers or fixtures from top to mains so that the entire system can be drained at low point.

c. Provide hot water supply to all fixtures except water closets.

d. Support piping from the building structure by means of hangers to maintain required grading and pitching of lines and to prevent vibration. Pad with felt all contacts with wood framing.

8. GAS SYSTEM

a. All gas lines shall be black steel

b. Pitch piping and provide natural drop pockets at low point

9. SOIL, WASTE & VENT LINES

a. Comply with the Los Angeles Plumbing Code as to kind and size of pipes and fittings.

b. All vent pipes passing through the roof shall be flashed with Semco 1110-5 seamless 6 pound lead roof flashing with steel reinforced boot.

c. Connect to public sewer.

10. FIXTURE SCHEDULE

a. Tubs where indicated in new living units of Building "C" shall be: American Standard Recessed #P-2225 or P-2227, Pembroke, 5'-0" enameled tub, with shower diverter valves #N 1010 and trip lever waste #N 1700-16.

b. Shower Fixtures in stall showers where indicated in Buildings "A", "B" and "C", American Standard #N1110 Valves, ball joint shower head with regulator #N1303.

c. Water closets in all new living units and replacements in Building "A" American Standard Cadet #F 2110-11 water closet with seat.

d. Water closets in toilet rooms, Building "D" "Stanton" 3-300-T Siphon jet, elongated rim, 1½" top speed bowl floor mounted. Flush valve Sloan #110 FYVW Royal, seat Church #6100.

e. Lavatories in Buildings "C" and "D", American Standard "Comrade", 20 inch, wall hung, F-112-40, supply and drain fittings N2001.

f. Lavatory-dressing tables in all units of Building "B", American Standard, "Gracylyn" lavatory-dressing table F-117-40-1, 31" legs, trim N2105-10.

g. Water heater replacements in Building "A", Day and Night Automatic Instantaneous heater, 40-135, natural gas.

h. Furnish and install where indicated on Sheet #A-3, two (2) 100 JSB, 100 gallon, "Jetglas" storage boosters as manufactured by Day and Night Mfg. Co. connected in parallel with a circulating pump and the necessary piping, valves, connections and controls to serve laundry room and all new living units in Buildings "B" and "C".

i. Floor drains in kitchen: Zurn Figure Z-415 with cast iron body L.A. Pattern "P" trap, Type H square 5" nickel-bronze strainer.

j. Floor Sinks at Air Conditioning units: Zurn Figure 324, cast iron acid resisting white enamel, complete with top grate and non-clog splash preventing slotted semi-dome strainer.

k. Furnish and install where indicated in Buildings "B" and "C", "Voss", Model #201, Roman White, Florentine Terrazzo Pre-cast Shower Receptors, as manufactured by Pacific Pre-cast Products, Inc., 2375 E. 120th Street, Los Angeles, California.

11. KITCHEN EQUIPMENT

a. Dishwashing area sink: include waste, vent, hot and cold water piping, connections and trim for sink furnished and installed under the "Kitchen Equipment" section. Furnish and install Chicago No. 444-LD with L-7 swing spout and "Softflo", 1½" tailpiece and 1½" x 2" L.A. Pattern cast brass "P" trap, Crane 8-343 stops and 8-446 wall escutcheons.

DIVISION 15 MECHANICAL

Section 15B Heating and Air Conditioning

1. GENERAL

All provisions of the "General Conditions" and "Supplementary General Conditions" section form a part of this section.

2. WORK INCLUDED IN THIS SECTION

a. Forced air heating units as indicated on sheets M-1 and M-2.

b. Air cooled condensing units as indicated on sheets M-1 and M-2.

c. Multizone air handling units as indicated on sheets M-1 and M-2.

d. Ductwork, dampers, diffusers, registers, and grilles in new and existing construction.

e. Insulation for ducts, equipment and acoustic duct lining.

f. Unit temperature and humidity controls, low voltage wiring and accessories.

g. Condensate drain lines to floor sinks.

h. Roof mounted exhaust fans for range and dishwasher hoods.

3. WORK NOT INCLUDED IN THIS SECTION

a. Wood platform and curbs for heating and cooling units and exhaust fans.

b. Plumbing services and connections to units.

c. Electrical line voltage to units.

d. Openings, cutting and patching in both new and existing walls, roofs and ceilings for ductwork and piping.

4. DESIGN DATA

a. Location of equipment and piping on the drawings is diagramatic.

b. Within fifteen (15) days after contract execution, submit in manila bound folders six (6) brochures of the complete list, with descriptive literature of all material and equipment furnished under this section.

c. The capacity of air conditioner units shown in the schedule is based on a design condition of 86° DB, 65° WB entering the evaporator, with 72° WB ambient air entering the condenser, and a maximum condensing temperature of 105°.

5. FORCED AIR FURNACE UNITS

The Contractor shall furnish and install complete in the locations indicated on plans, AGA approved gas fired forced air furnaces, of the type, size and capacities set forth in the schedule. Furnaces shall be complete with coordinated safety controls, including automatic recycling type pilot, pressure regulating valve pilot cock, high limit and control, 2 stage gas manifold, gas shut-off valve, and draft diverter. Each furnace shall have vent flue through roof with approved vent cap and thimble.

---

b. Provide T & S Brass and Bronze Works, Inc., No. B-102A pot filler with No. B-199 softflo aerator end on pipe stanchion adjacent to range as shown. Support hot water piping securely to pipe stanchion bolted to floor. Provide shut off valve at pipe stanchion for pot filler in addition to the valve provided with the filler.

c. Dishwasher: Blakeslee EC-4 with FWPW pre-wash. Single type conveyor tank constructed of 16 gauge stainless steel complete with stainless steel front panel, gas burner with 100% safety pilot, thermostat on wash tank, thermometer and all standard equipment normally provided.

d. Atomic Disposer Corp., garbage disposer located at vegetable sink, Model No. 75-3-A-13-2, 3/4 hp, 208 V, 60 cycle, single phase, complete with pre-rinse, scrap ring and silver guard.

e. Atomic Disposer Corp., garbage disposer located in dishwashing counters Model No. 50-1-A-13-2, ½ hp, 208 V, 60 cycle, single phase, complete with pre-rinse, scrap ring and silver guard.

f. Josam Manufacturing Co., Model No. JH-6, grease interceptor finished inside and out with white porcelain enamel, furnish complete with basket baffle, cross hatched safety tread cover, automatic flow control and 3" cast iron soil pipe connections.

* * * * *

6. CONDENSING UNITS

"Supreme-Aire" Model ACCU 1003-2, complete with two 6½ hp compressors, air cooled condenser, two 3/4 hp condenser fans and prewired control panel, with special timers to prevent short cycling of the compressors. Motors and controls shall be 208 volt single phase with overload and undervoltage protection.

7. MULTIZONE UNITS

"Recold" Model MZH-66, complete with blower, 1 hp - 208 volt - single phase motor, 6 Row DX cooling coil with 2 equal circuits, split by face, 2 row non-freeze type heating coil, angle type filter box and 2" throwaway type filters. Provide an angle iron frame base for unit approximately 3 feet high and anchor to structure. Unit shall have 7 zones arranged as shown on the drawings. Zone dampers shall have felted edges for air tightness. Unit shall be insulated with 1" thick insulation on interior and be weatherproofed on outside for exterior installation.

8. TEMPERATURE CONTROL

Provide a complete temperature control system as shown on drawings. All low voltage wiring shall be run in conduit. Provide temperature indicators in each living unit, lobby and restaurant.

9. ROOF MOUNTED EXHAUST FANS

Exhaust fans for range and dishwasher hoods shall be as manufactured by Penn Ventilator Company, "Dynafan" unit size 22 with "Pyrotrol" heat shield, centrifugal type roof exhauster, suitable for curb mounting, and with heat shield and packing gland to insulate motor and drive against damaging heat transmission from below. Installed on roof curb, providing weathertight cover; 2" air space and gypsum board around framed opening.

10. VIBRATION ISOLATION

The Contractor performing the work under this Division shall make all or any necessary provisions in the installation of equipment under this section to insure that no objectionable vibration is transmitted by this equipment to the building structure.

11. DIFFUSERS AND REGISTERS

a. Diffusers: "Airfactors", of types and sizes as shown, removable core, with integral volume control, or extractor, in baked gray enamel.

b. Exhaust Registers: "Airfactors" Model RAH register with opposed blade damper in gray enamel, key operated.

c. Fire Dampers: Provide 12 ga. collars and fire dampers where indicated or required.

12. SHEET METAL WORK

a. Ducts shall be constructed of galvanized steel sheet to conform to the "Duct Construction Details" for low pressure ductwork, as outlined in Chapter 21 of the 1960 ASHRAE Guide.

b. Turning vanes shall be provided in all square elbows and where indicated and shall be "Airturns" as manufactured by "Barber-Colman"

c. Flexible connections shall be provided at the supply connections to the air unit, of asbestos cloth or "Ventglas".

d. Behind Registers, Diffusers and Grilles: Wherever ductwork or acoustic lining is visible through devices, the interior visible portions shall be painted flat black.

13. INSULATION AND ACOUSTIC LINING

a. Concealed Supply Ducts shall be insulated with 1" thick "Ultralite" #100 according to "Gustin-Bacon" Specification #DC-2.

b. Thermal and Acoustic lining shall be installed in all supply ducts exposed above roof. The duct size shall be increased 2" in both dimensions over that indicated to accommodate the duct liner. The insulation shall be coated with "Ultralite" #200, 1" thick, installed according to "Gustin-Bacon" Specification #DL-1; omit exterior insulation where lining occurs. All edges of duct liner exposed to the air stream shall be coated with adhesive.

14. TESTING AND ADJUSTING

a. The Architect shall be notified when the system is ready for testing.

b. The testing, adjusting and air proportioning of all fan systems shall be done by a qualified representative of the installing contractor.

c. Air volumes at the diffusers and registers shall be within 5% of the indicated quantities or adjusted as necessary to obtain the desired temperature within the space.

d. Contractor shall make all required adjustments to the fan system so that proper balancing of the system may be accomplished.

e. Before final acceptance of the work, the Contractor shall submit for approval three (3) certified copies of the report on the operation of the fan systems indicating air quantities at the diffusers, registers and fans, fan speeds, pulley and motor sizes, motor amperage and BHP, equipment pamphlets and operating instructions of all equipment.

15. OPERATING INSTRUCTIONS

The Contractor shall prepare three (3) descriptive booklets which shall contain all the necessary information required for operation, servicing and maintenance requirements of each piece of equipment.

16. GUARANTY

The Contractor shall warrant all equipment and materials to be in perfect condition when installed and guarantee to replace entirely at his own expense any portion of the equipment or materials which show structural defects or faulty workmanship for a period of one (1) year beginning with the filing of a notice of completion on the entire project.

*****

DIVISION 16 ELECTRICAL

Section 16A Electrical Work

1. **GENERAL**

   All provisions of the "General Conditions" and "Supplementary General Conditions" section form a part of this section.

2. **WORK INCLUDED IN THIS SECTION**

   a. 120/240, single phase, 3 wire lighting and power distribution system complete.

   b. Lighting fixtures and lamps.

   c. All line voltage connections for heating and air conditioning equipment.

   d. Connections to motors, signs and equipment specified in other sections.

   e. An adequate equipment grounding system.

   f. Conduit, pull wire and outlet boxes for telephone system.

   g. T.V. Antennas, lead-ins and outlets.

   h. Relocation of meter and rewiring as required or indicated in Building "A".

3. **WORK NOT INCLUDED IN THIS SECTION**

   a. Low voltage wiring for Air Conditioning and Heating.

   b. Neon signs

   c. Furnishing of underwater pool lights.

4. **CODE REQUIREMENTS**

   All work shall be done in accordance with the City of Los Angeles Electrical Code.

5. **COOPERATION WITH OTHER TRADES**

   Electrical outlets and equipment shall be furnished, installed and located in such a manner as to avoid interference with the work of other trades.

6. **MATERIALS**

   Materials shall be new and bear the Underwriter's label of approval.

7. **RECEPTACLES**

   All 120 volt receptacles shall be 2-wire 3-pole 15-amp. 125-volt. Surface mounted 120 volt single receptacles for damp locations shall be Hubbell Cat. #5261-I mounted in "FS" conduit with Crouse-Hinds Cat. #DS10G cover plate. 208 volt 1 phase single receptacles shall be 20 amp. 250 volts 2 wire 3 pole twist-lock Hubbell #7310-BG.

8. **LIGHTING SWITCHES**

   All flush toggle type switches shall be totally enclosed ivory handle bakelite or composition base with "T" rating for loads 0-800 watts, 20 amp. "T" rating for 800-1600 watts. Where more than one flush-mounted switch is shown at one outlet, a gang box shall be used. Surface-mounted switches shall be installed in a "FS" conduit box. Surface-mounted switches for damp locations with a Crouse-Hinds Cat. #DS32G cover plate. Surface-mounted switches for damp locations shall be installed in a "FS" conduit with a Crouse-Hinds Cat. #DS185 cover plate. All cover plates for flush-mounted devices shall be ivory phenolic plastic with matching screws. Cover plates for surface-mounted devices shall be Crouse-Hinds Cast Feraloy.

9. **LOCATIONS**

   The drawings indicate diagrammatically conduit runs, outlets, and equipment. In the event changes in the indicated locations of equipment or fixtures are necessary due to developed conditions in the building construction or rearrangement of furnishings, such changes shall be made without extra cost.

10. **MOUNTING HEIGHTS**

    Except where otherwise shown on the drawings, the following mounting heights from the floor to the center of the outlet shall govern: wall receptacles, 12"; wall switches, 54"; telephone outlets 12".

11. **LIGHTING PANEL CABINETS**

    a. Panelboards shall be mounted in a code gauge galvanized steel cabinet. Panel shall be provided with trim and door constructed from not less than No. 12 U.S. gauge sheet steel. Door shall be fitted with concealed hinges, spring catch latch and Yale cylinder lock. Front shall be flush type equipped with mounting clamps and set square with building lines.

    b. Provide in all main and sub panel cabinets directory cards typed with designation for each breaker as to location, room number, and type of load.

    c. Provide six (6) master keys to locks on all panels.

12. **CONNECTING EQUIPMENT FURNISHED BY OTHERS**

    The Contractor shall furnish all switches, push buttons, selector switches, pilot lights and make all connections to completely connect the plumbing, heating, ventilating, and air conditioning systems as indicated on the electrical and mechanical drawings and specifications.

13. **OUTLET BOXES**

    Outlet boxes and covers shall be pressed steel knockout type, galvanized or sheradized. Boxes shall not be smaller than 4" square x 1½" deep. Covers shall finish flush with the plaster or other surface. Boxes in concrete masonry shall be "concrete boxes". All switches and convenience receptacles in exposed conduit runs shall be installed in cast conduit fittings. Telephone outlets shall be 4-11/16" square box with telephone cover. Provide #14 gauge pull-in wire in conduits for telephone wiring. Install neoprene gaskets for weatherproofing junction boxes, pull boxes, and fittings.

14. **EXCAVATIONS**

Perform all excavating necessary for proper installation of the electrical work. Conduit runs where possible shall be 18" minimum below finished grade. After the installation of work requiring excavations has been inspected and approved, all excavations shall be filled with clean earth and tamped to a consistency that no settlement will occur and the ground is left firm at natural grade. All excavated earth which is not used for backfill shall be removed from the premises. No puddling of backfill will be allowed.

15. **LIGHTING FIXTURES**

Provide and install all lighting fixtures in accordance with the schedule and as specified. All fixtures shall be complete with fittings, wiring, supports and wiring connections. Lamps shall be furnished in all fixtures. All fluorescent tubes shall be rapid start. Lamps 200 watts and smaller shall be inside frosted except where installed behind lenses in recessed fixtures, they shall be clear.

16. **TESTS**

Before acceptance of the work, all portions of the electrical work shall be in operating condition satisfactory to the Owner.

17. **FIXTURE SCHEDULE**

Location	Description	Manufacturer & Catalog No.
New & Existing Baths New Dressing Rooms	Cylinder down lights Satin Chrome with L-6 louver perforations, 75W Type "A" Series	Prescolite #7022
Living Units Bldgs. "B" and "C"	Dormitory lights Fluorescent and 100W incandescent, walnut vinyl diffuser low power factor	Prescolite #3098-L
Lobby and Restaurant	Opal Spheres, 100W Incandescent, Pendant Type, Polished glass, Satin Chrome 12" to 4'-0" stems as directed	Prescolite #540
Restaurant and Lobby (Furred Soffits) Balcony lights Units 26 & 36	Square recessed, 200W Incandescent, 6130 Flat Alba Glass, Plated Polished Chrome Frame	Prescolite #1312-6130
Living Units Building "A" Restaurant Kitchen Rest Rooms	Round glass, ceiling mount 100W	Prescolite #GF-10X
Hall Lights (New & Existing Units)	Metal Cylinder, perforations, 30W, R-20 L-6 louver	Prescolite #WB-7022
Recessed Spots under Marquee	Directional, recessed eye ball, 75W type A Lamps, Matt White	Prescolite #39
Garden Lights	15W Fluorescent (face down) Jade green, garden light	Prescolite #5200F
Roof Spots	Cast Aluminum, 150W Projector Flood, 2 Sparlights	Multi Electric Mfg. Co. #6A-622
Ground & Marquee up-floods	Weatherproof recessed Floodlights with adjustable sockets 150W (Par-38)	Prescolite #5100
Pull Chains	Incandescent, Porcelain Lampholder, with pull chain	Alabax #AL 3140

* * * * *

Examination Questions

The following questions have come from several sources. Many were taken directly from examinations prepared by state licensing boards covering specifications, construction management, and professional practice. Others have been used in college courses in Specifications Writing and Professional Practice or have been prepared as a review of the material in this book. No attempt has been made to present technical information on materials or construction techniques.

A working knowledge of materials and construction techniques, is, to a great extent, the result of practical job experience. The questions cover professional practice, construction management, legal implications of the contract documents, and writing techniques necessary for a successful architect, engineer, or specifications writer. Although the questions are not segregated into chapters, they do follow the general arrangement of information as presented in the text.

1. Complete the following sentence: Specifications should be _____ , _____ , and _____.

2. Name five parts of the contract documents.

3. Discuss the use made of specifications in construction.

4. Describe a guide specification and how it is used.

5. What qualities should be possessed by a person who writes specifications?

6. How many free sketches does an architect usually furnish a client?

7. What records should an architect keep of preliminary sketches?

8. A structural engineer usually designs what portions of a building?

9. The work of a civil engineer covers what portions of a large building project?

10. Mechanical engineers usually design what portions of the work?

11. You are employed as an architect for an auditorium, and an acoustical engineer is to be employed. Who should pay for these services in the normal AIA contract?

12. When should an architect call in a structural engineer?

13. Who furnishes and pays for surveys of the site?

14. To what extent does the architect guarantee a preliminary cost estimate?

15. Is a preliminary cost estimate by an architect that is within 3 1/2 percent of the final cost of a building reasonable?

16. An architect should not accept any compensation for his services other than from whom?

17. Under what conditions may a member of the AIA practice architecture in other states?

18. When a firm of architects consists of three partners, Brown, Jones, and Doe, how should the names be listed on the firms letterhead if Doe is not a licensed architect?

19. The architect does not guarantee the estimated cost of a building and does not guarantee the contractor's performance of the contract. What does the architect guarantee, and what is the architect's relationship to the owner?

20. By whom is the state board of architectural examiners appointed?

21. The state board of architectural examiners operates under what department of the state?

22. What are duties of a job captain?

23. Explain briefly the advantages and disadvantages to the owner and the architect of a segregated contract.

24. In the firm of Smith, Doe, and Roe, Smith and Doe are architects, but Roe is not. What information must be included on their signs?

25. What two types of insurance must a practicing architect hiring several employees maintain, as required by law?

26. Name eight important items of overhead expense for running an architect's office.

27. During the construction of a church, certain subcontracts are removed from general contract (these subcontracts are

to be donated both in material and in labor). Upon what basis should the architect's fee be computed?

28. If the owner uses segregated contracts, does the architect get an additional fee?
29. An architect is asked to design a building for a public agency. What steps should he take before he proceeds with the design?
30. How is a list of bidders selected to bid on a public building?
31. How is a list of bidders selected on a privately financed project?
32. What steps can an architect take to assure that a bidder will sign an agreement if his proposal is accepted?
33. Name four state agencies that must check the contract documents during the design of a hospital.
34. In public work, the project must be submitted to what kind of a list of bidders?
35. Who should be present when bids are opened?
36. How can alternates affect the award of a contract?
37. What are some problems involved in requiring bidders to submit a list of subcontractors at the same time they submit their proposals.
38. When are addenda written?
39. Under what conditions would unit prices be made a part of a proposal?
40. Discuss the advantages of a small architectural office.
41. Discuss the advantages of a large architectural office.
42. When may an architect start the preparation of the working drawings?
43. Who should check drawings?
44. Who should check specifications?
45. List five items that may make a proposal invalid.
46. If an error has been made in a bid, under what conditions can the bid be withdrawn?
47. Describe the duties of an architect's full-time representative on a project.
48. Construction supervision and the employment of a "clerk of the works" are the financial responsibilities of whom?
49. When drawings are approved by the city planning department, can the city inspector require further changes in the actual construction?

50. Name four types of inspectors that may have authority on a project?
51. What is a specialty contractor?
52. Who must settle disputes between subcontractors?
53. What are change orders?
54. When are change orders written?
55. Under what conditions should the hiring of a watchman be required on a project?
56. Who is responsible for providing barricades on a project?
57. Who furnishes scaffolding for work on a project?
58. What items of furnishings, equipment, and services are usually required to be furnished in connection with a job office on a large project?
59. Who prepares shop drawings?
60. Why are shop drawings necessary?
61. What are the general contractor's responsibilities in regard to change orders?
62. Who is responsible for the storing of samples?
63. Describe two tests usually made when concrete is being poured.
64. How is concrete or masonry tested after the material is in place?
65. Who pays for materials testing?
66. Who selects testing laboratories, and who pays for their services?
67. Describe three methods commonly used in determining the money due a contractor as the work progresses.
68. After stripping the forms from the concrete foundation, you discover rock pockets in the walls. What instructions do you give the contractor?
69. The contractor receives some floor joists that are not grade-marked as required by the specifications. What is your procedure?
70. What tolerance in elevations can be allowed on concrete floors to receive resilient floor coverings before they become unsatisfactory?
71. How can you check the number of coats of paint on a job?
72. A contractor has poured a concrete wall which the engineer believes to be defective. What steps may be taken by the engineer, and who will pay any costs involved in the action taken?

73. Why is a percentage of the money due a contractor retained during the construction of a project?

74. What is the normal percentage of money retained from that due the contractor during construction? Does this vary as the project nears completion?

75. No notice of completion was filed on a project. For how many days should the final payment to the contractor be withheld?

76. What time limits are set on the filing of liens by material dealers, mechanics, and contractors?

77. Can an architect or an engineer file a mechanic's lien? Under what conditions?

78. What is the procedure for obtaining the release of a lien against a property?

79. The contractor has failed to pay his subcontractor, and the public agency for whom the work was executed will not allow the filing of a lien against the public work. What steps should the contractor take?

80. What is meant by "substantial completion" of a project, and how does it affect the payments to be made to a contractor?

81. When may an owner occupy a project?

82. After work on a construction project has ceased and after the owner has accepted the project, what is the maximum number of days allowed for the filing of a notice of completion?

83. Who must file a notice of completion, and when will the project be considered completed if this notice is not filed?

84. Where is the notice of completion filed?

85. Define the word "plans."

86. If there is a conflict between what is shown on the drawings and what is specified, which will govern?

87. What is the relationship between the drawings and the specifications?

88. What type of abbreviations should be included in the drawings?

89. Describe the use of legends on drawings.

90. How much information, in the form of notes, should be included in the drawings?

91. Give the seven most common scales used in architectural drawings.

92. How does an engineer's scale differ from an architect's scale?

93. Describe open-end dimensions and their use on architectural drawings.

94. What determines the scale to be used when preparing drawings and details?

95. List six main headings into which the construction drawings of a large project may be divided.

96. How is an intermediate produced and used?

97. Discuss the arrangement of a set of construction drawings.

98. What information is usually included in civil drawings?

99. What information is usually included in structural drawings?

100. What information is usually included in mechanical drawings?

101. What type of drawings must be prepared by the architect after a contract has been signed?

102. Who should check the working drawings?

103. Define as-built drawings.

104. Discuss the use of the following statement, which is sometimes placed on drawings: "see specs."

105. How often should dimensions be repeated on the drawings?

106. Why is it important for a specifications writer to understand working drawings?

107. The following abbreviations represent associations in the construction industry. Give the full name and briefly state the purpose of each. ASTM, ASA, NBFU, ACIL.

108. What is a commodity standard?

109. How can Federal specifications be used on private work?

110. What publication by the FHA can be used as a reference for residential specifications?

111. What is Sweet's Catalog Service, and how can it be used?

112. What is the AIA Building Products Register, and how can it be used?

113. List six basic references that are available to the specifications writer.

114. Who may join the CSI?

115. Describe three types of manufacturers literature.

116. What are the duties of a manufacturers' representative?

117. Who usually pays the salary of a hardware consultant?

118. What is a uniform building code? How is it amended? How is it administered?
119. If a new edition of a regional building code is published, is this automatically put in force in a city operating under this code? Why?
120. Are building codes the same throughout the United States? Each state? Each county?
121. Which state act governs the construction of apartment houses?
122. The architect's working drawing indicates a detail that is contrary to code requirements. To comply with code requirements will cost an additional amount of money. Who pays the additional cost?
123. The Uniform Plumbing Code and the National Electric Code are enforced in some communities. Under what conditions are they enforced, and who administers their enforcement?
124. Does the state housing act take precedence over local codes?
125. What information must the specifications writer have at hand when he starts writing?
126. Describe outline specifications?
127. Describe three systems for identifying or numbering trade sections.
128. Describe the block system of typing.
129. Describe the indented system of typing.
130. What factors affect the choice of a particular typing style?
131. Describe five processes used to reproduce specifications.
132. What are streamlined specifications?
133. Give four problems that can arise when old specifications are used as a reference for new specifications.
134. What is the paragraph method of assembling specifications?
135. What are guide specifications?
136. Give three problems involved in the use of guide specifications.
137. Give three advantages in the use of guide specifications.
138. Define standard specifications and describe their use.
139. What is a dual system of specifications?
140. When should the writing of specifications be started?
141. Name four factors that affect the grouping of information into sections.
142. What information should appear on a title page of a book of specifications?

143. Describe five methods of binding a book of specifications. Discuss advantages and disadvantages of each.
144. How are the specifications affected by a contract let on a segregated basis?
145. How do union jurisdictions affect the grouping of information into trade sections?
146. What laws or codes affect the grouping of information?
147. How do most general contractors desire the work to be segregated in the specifications?
148. What are specification briefs, and how are they used?
149. What are the four essential elements of a binding contract?
150. When is a contract enforceable?
151. Is an oral contract binding?
152. What limits are placed upon the work of an engineer or architect in the preparation of contracts?
153. Decisions made by courts of law will be made to a great extent on what three bases?
154. When an agreement is being written for the construction of a public building, who is designated as the owner?
155. What form of an agreement is used in contracts between the owner and a subcontractor?
156. Define a subcontractor.
157. Outline the information that should be included in an invitation to bid.
158. Should any information included in an invitation to bid be included in the instructions to bidders?
159. Who prepares the proposal on a construction project?
160. Should a bidder be required to make a recap of the items he has included in his bid? Why?
161. Should a bidder be allowed to present a proposal on a bid form developed in his office? Why?
162. What is included in a bid schedule?
163. What is the purpose of requiring unit prices in a proposal?
164. What are alternates, and why are they included in a proposal?
165. Under what conditions would unit prices be requested of a bidder?
166. What is the deciding factor when determining the units of work to be requested when asking for unit prices?

167. What is meant by the term "contractor's option"?

168. When are materials lists included in a proposal?

169. On what type of jobs, and when, should the subcontractor be listed at the time of bidding?

170. How may changes be made in the plans or specifications prior to receiving of bids?

171. How much information should be given in an addendum?

172. What steps can an architect take to help determine whether a bidder is qualified to perform?

173. Under what conditions should quotations on alternates be required from bidders?

174. If the subcontractor has no contract with the owner, how and why is he sometimes required to use a prescribed form in submitting a bid to a contractor?

175. Describe two types of subcontract forms as published by the AIA.

176. What information should be obtained from a new contractor who wishes to bid on one of your jobs?

177. Name three signatures required on a bond.

178. How do you determine the reliability of a bonding company?

179. What document should you require as a supplement to the bonds?

180. Either partner in a contracting firm can sign the contract documents. What is the nature of the document you should require in addition to the signature?

181. When the contractor for a project is a corporation, what official of the corporation normally signs the contract?

182. What additional document may be required when a corporation is a party to an agreement?

183. What type of document is required to guarantee that a bonding company will issue a bond to the contractor?

184. In agreements with a construction company which operates as a partnership, what signatures must appear on an agreement between the owner and the contractor?

185. Most public subdivisions are unable to enter a contract containing a penalty clause. What other type of clause may be entered in the contract that will tend to force an early completion of the project?

186. An architect prepares a recommended form of contract for the owner, and the owner signs the contract. Can the architect then act as legal adviser to the owner?

187. How is the amount of liquidated damages determined?

188. When should the AIA short-form agreement be used?

189. An agreement is to be signed between the owner and a construction corporation. What signatures must appear on the agreement?

190. Why is it necessary for the specifications writer to be familiar with the general conditions?

191. Who usually writes the general conditions?

192. Name ten points generally covered in the general conditions of a contract.

193. How are the general conditions related to the contract documents?

194. How are the general conditions related to the trade sections?

195. Discuss the problems involved in writing general conditions.

196. How do the general conditions used by Federal agencies differ from those used on private projects?

197. How do standard general conditions developed by various associations differ?

198. How do new editions of standard general conditions affect their use?

199. How and why were the AIA standard general conditions developed?

200. How may conflicts between information shown on the drawings and that described in the specifications be resolved?

201. What steps can an architect take to assure that a project will be completed?

202. The owner may require the contractor to stop work on a project under what conditions?

203. Under what conditions can the architect instruct the contractor to make changes in the work when said changes will increase or decrease the cost of the project?

204. The owner instructs the contractor to install an extra access door to a heating room. What is the architect's responsibility?

205. Under what insurance policy is "malicious mischief and vandalism" normally covered?

206. What steps can an architect take to assure himself that all bills for materials or labor will be paid at the completion of a project?

207. A certificate of payment is signed by both the architect and the contractor. In the event that it is later determined that there was an error in the certificate, what are the rights of the contractor and owner?

208. The contractor submits shop drawings which are not in agreement with the architect's drawings. Your draftsman forwards the drawing with approval. What recourse do you, as the architect, have?

209. Must a contractor furnish items that are shown on the drawings but not mentioned in a trade section?

210. The architect checks shop drawings for what type of information?

211. When does a contractor have a valid claim for extra costs above the contract price?

212. When must a contractor make a claim for extras?

213. Who pays for all royalties and license fees?

214. Why should an architect take out errors and omissions insurance?

215. Claims for damage for personal injury which may arise from operations by anyone indirectly employed by a subcontractor shall be covered by insurance maintained by whom?

216. Under what conditions may an owner direct the contractor to stop work on a project that is under construction?

217. A subcontractor is performing work which is unsatisfactory to the owner. What procedure should the owner follow?

218. A subcontractor has been declared bankrupt. Is the general contractor responsible for repairs to the work of the subcontractor?

219. Can the contractor be held for faults that appear after the notice of completion has been filed?

220. Why are supplemental general conditions needed?

221. How do supplemental general conditions relate to the trade sections?

222. Where are special-conditions sections located in the construction documents?

223. In the event of a conflict between the general conditions and supplemental general conditions, which would govern?

224. The technical provisions in the specifications are written primarily for what four people?

225. Name four important subdivisions of any trade section in a specification.

226. What is a scope paragraph?

227. Under what conditions would the work of more than one trade be grouped into a trade section?

228. What is the relationship of a trade section and the special conditions?

229. Give three reasons why all trade sections should follow the same format.

230. Why is the heading "work excluded" placed in a trade section?

231. Prepare, in brief outline form, a trade section covering concrete, ceramic tile, or brick masonry.

232. An item is described under one trade section, and its installation is to be described under another trade section. How would this be handled?

233. Define a guaranty.

234. Define a warranty.

235. A subcontractor furnishes metal windows for a project and agrees to guarantee that they will not leak. How can the owner assure himself that any defects that appear in these windows at a later date will be remedied?

236. Resilient floor tiles are to be delivered to the project site. What precautions must be included in the trade sections regarding delivery, storage, and checking of this material?

237. What are the determining factors that affect the persons or trades who will furnish the scaffolding or staging necessary for the performance of a particular item of work?

238. Special steel anchors, to which plumbing fixtures will be attached at a later date, are to be cast into a concrete floor slab. How would this be covered in the trade sections?

239. Write a specification outline for "D"-group asphalt tile floor.

240. Write a specification in outline form for one of the following: glass and glazing, sheet metal, tile. (List the major divisions and items to be included.)

241. Write a brief outline specification for metal-lath ceiling on metal furrings suspended from a steel roof deck.

242. Consider a reinforced architectural concrete building. The building is to have a smooth painted finish. Write an outline for a concrete specification, listing the main topic heads, such as general conditions, scope, work included, etc.

243. Describe a firm specification.

244. What is a standard?

245. How may standards be used in specifications?

246. On what type of job are open specifications generally used?

247. What are some advantages of a closed specification?

248. What are some objections to a closed specification?

249. What is a performance specification?

250. What are some precautions to be observed when using a manufacturer's specification?

251. How can manufacturer's specifications be used in a trade section?

252. Write a brief paragraph that could be inserted in the specifications to allow the contractor to propose substitutes for items specified.

253. The following statement has been included in a specification: "Only the best grade of paint shall be used." How would you interpret this phrase?

254. Discuss the following words or phrases and their use in specifications: "shall," "will," "must," "is to," "should."

255. When should the pronoun "he," "his," "this," and "it" be used in specifications?

256. Define an escape clause.

257. List three words that are usually capitalized in specifications.

258. Name six important changes that have been made in the West Coast Lumber Grade Rule #15.

259. When curing compound has been used on interior concrete-slab floors, what instructions should you give the contractor regarding the following floor coverings?
a. Asphalt tile
b. Vinyl tile

260. What type of hardware must be specified for school classrooms under the following conditions?
a. Less than fifty occupants
b. More than fifty occupants

261. What is most important in the construction of a walk-in refrigerator, excluding insulation?

262. A grand jury verbally requests that you submit all your records for a project. What action would you take?

263. The contractor has just commenced work on a project. Give important items you would check upon making your first field inspection.

264. Electric service wiring is to be installed in fiber conduit. Give three precautions that must be included in the specifications.

265. What four items must be specified if a terrazzo floor must match an approved sample in appearance?

266. Under what conditions could you ask a contractor to cease work without his having a valid claim because of delay?

267. How can you tell whether the proper bolts have been installed in a structural-steel frame when high-tensile bolts have been specified?

268. What is Title 19, and who administers it?

269. What major type of occupancy is included under the UBC in groups A, B, C, and D?

270. Define the major features of the following types of construction: Types I, II, III, and IV.

271. What are the minimum fees recommended by the AIA for architect's compensation for the following?
a. Homes
b. Large commercial structures
c. Schools
d. Hospitals

272. A contractor has submitted shop drawings indicating a more expensive brand of equipment than that originally specified. What procedure should the architect follow in issuing an approval of the shop drawings?

273. How has the role played by specifications in construction changed through the years?

274. What effects has modern mass production of building materials had on architects and engineers?

275. Why is a thorough knowledge of business law essential to a specifications writer?

276. What aspects of a finished project are most affected by good specifications?

277. What documents are necessary to complete a modern complex building project?

278. An architect should not offer his services in a competition except under what conditions?

279. Which type of contract would be recommended to a client with limited funds, cost-plus or guaranteed-price?

280. When would you specify that cross bridging be nailed up tight in the floor construction of a single-story residence?

281. What are the advantages of a bonded roof?

282. What are the disadvantages of a bonded roof?

283. Which of the following are usually furnished and paid for by the owner?
    a. Survey
    b. Site restrictions
    c. Test borings

284. Glued laminated-wood arches are to be installed on a project. What important points must be specified in regard to them after erection?

285. Name four types of resilient floors and give the advantage and limitations of each.

286. Give five reasons for specifying the use of additives to concrete.

287. When would the following types of portland cement be specified?
    a. Type I
    b. Type II
    c. Type III
    d. Type IV

288. What are the actual dimensions of the following nominal sizes of lumber?
    a. 2" x 4"
    b. 2" x 6"
    c. 2" x 10"
    d. 3" x 4"
    e. 3" x 8"
    f. 4" x 6"

289. Describe the process of constructing a prestressed concrete slab.

290. Describe the process of constructing a post-tensioned concrete slab.

291. Describe the process of tilt-up construction and list its advantages.

292. Check those products used by the plastering trade:
    a. Bauxite
    b. Alumilite
    c. Vermiculite
    d. Sampsonite
    e. Pearlite
    f. Keene's cement
    g. Hydraulic cement

293. List the steps you would specify in the purification of a domestic drinking-water supply system at the completion of a project.

294. What is a polysulfide compound, and where would it be used on a construction project?

295. What kind of pipe and fittings would you specify for natural-gas lines?

296. Match the following:
    a. Cellular glass
    b. Polyvinyl acetate
    c. Cellulose fiber tile
    d. Asphalt-saturated rag felt
    e. Vermiculite plaster
    ___ Paint material
    ___ Fire-protection material
    ___ Roofing insulation
    ___ Insulation material
    ___ Acoustic material

297. Why is it desirable to let a separate contract under some conditions for structural steel?

298. In specifying an acoustical material, what association's standards are generally referred to?

299. In specifying acoustical material, what does "NRC" stand for?

300. The abbreviation "MBFU" can normally be used in several sections of the specifications. What does this abbreviation stand for?

301. What is a "trap" in building construction, and what is its purpose?

302. What is the "step-back" ordinance, and what is its purpose?

303. What is the purpose of a water softener, and where it is needed?

304. The superficial floor area in an apartment kitchen allowed under the code is what?

305. What is the minimum flue area of a gas-fired kitchen range?

306. In a residence, what is the minimum size of a room used for sleeping?

307. Describe the process of preparing ferrous-metal surfaces to receive paint.

308. Who is responsible for the puttying of nail holes before painting?

309. Describe three types of finish that may be specified for aluminum.

310. What is the thickness of standard-gauge linoleum?

311. What is particle board, and how is it manufactured?

312. Describe the difference between exterior-grade and interior-grade plywood.

313. Define three grades of glass and tell where each would be used.

314. What is a two-part mastic, and where would it be used?

315. What is efflorescence, and how is it treated?

316. What effect does the addition of lime to mortar have, and why should this addition be limited?

317. What does the word "buttering" mean in a masonry section of the specifications?

318. What is meant by the term "hydraulic cement"?

319. What is "Cornerite," and why is it used?

320. What are the results of excessive limes in finish plaster?

321. Why are air-conditioning ducts usually specified as galvanized iron?

322. What is a square in relation to roofing?

323. How many bundles of shingles are usually required for a square of roofing?

324. Why are wood shingles usually laid on wood stripping?

325. Describe and tell where a standing seam is used?

326. What is the meaning of the term "5/2-16 wood shingle"?

327. How is marble graded?

328. What is meant by the term "grout-locked"?

329. A brick course laid with its shorter dimension parallel to the face of a wall is called what kind of a course?

330. Name and sketch four types of brick bonds.

331. What is used to clean a mortar-stained brick wall?

332. Name 4 types of masonry joints.

333. What is the size of a common firebrick?

334. How are rivets inspected?

335. A hole drilled in a girder is usually how much larger than the rivet that is to be inserted?

336. Give three methods that may be specified to fireproof steel.

337. What is meant by the W/C ratio of concrete?

338. What is meant by cement factor in concrete?

339. Explain the method used to test the strength of Gunite concrete after it is in place?

340. What is dry pack, and when would this method be used?

341. Write a cleanup paragraph to be placed at the end of a brick-masonry trade section.

342. The compressive strength of a brick-mortar assembly is governed mainly by what three factors?

343. When the laying of a brick wall has been temporarily stopped for eight hours or longer, what instructions must be included in the specifications?

344. Describe the process used when pouring concrete under water.

345. What two important capacities should be specified for water heaters?

346. What type of pipe would you specify in a waste system subject to highly corrosive wastes?

347. List six characteristics of the material which should be covered in your specifications for acoustical tile.

348. Describe two methods of specifying hardware.

349. What minimum face veneer for plywood should you specify where vinyl tile is to be the finish floor?

350. What does the word "trim" refer to in a plumbing specification?

351. What method of preservation should be specified for the protection of a metal grating to be installed in a sidewalk?

352. For a school, your specifications require that all lumber be grade-marked. A load of lumber is delivered without grade markings. What would you instruct the contractor to do?

353. What instructions would you include in your specifications regarding the storage of wood doors before installation?

354. Write a brief paragraph to be included in a trade section on the nailing of 25/32" x 3-1/4" oak flooring.

355. What precautions should you include in a plastering specification regarding extreme weather conditions?

356. Under what conditions is a contract entitled to compensation for extras not ordered by the owner?

357. Name three types of ceramic tile and describe the properties of each.

BIBLIOGRAPHY

The American Institute of Architects: "Building Products Registry," 2d ed., Washington, D.C., 1962.

Blake, Clinton H., Jr.: "The Architect's Law Manual," Pencil Points Press, Inc., New York, 1924.

Clough, Richard H.: "Construction Contracting," John Wiley & Sons, Inc., New York, 1960.

Cohen, Henry A.: "Public Construction Contracts and the Law," McGraw-Hill Book Company, New York, 1961.

Colling, R. C.: "Modern Building Inspection," 2d ed., Building Standards Monthly Publishing Company, Los Angeles, Calif., 1951.

Cooper, George H.: "Building Construction Estimating," 2d ed., McGraw-Hill Book Company, New York, 1959.

Cowgill, Clinton, and B. J. Small: "Architectural Practice," Reinhold Publishing Corporation, New York, 1959.

Dallavia, Louis: "Estimating General Construction Costs," 2d ed., McGraw-Hill Book Company, New York, 1957.

Day, Frank Miles: "Handbook of Architectural Practice," American Institute of Architects, Washington, D.C., 1962.

Dietz, Albert G. H.: "Dwelling House Construction," D. Van Nostrand Company, Inc., Princeton, N.J., 1946.

Dyer, Ben H.: "Specification Work Sheets," American Institute of Architects, Washington, D.C., 1951.

Edwards, H. Griffith: "Specifications," 2d ed., D. Van Nostrand Company, Inc., Princeton, N.J., 1961.

Foster, Norman: "Construction Estimates from Take-off to Bid," McGraw-Hill Book Company, New York, 1961.

Gay, Charles Merrick, and Harry Parker: "Materials and Methods of Architectural Construction," 2d ed., John Wiley & Sons, Inc.. New York, 1947.

Goldsmith, Goldwin: "Architect's Specifications and How to Write Them," American Institute of Architects, Washington, D.C., 1948.

Hayward, Norris L.: "Contractor's Legal Problems," McGraw-Hill Book Company, New York, 1958.

Merritt, Frederick S.: "Building Construction Handbook," McGraw-Hill Book Company, New York, 1958.

Parker, William Stanley, and Faneuil Adams: "The A. I. A. Standard Contract Forms and the Law," Little, Brown and Company, Boston, 1954.

Seelye, E. E.: "Specifications and Costs," vol. 2, John Wiley & Sons, Inc., New York, 1946.

Sleeper, Harold Reeve: "Architectural Specifications," John Wiley & Sons, Inc., New York, 1940.

Small, Ben John: "Streamlined Specifications Standards," vol. 1, Reinhold Publishing Corporation, New York, 1952.

Small, Ben John, and Louis Axelbank: "Streamlined Specifications Standards," vol. II, Reinhold Publishing Corporation, New York, 1956.

Stevens, F. B.: "Stevens Master Specifications," Stevens Master Specifications, Inc., Chicago, 1932.

Thompson, Bernard: "It's the Law," Channel Press, New York, 1960.

Thompson, Bernard: "Architectural and Engineering Law," Reinhold Publishing Corporation, New York, 1951.

Tucker, James Irwin: "Contracts in Engineering," 2d ed., McGraw-Hill Book Company, New York, 1933.

Wills, Royal Barry: "This Business of Architecture," Reinhold Publishing Corporation, New York, 1941.

Index